# CHEMISTRY PROBLEMS

## AND HOW TO SOLVE THEM

## The Author

Paul R. Frey received his doctor's degree in physical chemistry from Oregon State College in 1936. Since that time he has been associated with the chemistry department at Colorado State University. Dr. Frey also has held teaching positions at York College, Colorado University, and Oregon State College.

The author has written numerous articles based upon original research, principally in the fields of dipole moment values of organic compounds and the utilization of carotene in the animal body. His articles have been published in the *Journal of the American Chemical Society, American Journal of Physiology, Journal of Nutrition, Science, Journal of the American Veterinary Medical Association*, and the *Journal of the Colorado-Wyoming Academy of Science*. Professor Frey is the author of a standard textbook, *College Chemistry*. In addition, he is a member of the American Chemical Society, the Society for Experimental Biology and Medicine, the American Association for the Advancement of Science, the Colorado-Wyoming Academy of Science, Sigma Xi, Phi Kappa Phi, Phi Lambda Upsilon, and Sigma Pi Sigma.

College Outline Series

# CHEMISTRY PROBLEMS

## AND HOW TO SOLVE THEM

PAUL R. FREY

Barnes & Noble, Inc.   New York

Publishers · Booksellers · Since 1873

©

Fifth Edition, 1958

Copyright, 1938, 1940, 1944, 1953, 1958
By BARNES & NOBLE, INC.

*All rights reserved*

Reprinted, 1959

*L. C. catalogue card number: 58–11383*

# Preface

This book was written as an aid to the student in outlining a logical method of attack in the solution of problems in general chemistry. The thorough understanding of a few elementary principles of mathematics and their use in the solution of chemical problems will help eliminate the all too common practice of solving problems according to prescribed formulas. The working of a problem by routine procedure is usually indicative of a lack of understanding of the concepts involved and their relationship one to the other. The solved problems in the book stress the chemical, physical, and mathematical concepts involved. Consistent use is made of dimensions and the rules applying to significant digits. Such usage tends to promote deductive reasoning on the part of the student. Each type of problem is presented as an independent unit. The order of study of the types of problems is therefore immaterial and may be adapted readily to any course of instruction.

In the fifth edition, the text has been reorganized and rewritten, two chapters have been added on the writing of chemical equations, and the number of problems has been almost doubled. Except for Chapter 1, the problems in each list are divided into two groups, Part I and Part II. The problems in Part I represent a minimum coverage of the types of problems presented. The problems in Part II are more extensive and include more difficult problems as regards the method of solution. Answers are given to all arithmetical problems.

The author is greatly indebted to the many coworkers who submitted criticisms of the earlier editions of the book, and to Dr. Gladys Walterhouse for her many constructive suggestions as editor of the new edition.

PAUL R. FREY

Colorado State University

# Table of Contents

# TABULATED BIBLIOGRAPHY
# AND QUICK REFERENCE TABLE

# Tabulated Bibliography of Standard Textbooks

The following list gives the author, title, publisher, and publication date of the standard textbooks referred to in the table on pages xiv–xxi.

Barker, John W., and Glasoe, Paul K. *First Year College Chemistry.* McGraw-Hill, 1951.

Bogert, L. Jean. *Fundamentals of Chemistry.* Eighth ed. Saunders, 1958.

Brescia, Frank. *General College Chemistry.* Blakiston, 1953.

Briscoe, Herman T. *College Chemistry.* Fourth ed. Houghton Mifflin, 1951.

Cavelti, John E. *Introductory General Chemistry.* Blakiston, 1952.

Compton, Charles. *An Introduction to Chemistry.* Van Nostrand, 1958.

Cragg, L. H., and Graham, R. P. *An Introduction to the Principles of Chemistry.* Rinehart, 1955.

Deming, Horace G. *General Chemistry.* Sixth ed. Wiley, 1952.

Ehret, William F. *Smith's Introductory College Chemistry.* Third ed. Appleton-Century-Crofts, 1950.

Frey, Paul R. *College Chemistry.* Second ed. Prentice-Hall, 1958.

Garrett, Alfred B.; Haskins, Joseph F.; and Sisler, Harry H. *Essentials of Chemistry.* Second ed. Ginn, 1959.

Graham, R. P., and Cragg, L. H. *The Essentials of Chemistry.* Rinehart, 1959.

Gregg, Donald C. *Principles of Chemistry.* Allyn and Bacon, 1958.

Hildebrand, Joel H., and Powell, Richard E. *Principles of Chemistry.* Sixth ed. Macmillan, 1952.

Holmes, Harry N. *General Chemistry.* Fifth ed. Macmillan, 1951.

Holmes, Harry N. *Introductory College Chemistry.* Fifth ed. Macmillan, 1951.

Hopkins, B. Smith, and Bailar, John C. *General Chemistry for Colleges*. Fifth ed. Heath, 1956.

Hutchinson, Eric. *Chemistry, The Elements and Their Reactions*. Saunders, 1959.

Jones, W. Norton. *General Chemistry*. Blakiston, 1954.

King, G. Brooks, and Caldwell, William E. *The Fundamentals of College Chemistry*. Third ed. American Book Co., 1959.

Laubengayer, A. W. *General Chemistry*. Revised ed. Rinehart, 1957.

Luder, W. F.; Vernon, Arthur A.; and Zuffanti, Saverio. *General Chemistry*. Second ed. Saunders, 1959.

Mack, Edward; Garrett, Alfred B.; Haskins, Joseph F.; and Verhoek, Frank H. *Textbook of Chemistry*. Second ed. Ginn, 1956.

Markham, Edwin C., and Smith, Sherman E. *General Chemistry*. Houghton Mifflin, 1954.

Meyer, Lillian Hoagland. *Introductory Chemistry*. Second ed. Macmillan, 1959.

Nebergall, William H., and Schmidt, Frederic C. *College Chemistry*. Heath, 1957.

Nebergall, William H., and Schmidt, Frederic C. *General Chemistry*. Heath, 1959.

Nitz, Otto W. *Introductory Chemistry*. Van Nostrand, 1956.

Pauling, Linus. *College Chemistry*. Second ed. Freeman, 1955.

Pauling, Linus. *General Chemistry*. Second ed. Freeman, 1953.

Quagliano, James V. *Chemistry*. Prentice-Hall, 1958.

Roe, Joseph H. *Principles of Chemistry*. Eighth ed. Mosby, 1956.

Routh, Joseph I. *20th Century Chemistry*. Second ed. Saunders, 1958.

Scarlett, A. J. *College Chemistry*. Holt, 1956.

Scarlett, Andrew J., and Gomez-Ibanez, Jose. *General College Chemistry*. Fifth ed. Holt, 1954.

Schwenck, J. Rae, and Martin, Raymond M. *Basic Principles of Chemistry*. Prentice-Hall, 1958.

Selwood, P. W. *General Chemistry*. Third ed. Holt, 1959.

Sienko, Michell J., and Plane, Robert A. *Chemistry*. McGraw-Hill, 1957.

Sisler, Harry H.; Vander Werf, Calvin A.; and Davidson, Arthur W. *College Chemistry*. Macmillan, 1953.

Sisler, Harry H.; Vander Werf, Calvin A.; and Davidson, Arthur W. *General Chemistry*. Second ed. Macmillan, 1959.

Sneed, M. Cannon; Maynard, J. Lewis; and Brasted, Robert C. *General College Chemistry*. Second ed. Van Nostrand, 1954.

Sorum, C. H. *General Chemistry*. Prentice-Hall, 1955.

Steiner, L. E., and Campbell, J. A. *General Chemistry*. Macmillan, 1955.

Timm, John Arrend. *General Chemistry*. Third ed. McGraw-Hill, 1956.

Watt, George W. *Basic Concepts in Chemistry*. McGraw-Hill, 1958.

Watt, George W., and Hatch, Lewis F. *The Science of Chemistry*. Second ed. McGraw-Hill, 1954.

Winslow, Eugene C. *Basic Principles of Chemistry*. Van Nostrand, 1958.

Wood, Jesse Hermon, and Keenan, Charles William. *General College Chemistry*. Harper, 1957.

Young, L. E., and Porter, C. W. *General Chemistry, A First Course*. Fourth ed. Prentice-Hall, 1958.

| CHAPTER IN CHEM. PROBS. | TOPIC | BARKER & GLASOE | BOGERT | BRESCIA | BRISCOE |
|---|---|---|---|---|---|
| 1 | Mathematics and Chemistry | | | | |
| 2 | Units of Measurement Used in Chemistry | 1, 10 | App. | 2, App. | 7, Introd. |
| 3 | Significant Digits | | | | |
| 4 | Dimensional Analysis | | | | |
| 5 | Density and Specific Gravity | 1 | 6 | | 13, Introd. |
| 6 | Chemical Units of Mass | 3 | 11 | 3 | 2, 8 |
| 7 | The Physical Behavior of Gases | 10 | | 2 | 7 |
| 8 | Chemical Equations | 3 | 4 | 6 | 9 |
| 9 | Equivalent Weights of the Elements | 12 | | 3, 4 | 2, 8 |
| 10 | Chemical Formulas | 3, 10, 11 | 4 | 3, 6 | 8, 9 |
| 11 | Chemical Equations | 3, 11 | 4 | 6 | 9 |
| 12 | Relationships Involving Energy | 16 | 6, 8 | 3, 6, 15 | 9 |
| 13 | Atomic Weights of the Elements | 3 | | 3 | 8 |
| 14 | Oxidation-Reduction Equations | 6 | 9 | 20 | 21 |
| 15 | Solutions | 13 | 11 | 16 | 15 |
| 16 | Volumetric Analysis | 13, 16 | | 21 | 15, 21 |
| 17 | Molecular Weights of Compounds | 13 | | 17 | 15 |
| 18 | Chemical Equilibria | 16 | 12 | 19 | 25, 26 |
| 19 | Electrochemistry | 15 | 12 | 18, 22 | 16, 36 |
| 20 | Nuclear Chemistry | 29 | 15 | 8, 9 | 11 |

*See pp. xi–xiii for*

# TO STANDARD TEXTBOOKS
*to chapters.*

| CAVELTI | COMP-TON | CRAGG & GRAHAM | DEMING | EHRET | FREY | GARRETT, HASKINS, & SISLER | GRAHAM & CRAGG |
|---|---|---|---|---|---|---|---|
| App. | App. | | App. | | 1 | App. | 2 |
| 6, App. | App. | App. | 4, 6, App. | 7, App. | 1, App. | 2 | 2, App. |
| | | | App. | | 1 | | App. |
| App. | | | 6 | | 1 | | |
| 2 | 5 | 7 | 13 | 1 | 1 | 6, App. | 4 |
| 4, 6, 9 | 11 | 6 | 4 | 1!, 14 | 2 | 3 | 8 |
| 8 | 5, 11 | 7, 8 | 8 | 7 | 3 | 9 | 6 |
| | 11 | | 4, 17 | 5, 11 | 2 | 2, App. | 2, 10 |
| 22 | 20 | 6 | 9 | 3, 8, 9 | 10 | | 7 |
| 4, 9 | 11 | 6, 12 | 4, 9 | 5, 11 | 3, 10 | App. | 7, 8, 9 |
| 13 | 11 | 12 | 4, 9 | 5, 10, 11 | 10 | App. | 7, 10 |
| 7, 12, 17 | 5 | 14, 18 | 6, 11, 18 | 10, 35 | 1, 4, 11 | 6, 10, App. | 4 |
| 10 | | 6 | 9 | 4, 11 | 4 | | 9 |
| 16 | 18 | 16 | 25 | 26 | 15 | App. | 27 |
| 22 | 15, 20 | 10 | 13 | 12 | 14 | 11 | 21 |
| 16 | 20 | 15, 16 | 17, 23 | 24, 26 | 14, 15 | 11 | 21 |
| 14 | 15, 20 | 11 | 13 | 12 | 14 | 11 | |
| 17 | 14, 16 | 13, 15 | 22, 23 | 24 | 18, 19 | 12 | 25 |
| 14 | 18 | 17 | 43 | 22, 46 | 23 | 38 | 26 |
| | 9 | 19, 20 | 32 | 18, 19 | 36 | 17 | 30 |

*list of complete titles.*

| CHAPTER IN CHEM. PROBS. | TOPIC | GREGG | HILDE-BRAND & POWELL | HOLMES General | HOLMES Introd. |
|---|---|---|---|---|---|
| 1 | Mathematics and Chemistry | | | | |
| 2 | Units of Measurement Used in Chemistry | 1, App. | 3 | 1, 7, App. | 2, 9, App. |
| 3 | Significant Digits | | | | |
| 4 | Dimensional Analysis | | | | |
| 5 | Density and Specific Gravity | 1 | 17 | 11 | |
| 6 | Chemical Units of Mass | 3 | 1 | 7, 13 | 13 |
| 7 | The Physical Behavior of Gases | 6 | 3 | 7 | 9 |
| 8 | Chemical Equations | 12 | 2 | 4 | 5 |
| 9 | Equivalent Weights of the Elements | 12 | 9 | 2, 10, 15 | 4 |
| 10 | Chemical Formulas | 3, 6 | 2, 4 | 4, 13 | 5, 13 |
| 11 | Chemical Equations | 3, 4 | 2 | 4, 9 | 5, 6, 8 |
| 12 | Relationships Involving Energy | 1, 5 | 7 | 5, 8, 11, 13, 45 | 12 |
| 13 | Atomic Weights of the Elements | | 2 | 13 | 13 |
| 14 | Oxidation-Reduction Equations | 12 | 15 | 10 | 17 |
| 15 | Solutions | 15 | 6 | 15 | 15 |
| 16 | Volumetric Analysis | 12, 18 | 6 | 21 | 22 |
| 17 | Molecular Weights of Compounds | 15 | 4 | 15 | 15 |
| 18 | Chemical Equilibria | 14, 18, 20 | 12 | 22, 23 | 23, App. |
| 19 | Electrochemistry | 13 | 8, 15 | 20, 50 | 21, 46 |
| 20 | Nuclear Chemistry | 9, 21 | 16 | 27, 28 | 25 |

*See pp. xi–xiii for*

to chapters.

| HOP-KINS & BAILAR | HUTCH-INSON | JONES | KING & CALD-WELL | LAUBEN-GAYER | LUDER, VERNON & ZUFFANTI | MACK et al. | MARK-HAM & SMITH |
|---|---|---|---|---|---|---|---|
|  |  | 3 |  | App. | App. | App. | 3 |
| 2, App. | 3 | 3 | 2, App. | App. | 1, App. | 2 | 3 |
|  |  | 3 |  | App. |  |  | 3 |
|  |  |  |  |  |  |  | 3 |
| 8 | 4 | 2 | 2 |  | 1 | 2, App. | 3 |
| 2, 3, 13 | 5 | 8 | 3 | 1, 2, 6 | 3 | 6, 9 | 10, 11 |
| 6 | 5, 8 | 9 | 8 | 9 | 2 | 6 | 5, 6 |
| 3 |  | 5 | 5 | 6 | 3 | 10 | 13 |
| 3 | 6 | 8 | 2 | 2, 6 | 1 | 7, 9 | 27 |
| 2, 12 | 5, 6 | 8 | 5, 8, 13 | 2, 9 | 1, 3 | 3, 10 | 11, 13 |
| 3 | 5 | 8 | 14 | 6 | 1, 3 | 9, 10 | 13 |
| 3, 8 | 7 | 8 | 2 | 3, 6, 10, 11 | 1, 2 | 2, 8, 11, 14 | 3, 7, 36 |
| 12 | 6 | 3, 8, 11 | 13 | 2, 3 |  | 9 | 11, 12 |
| 15 | 14 | 5 | 20, App. | 8, 18, App. | 11 | 15 | 22, 27 |
| 19 | 8, 19 | 15 | 15 | 12, 17 | 26 | 12, 14 | 23 |
| 19 | 8, 19 | 22 | 15 | 17 | 26 | 14 | 23, 27 |
| 9 | 9 | 15 | 15 | 12 | 8 | 12 | 26 |
| 19 | 10, 18 | 21, 22 | 17, 19 | 15, 16, 17 | 9, 13 | 24, 25 | 24 |
| 18 | 16, 17 | 17 | 32 | 19 | 27 | 13 | 27, 40 |
| 41 | 35 | 40 | 31 | 36 | 24 | 21 | 51 |

list of complete titles.

# QUICK REFERENCE TABLE

*Numbers refer*

| CHAPTER IN CHEM. PROBS. | TOPIC | MEYER | NEBER-GALL & SCHMIDT College | NEBER-GALL & SCHMIDT General | NITZ |
|---|---|---|---|---|---|
| 1 | Mathematics and Chemistry | | App. | App. | App. |
| 2 | Units of Measurement Used in Chemistry | 3 | 1, 7 | 1 | 2, 10, App. |
| 3 | Significant Digits | | App. | App. | |
| 4 | Dimensional Analysis | | | | |
| 5 | Density and Specific Gravity | 3 | 1 | 1 | 9 |
| 6 | Chemical Units of Mass | 2 | 2 | 2, 11 | 3 |
| 7 | The Physical Behavior of Gases | 7 | 7 | 7 | 10 |
| 8 | Chemical Equations | 4 | 2 | 2 | 4 |
| 9 | Equivalent Weights of the Elements | 6 | 9 | 9 | 4 |
| 10 | Chemical Formulas | 2, 7 | 2, 9 | 2, 9 | 4, 10 |
| 11 | Chemical Equations | 4, 7 | 2 | 2 | 4 |
| 12 | Relationships Involving Energy | 7 | 1, 5, 8 | 1, 8 | 9 |
| 13 | Atomic Weights of the Elements | | 9 | 9 | |
| 14 | Oxidation-Reduction Equations | 17 | 14 | 14 | 15 |
| 15 | Solutions | 12, 15 | 11 | 11 | 12 |
| 16 | Volumetric Analysis | 15 | 11, 14 | 11 | |
| 17 | Molecular Weights of Compounds | | 11 | 11 | 12 |
| 18 | Chemical Equilibria | 15 | 16, 41, 42, App. | 16, 33, 44, App. | 13, 14 |
| 19 | Electrochemistry | | 20 | 20 | 16 |
| 20 | Nuclear Chemistry | 8 | 3, 30 | 30 | 25 |

*See pp. xi–xiii for*

| PAULING College | PAULING General | QUAG-LIANO | ROE | ROUTH | SCARLETT | SCARLETT & GOMEZ-IBANEZ | SCHWENCK & MARTIN |
|---|---|---|---|---|---|---|---|
| | | 2 | | | App. | App. | |
| 1, App. | 1, 2 | 2 | App. | 2 | App. | App. | 6, App. |
| | | | | | | | |
| | 1 | | | | | | |
| 1 | | 2 | 9, App. | 11 | 1 | | 6 |
| 8 | 4 | 3, 4 | 13 | 3 | 2 | 2 | 6 |
| 9 | 14 | 8, 9 | | 10 | 8 | 5 | 14 |
| 4, 6 | 4 | 4 | 2 | 6 | 6 | 2 | 10 |
| 8 | 7 | 3, 5, 7 | 2 | | 2, 11 | 2 | 19 |
| 8, 9 | 7, 14 | 4, 8 | 2, 9 | 10 | 2 | 2, 4 | 10 |
| 8 | 7 | 4 | 9 | 10 | 6, 12 | 2 | 7, 10 |
| 1, 23 | 31 | 2, 4, 10 | App. | 10 | 6, 9, 10 | 9, 37 | 26 |
| 8, 9 | 7, 14 | | | | 11 | 2, 4 | 4 |
| 12 | 11 | 6, 17, App. | 8 | 9 | 17 | 15 | 24, 25 |
| 18 | 21 | 16 | 12, 13 | 12, 14 | 13 | 7, 9 | 19, 20 |
| 20 | 21 | 16 | 12, 13 | 12, 14 | 15 | 9 | 19 |
| 9, 18 | 16 | 16 | | 12 | 13 | 7 | 18 |
| 20 | 20, 21 | 21, 22 | 13 | 15 | 15, 16 | 16, 18 | 21, App. |
| 10 | 13 | 18 | 11 | 15 | 15, 25 | 14, 19 | 28 |
| 32 | 33 | 32 | 18 | 4 | 34 | 39 | 29 |

*list of complete titles.*

# QUICK REFERENCE TABLE

*Numbers refer*

| CHAPTER IN CHEM. PROBS. | TOPIC | SEL-WOOD | SIENKO & PLANE | SISLER et al. College | SISLER et al. General | SNEED, MAYNARD & BRASTED |
|---|---|---|---|---|---|---|
| 1 | Mathematics and Chemistry | 4 | App. | | | |
| 2 | Units of Measurement Used in Chemistry | App. | 1, App. | 1, 2, App. | 2, App. | 1, App. |
| 3 | Significant Digits | | 1 | | | |
| 4 | Dimensional Analysis | | | | | |
| 5 | Density and Specific Gravity | 1 | 1 | 1 | 2 | 1 |
| 6 | Chemical Units of Mass | 4, 7, 13 | 2, 5 | 4 | 6 | 5 |
| 7 | The Physical Behavior of Gases | 5 | 6 | 2 | 3 | 8 |
| 8 | Chemical Equations | 3 | 5 | 5 | 7 | 5 |
| 9 | Equivalent Weights of the Elements | 4 | 5 | 4 | 5 | 1, 2, 10 |
| 10 | Chemical Formulas | 4, 7 | 5 | 4, 5 | 6, 7 | 5, 10 |
| 11 | Chemical Equations | 4 | 2, 5 | 5 | 7 | 5 |
| 12 | Relationships Involving Energy | 5, 11 | 1, 5 | 5 | 2, 4, 7 | 7 |
| 13 | Atomic Weights of the Elements | 7 | 2 | 4 | 6 | 10 |
| 14 | Oxidation-Reduction Equations | 21 | 10, 14 | 9 | 12 | 13 |
| 15 | Solutions | 12 | 10 | 13, 15 | 16, 18 | 14, 18 |
| 16 | Volumetric Analysis | 13 | 10 | 15 | 18 | 18 |
| 17 | Molecular Weights of Compounds | 12 | 10 | 13 | 16 | 14 |
| 18 | Chemical Equilibria | 11, 21 | 13, 17 | 12, 15, 16 | 15, 18, 19 | 16, 18 |
| 19 | Electrochemistry | 18 | 3, 14 | 14, 20 | 17, 24 | 19 |
| 20 | Nuclear Chemistry | 24 | 3, 29 | 38 | 10 | 34 |

*See pp. xi–xiii for*

*to chapters.*

| SORUM | STEINER & CAMP-BELL | TIMM | WATT | WATT & HATCH | WINS-LOW | WOOD & KEENAN | YOUNG & PORTER |
|---|---|---|---|---|---|---|---|
|  |  | App. | 8 |  |  | 1, 10 |  |
| 1 | App. | 5, App. | 1, App. | 2, App. | 2 | 1, App. | 2, App. |
|  | 4 |  | 8 |  |  |  |  |
|  |  |  | 8 |  |  |  |  |
| 1 | 2 |  | 9 | 7 |  | 1 | 2 |
| 1, 2 | 5 | 6 | 2 | 3 | 1 | 5, 10 | 1 |
| 2 | 9 | 4 | 9 | 7 | 3 | 4, 5 | 2 |
| 3, 13 | 5 | 6 | 2 | 3 | 2 | 6 | 2, 3, 4 |
| 1, 5, 13 | 4 | 6, 7 | 6 |  | 12 | 18 | 5 |
| 1, 2, 4 | 5 | 6, 7 | 3, 8, 10 | 3 | 1, 2, 4 | 5, 10 | 2, 5 |
| 1, 5 | 5 | 13 | 8 | 3 | 2 | 10 | 2, 5 |
| 1, 2, 3 | 5, 11 | 3 | 19 | 2, 11 | 3 | 1, 4 | 2 |
|  | 11, 13 | 6 | 2 |  |  | 1 | 1 |
| 16 | 19 | 30 | 21 |  | 7 | 20 | 8 |
| 11 | 17 | 20, 23 | 13, 15 | 12 | 12 | 12 | 2, 5 |
| 13 |  | 23 | 15 | 14 | 12 | 12 | 5 |
| 12 | 17 | 20, 23 | 14 | 12 | 12 | 12 | 2 |
| 14 | 18 | 21, 22, 23, 26 | 16, 17, 18, App. |  |  | 13, 14, App. | 5 |
| 15 | 15, 26 | 30 | 20 | 18 | 20 | 25 | 15 |
| 8, 36 | 13, 21 | 45, 46 | 27 | 5 | 21 | 15 | 19 |

*list of complete titles.*

# 1

# Mathematics and Chemistry

Most natural laws may be expressed in the form of mathematical equations. Problems involving mathematics therefore become an essential part of the first course in college chemistry. Each problem in chemistry is based upon one or more scientific principles. To work a problem in chemistry one must know and understand the scientific principles involved, and have sufficient knowledge of arithmetic and algebra to solve the problem numerically. For example, two weights of 50 lb. and 75 lb., respectively, are attached to a bar. What is the downward force, F, exerted on the bar by the two weights? In order to solve the problem one must know and apply mathematically the principle that forces acting in parallel must be added in order to obtain the resultant force. That is:

$$F = 50 \text{ lb.} + 75 \text{ lb.} = 125 \text{ lb.}$$

The brief review of *fractions*, *exponential quantities*, and elementary *algebra* which follows will help the student recall their meaning and usage.

## Fractions

**1.1. Common Fractions.** When *adding* or *subtracting* common fractions the quantities involved in the mathematical operation must first be reduced to a *common denominator*.

**Example 1.1.** Find the value of $x$ in the expression:

$$x = \tfrac{3}{4} - 3\tfrac{1}{6} + 8\tfrac{5}{12}.$$

**Solution.** The common denominator is 12. That is, 12 is divisible by 4, 6, and 12. Therefore:

$$x = \frac{3}{4} - 3\tfrac{1}{6} + 8\tfrac{5}{12} = \frac{3}{4} - \frac{19}{6} + \frac{101}{12} = \frac{9 - 38 + 101}{12} = 6.$$

1

When *multiplying* common fractions, multiply the numerators for a new numerator, and the denominators for a new denominator; then reduce the resulting fraction to its *lowest terms*.

**Example 1.2.** Find the value of $x$ in the expression:

$$x = 16 \times \tfrac{3}{4} \times \tfrac{5}{6}.$$

**Solution.**

$$x = \frac{16}{1} \times \frac{3}{4} \times \frac{5}{6} = \frac{16 \times 3 \times 5}{4 \times 6} = 10.$$

When *dividing* one fraction by another, *invert* the divisor and multiply.

**Example 1.3.** Find the value of $x$ in the expression:

$$x = 6\tfrac{1}{2} \div \tfrac{3}{4}.$$

**Solution.**

$$x = 6\tfrac{1}{2} \div \frac{3}{4} = 6\tfrac{1}{2} \times \frac{4}{3} = \frac{13 \times 4}{2 \times 3} = 8\tfrac{2}{3}.$$

Only *common factors* may be canceled when they appear in both the numerator and denominator of a fraction.

**Example 1.4.** Find the value of $x$ in the expression:

$$x = 36 \times \frac{18}{5 \times 18} \times \frac{24 + 6}{6}.$$

**Solution.**

$$x = 36 \times \frac{18}{5 \times 18} \times \frac{24 + 6}{6} = \frac{36 \times \cancel{18} \times (24 + 6)}{5 \times \cancel{18} \times 6} = \frac{36 \times \cancel{30}}{\cancel{30}} = 36.$$

## Problems

1.1. Find the value of $x$.

a. $x = 3\tfrac{3}{4} + 5\tfrac{7}{8}.$      *Ans.* $9\tfrac{5}{8}.$

b. $x = 2\tfrac{1}{3} \times 6\tfrac{1}{4}.$      *Ans.* $14\tfrac{7}{12}.$

c. $x = 6\tfrac{5}{8} - 3\tfrac{3}{4}.$      *Ans.* $2\tfrac{7}{8}.$

d. $x = 5\tfrac{1}{4} \div 1\tfrac{2}{3}.$      *Ans.* $3\tfrac{3}{20}.$

e. $x = \left(\dfrac{231}{6} \times \dfrac{6}{11}\right) + \left(\dfrac{18 + 3}{3}\right).$      *Ans.* 28.

f. $x = \dfrac{760}{124} \times \dfrac{(272 + 18)}{580} \times \dfrac{744}{760}.$      *Ans.* 3.

g. $x = \dfrac{3\tfrac{1}{3} \times 12\tfrac{3}{4}}{3} \div \tfrac{1}{6}.$      *Ans.* $3\tfrac{2}{5}.$

**1.2. Decimal Fractions.** When *adding* or *subtracting* decimal fractions, the decimal points must be in a vertical column.

**Example 1.5.** Find the value of $x$.

(a) $x = 16.34 + 176.00 + 3.41$, and (b) $x = 1.436 - 0.471$.

**Solution.**

(a)        16.34          (b)          1.436
          176.00                      0.471
           _3.41_              $x = \overline{0.965}$
    $x = \overline{195.75}$

The *product* of two decimal fractions contains as many decimal places as the *sum* of the decimal places in the two quantities multiplied.

**Example 1.6.** Solve for $x$: $x = 7.33 \times 4.7$.
**Solution.** $x = 7.3\underline{3} \times 4.\underline{7} = 34.4\underline{51}$.

The *quotient* involving two decimal fractions contains as many decimal places as there are places in the *dividend* minus the number of places in the *divisor*. Note: zeros added to the dividend must be counted as decimal places.

**Example 1.7.** Solve for $x$: $x = 258.98 \div 28.4$.
**Solution.**   28.4 | 258.980 | 9.12   That is, $x = 9.12$.
                     255 6
                    _____
                      3 38
                      2 84
                    _____
                       540
                       568

To change a common fraction to a decimal fraction, divide the numerator by the denominator. For example, $\frac{4}{5} = 0.8$.

## Problems

1.2. Find the value of $x$.

  a. $x = 1.634 + 0.880 + 15.223$.                    *Ans.* 17.737.
  b. $x = 221.68 - 96.73$.                            *Ans.* 124.95.
  c. $x = 3.48 \times 0.775$.                         *Ans.* 2.697.
  d. $x = 3654 \div 311.1$.                           *Ans.* 11.75.
  e. $x = 12.36 \div 54.7$.                           *Ans.* 0.226.

1.3. Change each of the following to the corresponding decimal fraction.

  a. $\frac{13}{15}$                                  *Ans.* 0.87.
  b. $3\frac{7}{8}$                                   *Ans.* 3.9.

1.4. Reduce $\dfrac{2.125}{0.27}$ to the simplest decimal fraction.        *Ans.* 7.9.

1.5. Reduce 0.16 to the simplest common fraction.        *Ans.* $\frac{4}{25}$.

1.6. Mental exercises.

| | |
|---|---|
| a. $25 \times 10$ | f. $764 \div 100$ |
| b. $33 \times 100$ | g. $61.7 \div 100$ |
| c. $2.75 \times 10$ | h. $2174 \div 1000$ |
| d. $125 \times 1000$ | i. $0.089 \times 100$ |
| e. $32 \div 10$ | j. $1.42 \div 1000$ |

## Exponential Numbers

**1.3. Introduction.** In scientific work it is often necessary to use quite large numbers such as 602,000,000,000,000,000,000,000, or extremely small numbers such as 0.00000000048. A method whereby such numbers can be presented in a more condensed form will be given. For example, 10,000 may be written $10^4$ where 4 is the *exponent* to the *base* 10. Table 1.1 gives a sequence of powers of 10. The table could be extended indefinitely.

TABLE 1.1

SOME POWERS OF TEN

| | | |
|---|---|---|
| $10^3$ | $=$ | 1000. |
| $10^2$ | $=$ | 100. |
| $10^1$ | $=$ | 10. |
| $10^0$ | $=$ | 1. |
| $10^{-1}$ | $=$ | 0.1 |
| $10^{-2}$ | $=$ | 0.01 |
| $10^{-3}$ | $=$ | 0.001 |

Numbers other than 10 may be used as a base. For example, $6^2 = 36$ and $12^2 = 144$. The base 10 is the most convenient to use.

In Table 1.1 it will be observed that $10^0 = 1$. Any expression (other than zero) to the exponent zero is equal to one. That is, $x^0 = 1$ if $x \neq 0$. It is important to remember this fact since zero frequently occurs as an exponent in mathematical expressions. Also, reference to Table 1.1 will show that a quantity expressed in the negative exponential form may be written as the reciprocal of the number with the sign of the exponent changed. That is:

$$10^{-1} = \frac{1}{10}, \quad 10^{-2} = \frac{1}{10^2}, \quad 10^{-3} = \frac{1}{10^3}, \quad \text{or} \quad x^{-a} = \frac{1}{x^a}.$$

Any factor may be interchanged between the numerator and denominator of a fraction by changing the sign of the exponent.

**1.4. Numbers Expressed as a Power of Ten.** The question now arises as to how a number such as 600 could be expressed as a power of ten. Since $10^2 = 100$ and $10^3 = 1000$, it is evident that a fractional exponent having a value between 2 and 3 must be used to express 600 as a power of ten. That is, in the expression $10^x = 600$, $x$ has a value lying between 2 and 3. In the particular case $x = 2.77815$. That is, $10^{2.77815} = 600$. The value 77815 was obtained from the logarithm table in Appendix IV. Appendix III describes the procedure for obtaining the logarithm of a number.

It is also possible to express a number as the product of two numbers, one of which is an integer power of ten.

**Example 1.8.** Express each of the following as a product of two numbers, one of which is an integer power of ten.

(a) 600, (b) 0.006, and (c) 674,000.

**Solution.**

(a) $600 = 6 \times 100 = 6 \times 10^2$.

(b) $0.006 = \dfrac{6}{1000} = 6 \times \dfrac{1}{1000} = 6 \times \dfrac{1}{10^3} = 6 \times 10^{-3}$.

(c) $674,000 = 674 \times 1000 = 674 \times 10^3$
$\qquad\qquad = 67.4 \times 10,000 = 67.4 \times 10^4$
$\qquad\qquad = 6.74 \times 100,000 = 6.74 \times 10^5$
$\qquad\qquad = 0.674 \times 1,000,000 = 0.674 \times 10^6$.

In Example 1.8c the quantity 674,000 is expressed as a power of ten in four different ways, all of which are correct. It is purely a matter of choice as to which form of answer shall be used. The form most commonly used is the one containing one integer value to the left of the decimal place, which in the above example would be $6.74 \times 10^5$.

### Problems

1.7. Express each of the following as the product of two numbers, one of which is an integer power of ten.

     a. 22,400                 *Ans.* $2.24 \times 10^4$.

     b. 364                    *Ans.* $3.64 \times 10^2$.

     c. 0.364                 *Ans.* $3.64 \times 10^{-1}$.

     d. 0.000364          *Ans.* $3.64 \times 10^{-4}$.

     e. 2004                   *Ans.* $2.004 \times 10^3$.

1.8. Change each of the following to the nonexponential form.

    a. $2.3 \times 10^3$                             *Ans.* 2300.

    b. $2.3 \times 10^{-3}$                         *Ans.* 0.0023.

    c. $0.0076 \times 10^4$                    *Ans.* 76.

    d. $0.0076 \times 10^{-2}$.                 *Ans.* 0.000076.

    e. $\dfrac{23.4}{10^3}$                              *Ans.* 0.0234.

1.9. Mental exercises. Determine the value of $x$.

    a. $10^3 = x$.                 c. $10^x = 0.0001$.

    b. $10^x = 10,000$.         d. $10^{-4} = x$.

**1.5. Addition and Subtraction of Exponential Quantities.** In order to add or subtract exponential numbers, each number must be expressed to the same *power* and referred to the same *base*. For example, $10^3 + 10^3 = 2 \times 10^3$.

The above limitations greatly restrict the use of exponents in the operations of addition and subtraction. In fact, exponential expressions are seldom used in such mathematical operations.

**1.6. Multiplication and Division of Exponential Quantities.** In order to multiply or divide exponential quantities, each number needs only to be referred to the same base. Exponential quantities will therefore be found quite useful in simplifying the operations of multiplication and division. In multiplication the exponents are *added;* in division the exponent of the divisor is *subtracted* from that of the dividend.

**Example 1.9.** Find the value of $x$ in each of the following:

    (a) $x = 10^2 \times 10^3$.           (d) $x = 0.0035 \div 0.00078$.

    (b) $x = 10^7 \div 10^3$.           (e) $x = \dfrac{0.088 \times 760 \times 220,000}{4300}$.

    (c) $x = 3200 \times 75,000$.

**Solution.**

    (a) $x = 10^2 \times 10^3 = 10^{2+3} = 10^5$.

    (b) $x = \dfrac{10^7}{10^3} = 10^{7-3} = 10^4$.

    (c) $x = 3200 \times 75,000$

        $= (3.2 \times 10^3)(7.5 \times 10^4)$

        $= (3.2 \times 7.5)(10^3 \times 10^4)$

        $= 24 \times 10^7$.

Observe that rearranging the order in which a series of quantities are multiplied does not affect the answer.

    (d) $x = \dfrac{0.0035}{0.00078} = \dfrac{3.5 \times 10^{-3}}{7.8 \times 10^{-4}} = 0.45 \times 10^{-3-(-4)} = 0.45 \times 10 = 4.5$.

(e) $x = \dfrac{0.088 \times 760 \times 220{,}000}{4300}$

$\phantom{(e) x} = \dfrac{(8.8 \times 10^{-2})(7.6 \times 10^{2})(2.2 \times 10^{5})}{(4.3 \times 10^{3})}$

$\phantom{(e) x} = \left(\dfrac{8.8 \times 7.6 \times 2.2}{4.3}\right)\left(\dfrac{10^{-2} \times 10^{2} \times 10^{5}}{10^{3}}\right)$

$\phantom{(e) x} = \dfrac{147}{4.3} \times 10^{-2+2+5-3}$

$\phantom{(e) x} = 34 \times 10^{2}.$

By means of the following rule it is possible to determine the *numerical value* and *sign* of an exponent when expressing a number as a power of ten. **Rule:** A shift of the decimal point to the *right* requires the use of a *negative* exponent; to the *left*, a *positive* exponent. In either case the exponent is equal numerically to the number of places the decimal point has been moved. For example:

$$0.088 = 8.8 \times 10^{-2}, \quad \text{and} \quad 760. = 7.6 \times 10^{2}.$$
$$\rightarrow \phantom{0.088 = 8.8 \times 10^{-2}, \quad \text{and} \quad 760.} \leftarrow$$

### Problems

1.10. Evaluate $x$ in each of the following as a power of ten.

a. $x = 22{,}400 \times 250.$                       *Ans.* $5.6 \times 10^{6}.$

b. $x = 1.48 \times 0.0095.$                   *Ans.* $1.41 \times 10^{-2}.$

c. $x = \dfrac{73{,}000 \times 0.00075}{170}.$          *Ans.* $3.22 \times 10^{-1}.$

d. $x = 380 \times \frac{810}{760} \times \frac{300}{270}.$             *Ans.* $4.5 \times 10^{2}.$

e. $x = 72{,}400 \div 340.$                    *Ans.* $2.13 \times 10^{2}.$

f. $x = 340 \div 72{,}400.$                    *Ans.* $4.70 \times 10^{-3}.$

g. $x = 0.027 \div 0.009.$                   *Ans.* $3.$

h. $x = 2.68 \div 0.044.$                    *Ans.* $6.09 \times 10.$

i. $x = (10^{3})^{2}.$                            *Ans.* $10^{6}.$

j. $x = (10^{-3})^{2}.$                          *Ans.* $10^{-6}.$

**1.7. Fractional Exponents.** Exponents in the form of decimal fractions are obtained from logarithm tables (Appendix IV). The present discussion will be limited to exponents in the form of common fractions.

The expression $x^{\frac{a}{b}}$ is the general form for a quantity containing a fractional exponent. Fractional exponents may be written using the root sign, $\sqrt{\ }$. That is, $x^{\frac{a}{b}} = \sqrt[b]{x^{a}}$. Specific examples are, $100^{\frac{1}{2}} = \sqrt{100} = 10$; $1000^{\frac{1}{3}} = \sqrt[3]{1000} = 10$; and $10^{\frac{2}{3}} = \sqrt[3]{10^{2}} = 4.64.$

The square root of a quantity is obtained by dividing the exponent by two; the cube root is obtained by dividing the exponent by three.

**Example 1.10.** Evaluate $x$ in each of the following:

(a) $x = \sqrt{10^4}$.

(b) $x = \sqrt[3]{10^{-9}}$.

(c) $x = \sqrt{900}$.

(d) $x = \sqrt{80,000}$.

(e) $x = \sqrt{0.0001}$.

(f) $x = \sqrt[3]{0.000089}$.

Solution.

(a) $x = \sqrt{10^4} = 10^{\frac{4}{2}} = 10^2 = 100$.

(b) $x = \sqrt[3]{10^{-9}} = 10^{-\frac{9}{3}} = 10^{-3} = 0.001$.

(c) $x = \sqrt{900} = \sqrt{9 \times 100} = \sqrt{9 \times 10^2} = \sqrt{9} \times \sqrt{10^2} = 3 \times 10 = 30$.

(d) $x = \sqrt{80,000} = \sqrt{8 \times 10^4} = \sqrt{8} \times 10^2 = 2.83 \times 10^2 = 283$.

(e) $x = \sqrt{0.0001} = \sqrt{10^{-4}} = 10^{-\frac{4}{2}} = 10^{-2} = 0.01$.

(f) $x = \sqrt[3]{0.000089} = \sqrt[3]{89 \times 10^{-6}} = \sqrt[3]{89} \times 10^{-2} = 4.5 \times 10^{-2}$.

In the above examples note that the quantity under the root sign has been expressed as a power of ten such that the exponent is divisible by the root. Logarithms would be required to obtain the value of a quantity such as $\sqrt[3]{89}$ with any degree of accuracy.

## Problems

1.11. Evaluate $x$ in each of the following:

a. $x = \sqrt{640,000}$.      *Ans.* $8 \times 10^2$.

b. $x = 0.0000064^{\frac{1}{2}}$.      *Ans.* $8 \times 10^{-3}$.

c. $x = \sqrt{4 \times 10^8}$.      *Ans.* $2 \times 10^4$.

d. $x = (64 \times 10^{-9})^{\frac{1}{3}}$.      *Ans.* $4 \times 10^{-3}$.

e. $x = \sqrt{(4 \times 10^3)(16 \times 10^5)}$.      *Ans.* $8 \times 10^4$.

f. $x = \sqrt{16 \times 10^{-6}} \times \sqrt{9 \times 10^4}$.      *Ans.* $1.2$.

g. $x = \sqrt{22,400}$.      *Ans.* $1.50 \times 10^2$.

h. $x = (22,400)^{\frac{1}{3}}$.      *Ans.* $2.82 \times 10$.

i. $x = \sqrt[3]{0.0000042}$.      *Ans.* $1.61 \times 10^{-2}$.

j. $x = (602,000,000)^{\frac{1}{4}}$.      *Ans.* $1.57 \times 10^2$.

k. $x = \sqrt{(248)^2}$.      *Ans.* $248$.

l. $x = \sqrt{(10,000)^{\frac{1}{2}}}$.      *Ans.* $10$.

**1.8. Approximation of Answers.** In problems involving the successive multiplication and division of numbers, there is always the possibility of misplacing the decimal point in the answer. In such problems one may determine by inspection whether or not the answer is of the proper order of magnitude. This method involves what is termed "approximation of numbers," in which each number other than the power of ten is changed to the nearest integer value. For example, a number such as $7.65 \times 10$ becomes $8 \times 10$ as an approximation, and $1.25 \times 10^2$ becomes $1 \times 10^2$.

**Example 1.11.** Determine by the method of approximation the location of the decimal point in the following answer.

$$76.5 \times \tfrac{125}{2000} \times \tfrac{1600}{275} = 278.$$

**Solution.**

$$\frac{(7.65 \times 10)(1.25 \times 10^2)(1.6 \times 10^3)}{(2 \times 10^3)(2.75 \times 10^2)} = \frac{(8 \times 1 \times 2)(10^6)}{(2 \times 3)(10^5)} = \frac{16}{6} \times 10 = 30.$$

That is, the answer is of the order of magnitude of 30. The correct answer is therefore 27.8. With practice one can readily acquire the ability to carry out most of the above operations mentally.

### Problems

1.12. By the method of approximation determine the location of the decimal point in each of the following.

a. $\dfrac{2.76 \times 1300}{230} = 1560.$                     *Ans.* 15.60.

b. $\dfrac{1600 \times 4.6}{486 \times 76.5} = 1980.$                     *Ans.* 0.1980.

c. $38 \times \tfrac{735}{760} \times \tfrac{390}{273} = 4038.$                     *Ans.* 40.38.

d. $\dfrac{341 \times 0.00782}{1742 \times 3.07} = 4985.$                     *Ans.* $4.985 \times 10^{-4}$.

### Elementary Algebra

**1.9. Algebraic Equations.** Only coefficients of like factors may be added or subtracted. For example:

$$4x + 3x = 7x,$$
$$6x^2 - 2x^2 + x = 4x^2 + x,$$
and $$3x^2 - 2x - 5x = 3x^2 - 7x.$$

The rules relating to exponential quantities, as presented previously, apply to algebraic equations. Exponents of like factors are *added* when the exponential quantities are *multiplied*, and *subtracted* when the quantities are *divided*. For example:

$$3x \times 2x^2 = 6x^3,$$
$$12x^2 \div 3x = 4x,$$
and $$\frac{12x^2 \times x^2}{4x^3} = 3x.$$

The discussion which follows will be limited to the solution of problems involving only one unknown, usually represented by $x$.

**Example 1.12.** Solve for $x$.

$$36x = 756 + 8x.$$

**Solution.**

$36x = 756 + 8x.$   Collecting like terms gives
$$36x - 8x = 756$$
or
$$28x = 756$$
and
$$x = 27.$$

**Example 1.13.** Solve for $x$.

$$9x^2 + 5x - 8 = 0.$$

**Solution.**   This is a *quadratic* equation of the general form

$$ax^2 + bx + c = 0,$$

and may be solved for $x$ by substituting the values of the constants $a$, $b$, and $c$ in the formula:

$$x = \frac{-b \pm \sqrt{b^2 - 4ac}}{2a}.$$

Then
$$x = \frac{-5 \pm \sqrt{5^2 - (4)(9)(-8)}}{(2)(9)}$$

$$= 0.7 \quad \text{or} \quad -1.3.$$

## Problems

1.13. Determine the value of $x$ in each of the following expressions.

a. $3x - 9 = 0$.                                   *Ans.* $x = 3$.

b. $\dfrac{26 - x}{x} = 12$.                        *Ans.* $x = 2$.

c. $(560)(43 - 21x) = (150)(42.9)$.          *Ans.* $x = 1.5$.

d. $2x^2 - 3x - 50 = 0$.                        *Ans.* $x = 5.8$ or $-4.3$.

**1.10. Ratio and Proportion.**   A proportion is an expression of equality between *two ratios*.   In the most general form a proportion is expressed as $\dfrac{a}{b} = \dfrac{c}{d}$, where any one of the four quantities may be the unknown.   Solving the proportion gives $ad = bc$.   In this form the unknown may be expressed in terms of the other three.

**Example 1.14.** Solve for $x$.

$$\frac{122}{11.2} = \frac{24}{x}.$$

**Solution.**

$$122x = (11.2)(24)$$
and
$$x = 2.2.$$

**Example 1.15.** A sample of brass weighing 4.55 lb. was found to contain 3.18 lb. of copper and 1.37 lb. of zinc. How much copper would there be in 500 lb. of the brass?

**Solution.** The ratio of copper to brass must be constant in any given mass of the brass. Therefore:

$$\frac{3.18 \text{ lb. copper}}{4.55 \text{ lb. brass}} = \frac{x \text{ lb. copper}}{500 \text{ lb. brass}}$$

or
$$x = \frac{(3.18)(500)}{(4.55)} \text{ lb. copper}$$

$$= 349 \text{ lb. copper.}$$

### Problems

1.14. Solve for $x$: $\dfrac{12.2}{x} = \dfrac{4.8}{33.4}$. *Ans.* 84.9.

1.15. A 12 ft. rod of iron weighed 33.4 lb. What would be the weight of a section of the rod measuring 4 ft. 7 in., assuming the rod to be of uniform cross section? *Ans.* 12.8 lb.

1.16. If seven-tenths of a ton of coal costs \$11.25, what will 3.5 tons cost? *Ans.* \$56.25.

**1.11. Percentage.** Percentage is a *ratio* indicating the number of parts out of 100. That is, 5% means five parts out of 100, or $\frac{5}{100}$. A common fraction represents a ratio, and a decimal fraction a given portion of a unit value.

**Example 1.16.** Express each of the following as percentage: (a) $\frac{11}{36}$, and (b) 0.24.

**Solution.**

(a) Since percentage is parts per 100, then:

$$\frac{11}{36} = \frac{x}{100}$$

or
$$x = (\tfrac{11}{36} \times 100)\%$$
$$= 31\%.$$

(b) Since a decimal fraction represents a given portion of the unit value, then:

$$\frac{0.24}{1} = \frac{x}{100}$$

or
$$x = (0.24 \times 100)\%$$
$$= 24\%.$$

From Example 1.16 we see that both common fractions and decimal fractions may be expressed as percentage by multiplying the fractions by 100.

## Problems

**1.17.** Convert each of the following to percentage.

    a. 0.74                                        *Ans.* 74%.

    b. 0.01                                         *Ans.* 1%.

    c. $\frac{6}{100}$                                        *Ans.* 6%.

    d. $\frac{23}{25}$                                        *Ans.* 92%.

    e. $1\frac{3}{4}$                                        *Ans.* 175%.

**1.18.** Convert each of the following to the corresponding decimal fraction.

    a. 16%                                      *Ans.* $\frac{4}{25}$.

    b. 1.5%                                     *Ans.* $\frac{3}{200}$.

    c. 0.3%                                     *Ans.* $\frac{3}{1000}$.

    d. $6\frac{3}{4}$%                                 *Ans.* $\frac{27}{400}$.

**1.19.** What is 15% of $1500?              *Ans.* $225.

**1.20.** What is 2.75% of $1600?         *Ans.* $44.

**1.21.** What is 0.25% of $2000?         *Ans.* $5.

**1.22.** A sample of brass contains 65.0 per cent copper and 35.0 per cent zinc. How much copper and how much zinc would there be in 140 pounds of the brass?     *Ans.* 91 lb. copper, 49 lb. zinc.

**1.23.** An average sample of sea water contains $5 \times 10^{-6}$% bromine. How many tons of sea water would be required in order to obtain one ton of bromine?     *Ans.* $2 \times 10^7$ tons.

**1.24.** An average sample of sea water contains 3.5% dissolved solids. How many pounds of sea water would be required to obtain one pound of dissolved solids by evaporation of the water? *Ans.* 28.6 lb.

**1.25.** Stainless steel consists of approximately 74% iron and 26% chromium. How much iron and how much chromium would be required to prepare 250 tons of stainless steel?     *Ans.* 185 tons iron,

                                                            65 tons chromium.

# 2

# Units of Measurement Used in Chemistry

The metric system of measure and the centigrade scale of temperature are used almost exclusively in chemistry. Every student therefore must be familiar with these units of measure. It is for this reason that a survey is given at this time of the common metric units involving length, weight, and volume, and a comparison of the Fahrenheit, centigrade, and absolute scales of temperature. Table 2.4, p. 16, which gives the relationship between corresponding English and metric units, will be found helpful in visualizing the relative magnitude of the more commonly used metric units. The unit of time used universally is the second.

## Metric Units of Length, Mass, and Volume

**2.1. Introduction.** In any system of measurement there must be arbitrarily established units of *length*, *mass*, and *volume*. Examination of the apparatus used in laboratories will show that length is commonly measured in *meters*, mass in *grams*, and volume in *cubic centimeters* or *milliliters*. These are the fundamental units of length, mass, and volume in the metric system.

Metric units are based on a decimal system in which the prefix designates the multiple or submultiple value of the quantity in terms of the fundamental unit. See Table 2.1, p. 14.

The principal advantage of the metric system is that values of length, mass, and volume repeat in multiples of ten. English units are inconsistent — 12 in. equals one foot, 3 ft. equals one yard, and $5\frac{1}{2}$ yd. equals one rod. The metric system also represents a more international standard than does the English system. The meter, gram, and liter as used in the United States are identical to the corresponding units used in any other country. On the other hand, in England a quart is larger than the quart used in the United States, and in France an inch is longer than the inch used in England.

The *centimeter-gram-second* (cgs) system, called the metric system, and the *foot-pound-second* (fps) system, called the English system, are the two principal surviving standards in the world today. The unit of time, the second, is the same in each of the two systems.

TABLE 2.1

PREFIXES USED IN THE METRIC SYSTEM AND THEIR VALUES

|  |  |  |
|---|---|---|
| micro = | 0.000001 | part of fundamental unit |
| milli = | 0.001 | part of fundamental unit |
| centi = | 0.01 | part of fundamental unit |
| deci = | 0.1 | part of fundamental unit |
|  | 1.0 | fundamental unit |
| deka = | 10 | times fundamental unit |
| hecto = | 100 | times fundamental unit |
| kilo = | 1000 | times fundamental unit |

**2.2. The More Commnly Used Metric Units of Length.** The fundamental unit of length in the metric system is the *meter* (m.). Originally the meter was intended to represent one ten-millionth of the earth's quadrant. Although recent measurements with more precise measuring instruments than used originally have shown the meter to be slightly in error, the length as originally adopted has been retained. The meter is now defined as the distance between two parallel lines on a platinum-iridium bar kept in the International Bureau of Weights and Measures at Sèvres, France. Replicas of the bar are called secondary standards and are available to any country desiring them. The United States possesses two such secondary standards of the meter which, along with other standards, are kept in the National Bureau of Standards, Washington, D.C. In Tables 2.2 and 2.3, the more commonly used units are given in **boldface** type.

TABLE 2.2

METRIC UNITS OF LENGTH USING THE METER AS THE
FUNDAMENTAL UNIT

|  |  |  |  |
|---|---|---|---|
| 1 **millimeter** (mm.) | = | 0.001 | m. |
| 1 **centimeter** (cm.) | = | 0.01 | m. |
| 1 **decimeter** (dm.) | = | 0.1 | m. |
| 1 **meter** (m.) | = | 1 | m. |
| 1 **kilometer** (km.) | = 1000 |  | m. |

Three other units of length are used to express the size of extremely small particles such as atoms, and the magnitudes relating to extremely short waves such as light and X-rays. The units are the *micron* ($\mu$), the *millimicron* (m$\mu$), and the *angstrom* (A.).

$$1.00 \text{ A.} = 10^{-8} \text{ cm.}$$
$$1.00 \text{ m}\mu = 10^{-7} \text{ cm.} = 10 \text{ A.}$$
$$1.00 \ \mu = 10^{-4} \text{ cm.} = 10^{3} \text{ m}\mu = 10^{4} \text{ A.}$$

**2.3. The More Commonly Used Metric Units of Mass.** The fundamental unit of mass in the metric system is the *gram* (g.). The gram was originally intended to represent the volume occupied by 1 cm.$^3$ of water at 3.98° C., the temperature at which water possesses its greatest density. As with the meter, later measurements have shown that one gram of water at 3.98° C. occupies a volume of 1.000027 cm.$^3$ It is only in extremely accurate work that this discrepancy in volume must be taken into consideration.

A direct relationship thus exists between the centimeter as a unit of length and the gram as a unit of mass. Table 2.3 gives metric units of mass in terms of decimal fractions of a gram because of the common practice of recording weights in this manner.

TABLE 2.3

METRIC UNITS OF MASS USING THE GRAM AS THE
FUNDAMENTAL UNIT

| | | |
|---|---|---|
| 1 milligram (mg.) = | 0.001 | g. |
| 1 centigram (cg.) = | 0.01 | g. |
| 1 decigram (dg.) = | 0.1 | g. |
| 1 gram (g.) = | 1 | g. |
| 1 kilogram (kg.) = | 1000 | g. |

**2.4. The More Commonly Used Metric Units of Volume.** Units of area and volume in the metric system are obtained in the same manner as are corresponding units in the English system.

The *cubic centimeter* (cc. or cm.$^3$) is the metric unit of volume most commonly used in laboratory work. It is, however, a relatively small unit of volume. A larger unit of volume, the *liter* (*l.*), is defined as the volume occupied by one kilogram of water at 3.98° C. The liter was also designed to correct for the error involved when the cubic centimeter was adopted. One liter is therefore equal to 1000.027 cm.$^3$ Ordinarily in the laboratory it is assumed that one milliliter (ml.) is equal in volume to one cubic centimeter. That is, cc., cm.³, and ml. may be used interchangeably.

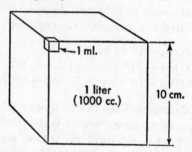

Fig. 2.1. The metric unit of volume, the liter.

**2.5. The Relationship between English and Metric Units of Length, Mass, and Volume.** By means of constants such as given in Table 2.4, one may change values in one system of units into the corresponding values in the other system of units.

TABLE 2.4

CONSTANTS RELATING ENGLISH AND METRIC UNITS

| A[1] | | C | B |
|---|---|---|---|
| centimeters | $\times$ | $10^8$ | $=$ angstroms |
| centimeters | $\times$ | $10^7$ | $=$ millimicrons |
| centimeters | $\times$ | $10^4$ | $=$ microns |
| cubic centimeters | $\times$ | $2.64 \times 10^{-4}$ | $=$ gallons |
| cubic inches | $\times$ | 16.4 | $=$ cubic centimeters |
| feet | $\times$ | 30.5 | $=$ centimeters |
| inches | $\times$ | 2.54 | $=$ centimeters |
| kilograms | $\times$ | 2.20 | $=$ pounds |
| kilometers | $\times$ | 0.621 | $=$ miles |
| liters | $\times$ | 0.264 | $=$ gallons |
| liters | $\times$ | 61.0 | $=$ cubic inches |
| liters | $\times$ | 1.06 | $=$ quarts |
| meters | $\times$ | 1.09 | $=$ yards |
| meters | $\times$ | 3.28 | $=$ feet |
| meters | $\times$ | 39.4 | $=$ inches |
| ounces | $\times$ | 28.3 | $=$ grams |
| pounds | $\times$ | 454 | $=$ grams |
| quarts | $\times$ | 946 | $=$ cubic centimeters |
| square inches | $\times$ | 6.45 | $=$ square centimeters |

[1] $A = \dfrac{B}{C}$.

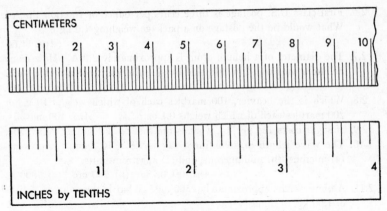

Fig. 2.2. A comparison of the English and metric units of length.

## Problems

### Part I

2.1. Linear units.  Change:
   a. 125 mm. to cm.                     *Ans.* 12.5 cm.
   b. 1.25 m. to cm.                      *Ans.* 125 cm.
   c. 2600 m. to km.                     *Ans.* 2.6 km.
   d. 1.65 cm. to A.                 *Ans.* $1.65 \times 10^8$ A.
   e. $2800\mu$ to mm.                    *Ans.* 2.8 mm.
   f. 25 in. to cm.                      *Ans.* 63.5 cm.
   g. 18 ft. to m.                        *Ans.* 5.49 m.
   h. 2.0 in. to A.                *Ans.* $5.08 \times 10^8$ A.

2.2. Volume units.  Change:
   a. 1500 ml. to *l.*                       *Ans.* 1.5 *l.*
   b. 0.025 *l.* to ml.                     *Ans.* 25 ml.
   c. 15 qt. to *l.*                       *Ans.* 14.2 *l.*
   d. 15 *l.* to gal.                      *Ans.* 3.96 gal.
   e. 2.35 qt. to ml.                    *Ans.* 2223 ml.

2.3. Weight units.  Change:
   a. 2.10 g. to mg.                     *Ans.* 2100 mg.
   b. 1.65 kg. to g.                      *Ans.* 1650 g.
   c. 3500 mg. to g.                    *Ans.* 3.5 g.
   d. 35 lb. to kg.                      *Ans.* 15.9 kg.
   e. 2.36 kg. to lb.                    *Ans.* 5.19 lb.

2.4. How many cm.³ are there in a rod of uniform cross section measuring 10 cm. by 2 cm. by 90 cm.?         *Ans.* 1800 cm.³

2.5. Calculate the volume in liters of a box measuring 12 cm. by 120 mm. by 1.2 m.                    *Ans.* 17.3 *l.*

2.6. First-class U.S. postage is three cents per ounce or fraction thereof. What would be the postage on a package weighing 1.0 kg.?

*Ans.* $1.06.

2.7. The diameter of a helium atom is approximately 2.0 A. How many helium atoms could be laid side by side the length of a meter stick?

*Ans.* $5 \times 10^9$.

2.8. Which is the heavier, 100 marbles each of which weighs 10 g., or 200 marbles each of which weighs 0.1 oz.?          *Ans.* 100 marbles.

2.9. If sugar costs 12¢ per lb., what is the cost per kilogram? *Ans.* 26¢.

2.10. The wave length of an infrared ray is $7.8 \times 10^{-5}$ cm. Express as (a) microns, (b) millimicrons, and (c) angstrom units.

*Ans.* (a) 0.78μ;  (b) 780 mμ;  (c) 7800 A.

2.11. A dime weighs approximately 2500 mg. What is the value in dollars of 1.00 kg. of dimes?          *Ans.* $40.

2.12. List in the order of increasing value:

a. Units of length — foot, meter, kilometer, yard, mile, millimeter, inch, and centimeter.

b. Units of mass — kilogram, ounce, milligram, pound, and gram.

c. Units of volume — milliliter, quart, cubic centimeter, cubic inch, cubic decimeter, and liter.

## Part II

2.13. Linear units.  Change:

| | |
|---|---|
| a. 0.235 m. to mm. | *Ans.* 235 mm. |
| b. 0.015 km. to cm. | *Ans.* 1500 cm. |
| c. 255 A. to mμ. | *Ans.* 25.5 mμ. |
| d. 0.75 mm. to μ. | *Ans.* 750 μ. |
| e. 2800 mμ to cm. | *Ans.* $2.8 \times 10^{-4}$ cm. |
| f. 25 cm. to in. | *Ans.* 9.85 in. |
| g. $\frac{5}{16}$ in. to mm. | *Ans.* 7.9 mm. |
| h. $5 \times 10^5$ mμ to in. | *Ans.* 0.02 in. |

2.14. Volume units.  Change:

| | |
|---|---|
| a. 1500 cm.³ to ml. | *Ans.* 1500 ml. |
| b. 2.25 m³ to *l*. | *Ans.* 2250 *l*. |
| c. 1.27 *l*. to cc. | *Ans.* 1270 cc. |
| d. 25 in.³ to *l*. | *Ans.* 0.41 *l*. |
| e. 1.75 yd.³ to kl. | *Ans.* 1.338 kl. |

2.15. Weight units.  Change:

| | |
|---|---|
| a. 0.0025 kg. to mg. | *Ans.* 2500 mg. |
| b. 125 g. to kg. | *Ans.* 0.125 kg. |
| c. 1000 g. to lb. | *Ans.* 2.2 lb. |
| d. 1.25 tons to kg. | *Ans.* 1136 kg. |
| e. 1000 g. to oz. | *Ans.* 35.3 oz. |

2.16. How many cm.³ are there in one cubic meter?          *Ans.* $10^6$ cm.³

2.17. How many liters are there in one cubic meter?          *Ans.* $10^3$ *l*.

2.18. What is the weight of one gallon of water in kilograms?  *Ans.* 3.78 kg.

2.19. How many cubic inches are there in one liter?  *Ans.* 61 in.³

2.20. Calculate the volume in liters of a box measuring 24 in. by 6.5 in. by 10 in.  *Ans.* 25.6 *l.*

2.21. A speed of 60 $\frac{mi.}{hr.}$ corresponds to how many kilometers per hour?

*Ans.* 97 $\frac{km.}{hr.}$

2.22. The wave lengths of the visible rays in sunlight vary from 4000 A. for violet to 7000 A. for red.  Express as centimeters.

*Ans.* $4 \times 10^{-5}$ cm.;  $7 \times 10^{-5}$ cm.

2.23. The wave lengths of X-rays vary from $10^{-9}$ cm. to $10^{-6}$ cm.  Express as angstrom units.  *Ans.* 0.10 A.;  100 A.

2.24. A uniform iron bar 15 in. long weighs 2 lb. 4 oz.  Calculate the weight of the bar in grams per centimeter of length.  *Ans.* 26.8 g.

2.25. At room temperature the linear velocity of an oxygen molecule is about $4 \times 10^4$ cm. per sec.  What would the velocity of the oxygen molecule be in mi. per hour?  *Ans.* 894 $\frac{mi.}{hr.}$

2.26. If gasoline costs 30¢ per gallon, what is the cost per liter?

*Ans.* 7.9¢.

2.27. When placed on water, 1.00 ml. of oil spreads uniformly over an area of 500 cm.²  Express the thickness of the film in (a) microns, and (b) millimicrons.  *Ans.* 20μ;  (b) $2 \times 10^4$ mμ.

2.28. Soap bubble films average about 60 A. in thickness.  Express as (a) millimeters, and (b) centimeters.

*Ans.* (a) $6 \times 10^{-6}$ mm.;  $6 \times 10^{-7}$ cm.

2.29. How much area in m.² would 1.00 cm.³ of oil cover on water if the oil film were 4 A. in thickness?  *Ans.* $2.5 \times 10^3$ m².

2.30. Parcels shipped to areas in which the humidity is high are sometimes coated with a gel, one gram of which will cover approximately $5 \times 10^6$ cm.² of surface.  Express this as micrograms of gel per square meter.  *Ans.* $2 \times 10^3$ μg.

2.31. A nickel weighs approximately 5 g.  What is the weight in kilograms of $100 worth of nickels?  *Ans.* 10 kg.

2.32. Calculate your height in meters and in centimeters.

2.33. Calculate your weight in grams and in kilograms.

## Temperature Scales

**2.6. Introduction.**  In the laboratory, temperatures are usually recorded as *centigrade* (°C.) or *absolute* (°K.).  The symbol K. for absolute temperatures is used in honor of Lord Kelvin, the first person to postulate the existence of such a scale and its possible use.  The

*Fahrenheit* (°F.) scale is used domestically and, to some extent, in industry in the United States and England. The mercury expansion type of thermometer is the most commonly used instrument to measure temperatures.

**2.7. Interconversion of Centigrade and Absolute Temperatures.** In the solution of mathematical problems it is common practice to represent absolute temperatures by T and centigrade temperatures by t in formulas involving the quantities.

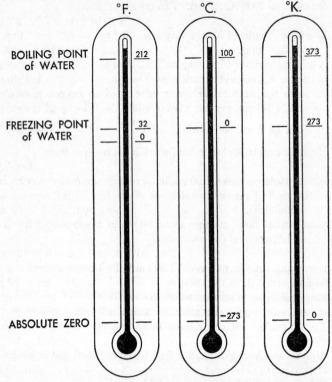

Fig. 2.3. A comparison of the Fahrenheit, centigrade, and absolute scales of temperature.

From Fig. 2.3 it will be observed that for any given temperature the values in °C. and °K. differ by the constant value 273. This constant difference is due to the choice of the zero point on each of the two scales. That is:

$$T = 273 + t$$

or $$t = T - 273.$$

**Example 2.1.** Normal body temperature is about 37° C. What would this be on the absolute scale?

**Solution.**

$$T = 273 + t$$

or

$$T = 273 + 37$$
$$= 310° K.$$

**2.8. Interconversion of Fahrenheit and Centigrade Temperatures.** The interconversion of Fahrenheit and centigrade temperatures is based upon the relationship shown in Fig. 2.3. That is:

an interval of 180° F. = 100° C.

or,    an interval of 1° F. = $(\frac{5}{9})$° C.

and,    an interval of 1° C. = $(\frac{9}{5})$° F.

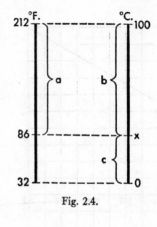

Fig. 2.4.

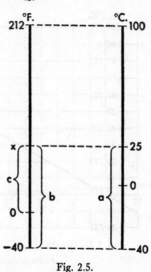

Fig. 2.5.

**Example 2.2.** Convert 86° F. to the corresponding centigrade value.

**Solution.** Let us see how we may reason out the answer to the problem. First, choose a reference temperature such as the boiling point of water as shown in Fig. 2.4. The solution to the problem now lies in converting the Fahrenheit scale interval "$a$" to the corresponding centigrade scale interval "$b$." The temperature to be found is "$c$," which is $100 - b$.

$$a = 212 - 86 = 126,$$
$$b = 126 \times \tfrac{5}{9} = 70,$$

and    $c = 100 - 70 = 30°$ C.

That is, 86° F. is equal to 30° C.

**Example 2.3.** Convert 25° C. to the corresponding Fahrenheit value.

**Solution.** It so happens that −40° C. and −40° F. are the same temperature. Using −40° C. as the reference temperature we see, from Fig. 2.5, p. 21, that:

$$a = 40 + 25 \quad = 65,$$
$$b = 65 \times \tfrac{9}{5} \quad = 117,$$

and

$$c = 117 - 40 = 77° \text{ F.}$$

That is, 25° C. is equal to 77° F.

**2.9. The Interconversion of Fahrenheit, Centigrade, and Absolute Temperatures by Means of a Graphical Method.** The interconversion of the three scales of temperature may be brought about by means of the graph shown in Fig. 2.6.

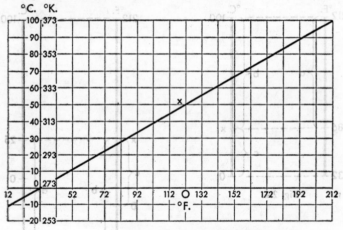

Fig. 2.6.  Graphical representation of the Fahrenheit, centigrade, and absolute scales of temperature.

Each scale division on the x-axis in Fig. 2.6 represents 10° F., and each division on the y-axis 10° C. or 10° K. The diagonal line was obtained by plotting Fahrenheit temperatures against the corresponding centigrade or absolute values.

**Example 2.4.** Convert 122° F. to the corresponding centigrade and absolute values, using Fig. 2.6.

**Solution.** Let O in Fig. 2.6 represent 122° F. Now draw a line from O parallel to the y-axis and intersecting the diagonal at x. A horizontal line drawn from x parallel to the x-axis intersects the y-axis at a point corresponding to 50° C. or 323° K. These are the temperatures to be found.

## Problems

### Part I

2.34. Convert:
   a. 50° C. to °F.          *Ans.* 122° F.
   b. 50° F. to °C.          *Ans.* 10° C.
   c. 50° F. to °K.          *Ans.* 283° K.
   d. 50° K. to °F.          *Ans.* −369° F.

2.35. A solution of salt water was found to freeze at 14° F. What is the freezing point of the solution in °C.?          *Ans.* −10° C.

2.36. Three thermometers are side by side. One is calibrated in °F., another in °C., and the third in °K. The Fahrenheit thermometer registers −22°. What is the temperature on each of the other two thermometers?          *Ans.* −30° C., 243° K.

2.37. Silver melts at 960.8° C. What is the melting point in °F.?          *Ans.* 1761° F.

2.38. The sublimation temperature of dry ice is −109° F. What is the temperature in °C.?          *Ans.* −78.3° C.

### Part II

2.39. Mercury boils at 630° K. Calculate the boiling point of mercury in (a) °C., and (b) °F.          *Ans.* (a) 357° C.; (b) 675° F.

2.40. Assuming the surface of the sun to be 10,832° F., calculate the temperature in °K.          *Ans.* 6273° K.

2.41. By means of Fig. 2.6 convert: (a) 50° C. to °F., (b) 50° F. to °C., and (c) 50° F. to °K.          *Ans.* (a) 122° F.; (b) 10° C.; (c) 283° K.

2.42. Show that Fahrenheit and centigrade temperatures are numerically the same at −40° C.

2.43. Mercury is used in some thermometers, and alcohol containing a colored pigment in others. Mercury freezes at −38.9° C. and boils at 356.6° C.; alcohol freezes at −117.3° C. and boils at 78.5° C. Over what limits of temperature range in °F. could each type of thermometer be used?
   *Ans.* Mercury, −38° F. and 674° F.; alcohol, −179° F. and 173° F.

2.44. If the freezing point of water had been used on the Fahrenheit scale as the zero of temperature, what would be the boiling point of water?          *Ans.* 180°.

2.45. Zero absolute corresponds to what temperature on the Fahrenheit scale?          *Ans.* −459° F.

2.46. A 10 degree interval on the centigrade scale corresponds to how many degrees interval on (a) the Fahrenheit scale, and (b) the absolute scale?          *Ans.* (a) 18°; (b) 10°.

2.47. List the following in order of increasing temperature: 100° K., 100° C., and 100° F.

# 3

# Significant Digits

In carrying out the mathematical operations of addition, subtraction, multiplication, and division, the student is confronted with the problem of the number of digits to retain in the answer. Very definite rules may be followed in such mathematical operations. Fortunately the rules are not difficult to remember and are easy to apply. Much unnecessary work may be avoided in mathematical operations by remembering the rules applying to significant digits.

## Significant Digits in Experimental Measurements

**3.1. Introduction.** Experimental data involving numbers are seldom absolutely accurate values. The accuracy of such data is dependent upon the precision of the measuring instrument used. For example, suppose the length of the iron rod shown in Fig. 3.1 is deter-

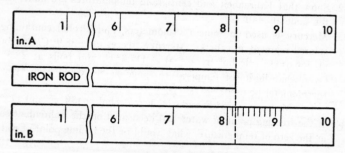

Fig. 3.1. The accuracy of a measurement depends upon the measuring instrument used.

mined by the measuring instruments A and B. Using instrument A, in which the centimeter is the smallest scale division, we see that the end of the rod lies between the 8 and 9 centimeter marks. Estimating the length to the nearest tenth of a centimeter gives the value 8.2 cm.

Using instrument B, in which the millimeter is the smallest scale division, gives the value 8.1̲6̲ cm. The underscored figure in each measured value has been estimated, and is therefore not absolutely reliable. Recorded data should represent the greatest accuracy possible with the measuring instrument used.

The discussion which follows deals primarily with the mathematical treatment of data. Such treatment should be consistent with the accuracy of the data used.

**3.2. Significant Digits.** Any figure representing a reasonably reliable value should be considered a *significant digit*. The value 8̲.2̲ cm., given in Sec. 3.1, represents two significant digits; the value 8.1̲6̲ cm. represents three significant digits. The number of significant digits in a quantity is independent of the location of the decimal point.

From the above it is apparent that the precision of the measuring instrument is a factor in determining the number of significant digits in a number. Another factor is the size of the object measured. For example, two objects were found to weigh 3̲.1̲ g. and 18̲.3̲ g., respectively, on a balance accurate to one-tenth of a gram. The weight of the larger object contains three significant digits, whereas the weight of the smaller object contains only two significant digits.

**3.3. Zero as a Significant Digit.** Zero occupies a unique position in our number system containing the ten symbols 1, 2, 3, 4, 5, 6, 7, 8, 9, and 0. Depending upon the manner in which it is used, zero may or may not be a significant digit when appearing in a number.

Zero may be used merely to give position value to a combination of one or more of the ten symbols in our number system. When so used, zero is not a significant digit. For example, in the expression 2̲.54̲ mm. = 0.254̲ cm. = 0.00254̲ m. = 0.00000254̲ km., none of the zeros are significant digits. In each case the zeros are used to give position value to the significant digits, 254̲. Zeros may also be used to give position value to integer numbers. For example, the statement that the earth is approximately 8̲000 miles in diameter represents one significant digit. Actually, the earth may be 7̲926̲ miles in diameter on a given axis, which value represents four significant digits. Exponential forms are sometimes used to indicate the number of significant digits in integer values. For example:

$$8000 \text{ miles} = 8̲ \times 10^3 \text{ miles},$$
$$7̲900 \text{ miles} = 7̲.9̲ \times 10^3 \text{ miles},$$
$$186000̲ \frac{\text{mi.}}{\text{sec.}} = 1̲.86̲ \times 10^5 \frac{\text{mi.}}{\text{sec.}}.$$

When used as one of the ten symbols in our number system, zero must be considered as a significant digit, regardless of the position of the decimal point. The zeros in each of the following expressions are significant: 1.06 m., 20.4 cm., 106 cm., 1004 ft., 2.20 lb., 9.600 g., 100.20 cm., and 1.0200 g. Observe that a zero following any of the other nine symbols, when to the right of the decimal point, is significant. One should be extremely careful in the use of zero when recording experimental data.

Some integer values are absolutely accurate values. For example, one egg represents 1.00000—— egg carried to an infinite number of significant digits. It is usually not difficult to recognize such integer values.

## Problems

### Part I

3.1. Give the number of significant digits in each of the following values.
  a. 15 cm.                                                      *Ans.* 2.
  b. 0.15 cm.                                                    *Ans.* 2.
  c. 15.0 cm.                                                    *Ans.* 3.
  d. 0.015 cm.                                                   *Ans.* 2.
  e. 1.250 g.                                                    *Ans.* 4.
  f. 13.002 g.                                                   *Ans.* 5.
  g. 0.0602 g.                                                   *Ans.* 3.
  h. 6.050 × 10² g.                                              *Ans.* 4.
  i. 3.00 × 10⁻² m.                                              *Ans.* 3.
  j. 8 silver dollars.                                           *Ans.* ∞.
3.2. Express each of the following as a power of ten, the number other than the power of ten containing the significant digits.
  a. One mile is equal to approximately 5300 ft.    *Ans.* 5.3 × 10³.
  b. One mile is equal to 5280 ft.                 *Ans.* 5.280 × 10³.
  c. Under ordinary room conditions sound travels approximately 1000 ft./sec.                              *Ans.* 1 × 10³ ft./sec.
  d. One yard is equal to 0.9144 m.               *Ans.* 9.144 × 10⁻¹.
  e. One yard is equal to approximately 900 mm.        *Ans.* 9 × 10².

### Part II

3.3. Give the number of significant digits in each of the following values.
  a. 1.01 l.                                                     *Ans.* 3.
  b. 250.10 m.                                                   *Ans.* 5.
  c. 0.00101 kg.                                                 *Ans.* 3.
  d. 9.0900 m.                                                   *Ans.* 5.
  e. 1.600 × 10² g.                                              *Ans.* 4.
  f. 2.0 × 10⁻³ ml.                                              *Ans.* 2.

g. $80.00 \times 10^2$ mm.                                    *Ans.* 4.

h. 3125 nails.                                                 *Ans.* $\infty$.

3.4. Express each of the following as a power of ten, the number other than the power of ten containing the significant digits.

a. One foot is equal to approximately 300 mm.     *Ans.* $3 \times 10^2$.

b. One foot is equal to 304.8 mm.              *Ans.* $3.048 \times 10^2$.

c. One cubic foot is equal to approximately 28,000 ml. *Ans.* $2.8 \times 10^4$.

d. One cubic foot is equal to 0.028 m³.          *Ans.* $2.8 \times 10^{-2}$.

e. At 0° C. sound travels with a velocity of 331.36 m./sec.

                                                    *Ans.* $3.3136 \times 10^2$.

## The Use of Significant Digits in Mathematical Operations

**3.4. Addition and Subtraction.** Only quantities representing like units and expressed to the same number of decimal places may be added or subtracted, regardless of the number of significant digits in the quantities.

**Example 3.1.** Add: 12.7 m. + 219.31 cm. + 332 mm.

**Solution.** First, change the quantities to like units, in this case the meter. The unit used is a matter of choice. Next, round off the numbers to one decimal place. One decimal place is chosen since this represents the least accurately measured quantity of the three to be added. Then,

$$
\begin{array}{llll}
12.7 \text{ m.} & = 12.7 \text{ m.} & = 12.7 \text{ m.} \\
219.31 \text{ cm.} & = 2.1931 \text{ m.} & = 2.2 \text{ m.} \\
332 \text{ mm.} & = 0.332 \text{ m.} & = \underline{0.3 \text{ m.}} \\
& & \text{Add: } 15.2 \text{ m.}
\end{array}
$$

**3.5. Rounding Off Numbers.** When rounding off numbers, the last figure retained is increased by one if the number immediately following is greater than five. Thus, in Example 3.1, 2.1931 m. becomes 2.2 m., and 332 mm. becomes 0.3 m.

The following rule may be applied when the terminal figure is five. If the figure preceding a terminal five is odd, increase the figure by one. That is, 2.175 becomes 2.18. If the figure preceding the terminal five is even, the figure remains unchanged. That is, 2.165 becomes 2.16.

**3.6. Multiplication and Division.** In multiplication and division the number of significant digits retained in the product or quotient is the same as the least number of significant digits occurring in either of the quantities involved. Note that the numbers are not rounded off before performing the mathematical operation, and that the units need not be similar.

**Example 3.2.** A rectangular sheet of platinum measures 5.29 mm. by 16.14 mm. What is the area of the sheet?

**Solution.**

$$\underline{5.29} \text{ mm.} \times \underline{16.14} \text{ mm.} = \underline{85.3806} \text{ mm.}^2 = \underline{85.4} \text{ mm.}^2$$

**Example 3.3.** A car traveled 277.68 mi. in 6.21 hr. What was the average speed in mi./hr.?

**Solution.**

$$\underline{277.68} \text{ mi.} \div \underline{6.21} \text{ hr.} = \underline{44.71} \text{ mi./hr.} = \underline{44.7} \text{ mi./hr.}$$

In the process of division it is customary to carry the quotient to one more significant digit than necessary in order to round off the answer to the required number of significant digits.

**Example 3.4.** Simplify the expression $\dfrac{5.8 \times 0.0899}{273}$.

**Solution.**

$$\frac{5.8 \times 0.0899}{273} = 0.00191 = 1.9 \times 10^{-3}.$$

**Example 3.5.** What is the surface area of a table measuring 2.63 m. by 76.5 cm.?

**Solution.** It is customary to use like units when calculating areas and volumes. Such treatment gives areas in terms of unit squares, and volumes in terms of unit cubes. Then:

$$2.63 \text{ m.} \times 0.765 \text{ m.} = 2.01 \text{ m.}^2$$

Only general rules relating to the use of significant digits in mathematical operations have been presented in the foregoing discussions. More comprehensive treatments can be introduced as the need for such arises.

## Problems

### Part I

3.5. Perform the indicated mathematical operations.

| | |
|---|---|
| a. 2.1 m. + 0.3 m. + 2.07 m. + 3.224 m. | *Ans.* 7.7 m. |
| b. 21.630 *l.* + 844 ml. + 0.036 *l.* + 10.196 ml. | *Ans.* 22.520 *l.* |
| c. 3.14 g. + 0.715 g. + 10.84 mg. | *Ans.* 3.87 g. |
| d. 13.22 cm. − 28.36 mm. | *Ans.* 10.38 cm. |
| e. 0.6260 g. − 15 mg. | *Ans.* 0.611 g. |
| f. 32.57 × 7.14 | *Ans.* 233. |
| g. 0.0482 × 0.2134 | *Ans.* 1.03 × 10⁻². |
| h. 7632 ÷ 173 | *Ans.* 44.1. |

   i.  $3.438 \div 0.988$                       *Ans.* 3.48.

   j.  $0.041761 \div 32.15$               *Ans.* $1.299 \times 10^{-3}$.

**3.6.** What is the area of a rectangle measuring 3.180 cm. by 22.4 mm.?

*Ans.* 7.12 cm.$^2$

**3.7.** Light travels $1.86 \times 10^5$ mi./sec. How far will a beam of light travel in one hour?          *Ans.* $6.70 \times 10^8$ mi.

**3.8.** A jar contains 10,000 lead shot averaging 0.2216 g. each. What is the weight of the shot?          *Ans.* 2216 g.

## Part II

**3.9.** Simplify each of the following expressions.

  a.  $\dfrac{2.56 \times 10^3}{454} \times 1.263$          *Ans.* 7.12.

  b.  $\dfrac{1566}{1.80} + 32$                *Ans.* 902.

  c.  $\dfrac{0.0154 \times 0.1276}{0.00891}$        *Ans.* $2.21 \times 10^{-1}$.

**3.10.** There are 2.54 cm. in one inch. How many centimeters are there in 15.0 in.?          *Ans.* 38.1 cm.

**3.11.** What is the cost of 1200 four-cent United States postage stamps?

*Ans.* \$48.00.

**3.12.** What is the circumference of a circle of 10.00 in. diameter, given that $\pi = 3.14$?          *Ans.* 31.4 in.

**3.13.** What is the circumference of a circle of 10.00 in. diameter, given that $\pi = 3.1416$?          *Ans.* 31.42 in.

**3.14.** A car travels $1.754 \times 10^2$ miles in 191.2 minutes. What is the average speed in miles per hour?          *Ans.* 55.04 mi./hr.

# 4

# Dimensional Analysis

Most quantities consist of both a numerical value and a dimensional value. The statement that a beaker contains 215 ml. of a liquid conveys two important ideas — the numerical value 215 and the dimensional value milliliters, both of which are necessary in order to express correctly the volume of liquid. The dimensional values commonly used in chemistry were discussed in Chapter 2. In the solution of a problem both the numerical and the dimensional values may be treated mathematically. When this is done the answer represents the correct numerical and dimensional values. The process of treating dimensions mathematically is called dimensional analysis.

**4.1. The Treatment of Dimensions in Addition and Subtraction.** Numbers which are added or subtracted must have the same dimensions. Obviously there would be no significance to the sum obtained by adding quantities such as 15 in. and 27 cm. without first converting to like units. This was discussed in Sec. 3.4.

**4.2. The Treatment of Dimensions in Multiplication and Division.** Quantities expressed either in like or unlike units may be multiplied or divided (Sec. 3.6). Also, the dimensions of the numbers may be treated mathematically in the same manner as the numbers.

**Example 4.1.** What is the area of a rectangular board 3.0 ft. long and 2.0 ft. wide?

**Solution.**

$$3.0 \text{ ft.} \times 2.0 \text{ ft.} = (3.0 \times 2.0)(\text{ft.} \times \text{ft.}) = 6.0 \text{ ft.}^2$$

Observe that both the numerical and the dimensional values have been multiplied.

**Example 4.2.** A car traveled 260 miles in 5.0 hours. Calculate the speed of the car in miles per hour $\left(\dfrac{\text{mi.}}{\text{hr.}}\right)$.

30

**Solution.**

$$\frac{260 \text{ mi.}}{5.0 \text{ hr.}} = \frac{260}{5.0} \frac{\text{mi.}}{\text{hr.}} = 52 \frac{\text{mi.}}{\text{hr.}}\cdot$$

In this case the dimensional value could not be simplified.

**Example 4.3.** How many centimeters are there in 15.0 in.?

**Solution.** There are 2.54 $\frac{\text{cm.}}{\text{in.}}\cdot$  Therefore:

$$2.54 \frac{\text{cm.}}{\text{in.}} \times 15.0 \text{ in.} = 38.1 \text{ cm.}$$

Cancellation of like units gives the desired dimensions, centimeters.

**Example 4.4.** How many feet are there in 200 cm.?

**Solution.** There are 30.5 $\frac{\text{cm.}}{\text{ft.}}\cdot$  Therefore:

$$\frac{200 \text{ cm.}}{30.5 \frac{\text{cm.}}{\text{ft.}}} = \frac{200}{30.5} \text{ cm.} \times \frac{\text{ft.}}{\text{cm.}} = 6.56 \text{ ft.}$$

**Example 4.5.** Given that there are 2.54 $\frac{\text{cm.}}{\text{in.}}\cdot$  Determine the number of inches per centimeter $\left(\frac{\text{in.}}{\text{cm.}}\right)\cdot$

**Solution.** Dimensionally $\frac{\text{cm.}}{\text{in.}}$ and $\frac{\text{in.}}{\text{cm.}}$ are reciprocals. Therefore:

$$\frac{1}{2.54 \frac{\text{cm.}}{\text{in.}}} = \frac{1}{2.54} \frac{\text{in.}}{\text{cm.}} = 0.394 \frac{\text{in.}}{\text{cm.}}\cdot$$

**Example 4.6.** Convert 2.36 kilograms to milligrams.

**Solution.** Dimensional analysis shows that the following operations must be carried out in order to obtain the value in milligrams.

$$\text{kg.} \times \frac{\text{g.}}{\text{kg.}} \times \frac{\text{mg.}}{\text{g.}} = \text{mg.}$$

Since there are 1000 $\frac{\text{g.}}{\text{kg.}}$ and 1000 $\frac{\text{mg.}}{\text{g.}}$, then:

$$2.36 \text{ kg.} \times 1000 \frac{\text{g.}}{\text{kg.}} \times 1000 \frac{\text{mg.}}{\text{g.}} = 2.36 \times 10^6 \text{ mg.}$$

**Example 4.7.** Convert $2\frac{7}{16}$ in. to millimeters.

**Solution.** There are 2.54 $\frac{\text{cm.}}{\text{in.}}$ and 10 $\frac{\text{mm.}}{\text{cm.}}\cdot$  Therefore:

$$\frac{39}{16} \text{ in.} \times 2.54 \frac{\text{cm.}}{\text{in.}} \times 10 \frac{\text{mm.}}{\text{cm.}} = 61.9 \text{ mm.}$$

**Example 4.8.** A car is traveling $60 \frac{\text{mi.}}{\text{hr.}}$. What is the speed of the car in $\frac{\text{ft.}}{\text{sec.}}$?

**Solution.** To obtain the desired answer it will be necessary to convert mi. to ft. and hr. to sec., and simplify. Since there are $5280 \frac{\text{ft.}}{\text{mi.}}$, $60 \frac{\text{min.}}{\text{hr.}}$, and $60 \frac{\text{sec.}}{\text{min.}}$, then

$$\frac{60 \text{ mi.} \times 5280 \frac{\text{ft.}}{\text{mi.}}}{1.0 \text{ hr.} \times 60 \frac{\text{min.}}{\text{hr.}} \times 60 \frac{\text{sec.}}{\text{min.}}} = \frac{60 \times 5280}{60 \times 60} \frac{\text{ft.}}{\text{sec.}} = 88 \frac{\text{ft.}}{\text{sec.}}.$$

**Example 4.9.** What is the weight in grams of 2.50 gallons of water, given that there are $231 \frac{\text{in.}^3}{\text{gal.}}$, $2.54 \frac{\text{cm.}}{\text{in.}}$, and that water weighs $1.00 \frac{\text{g.}}{\text{cm.}^3}$?

**Solution.**

$$2.50 \text{ gal.} \times 231 \frac{\text{in.}^3}{\text{gal.}} \times \left(2.54 \frac{\text{cm.}}{\text{in.}}\right)^3 \times 1.00 \frac{\text{g.}}{\text{cm.}^3} = 9.46 \times 10^3 \text{ g.}$$

$$\text{gal.} \times \frac{\text{in.}^3}{\text{gal.}} = \text{in.}^3$$

$$\text{in.}^3 \times \frac{\text{cm.}^3}{\text{in.}^3} = \text{cm.}^3$$

$$\text{cm.}^3 \times \frac{\text{g.}}{\text{cm.}^3} = \text{g.}$$

**4.3. Nondimensional Numbers.** In the introductory note to this chapter the statement was made that most quantities are dimensional. Nondimensional quantities are called *pure numbers*.

**Example 4.10.** Two iron rods are 75 ft. and 15 ft. respectively in length. The longer rod is how many times the length of the shorter rod?

**Solution.**

$$\frac{75 \text{ ft.}}{15 \text{ ft.}} = 5.$$

The dimensions cancel, giving the pure number 5. That is, the longer rod is 5 times the length of the shorter rod.

**Example 4.11.** What is the circumference of a circle having a diameter of 12.0 cm.?

**Solution.** The circumference, C, of a circle is directly proportional to the diameter, d. That is:

$$C \propto d.$$

The proportionality constant is 3.1416, commonly designated by the Greek letter pi, $\pi$. Or:

$$C = 3.1416 \times d.$$

Therefore $\qquad C = 3.1416 \times 12.0 \text{ cm.} = 37.7 \text{ cm.}$

Proportionality constants, such as $\pi$, are pure numbers.

**Example 4.12.** (a) Derive the dimensional formula for the conversion of $\frac{\text{mi.}}{\text{hr.}}$ to $\frac{\text{ft.}}{\text{min.}}$. (b) Determine the numerical value of the constant relating the two dimensions. (c) Change $25 \frac{\text{mi.}}{\text{hr.}}$ to $\frac{\text{ft.}}{\text{min.}}$.

**Solution.**

(a) $\frac{\cancel{\text{mi.}}}{\cancel{\text{hr.}}} \times \frac{\text{ft.}}{\cancel{\text{mi.}}} \times \frac{\cancel{\text{hr.}}}{\text{min.}} = \frac{\text{ft.}}{\text{min.}}$.

(b) Assign unit value to $\frac{\text{mi.}}{\text{hr.}}$. Then:

$$1.00 \frac{\text{mi.}}{\text{hr.}} = 1.00 \frac{\cancel{\text{mi.}}}{\cancel{\text{hr.}}} \times 5280 \frac{\text{ft.}}{\cancel{\text{mi.}}} \times \tfrac{1}{60} \frac{\cancel{\text{hr.}}}{\text{min.}} = 88 \frac{\text{ft.}}{\text{min.}}$$

(c) Since $1.00 \frac{\text{mi.}}{\text{hr.}} = 88 \frac{\text{ft.}}{\text{min.}}$, then:

$$25 \frac{\text{mi.}}{\text{hr.}} = (25 \times 88) \frac{\text{ft.}}{\text{min.}} = 2200 \frac{\text{ft.}}{\text{min.}}$$

## Problems

### Part I

4.1. Evaluate the following numerically and dimensionally:

| | |
|---|---|
| a. $18 \text{ ft.}^2 \div 3 \text{ ft.}$ | *Ans.* 6 ft. |
| b. $(6 \text{ ft.} \times 4 \text{ ft.}) \div 3 \text{ ft.}$ | *Ans.* 8 ft. |
| c. $350 \text{ cm.}^3 \div 7.0 \text{ cm.}$ | *Ans.* 50 cm.$^2$ |
| d. $\sqrt[3]{125 \text{ cm.}^3}$ | *Ans.* 5.0 cm. |
| e. $12.0 \text{ cm.} \times 15.0 \text{ cm.} \times 75.0 \text{ mm.}$ | *Ans.* $1.35 \times 10^3$ cm.$^3$ |

4.2. How many milliliters are there in 3.25 *l.*? $\qquad$ *Ans.* $3.25 \times 10^3$ ml.

4.3. How many liters are there in 325 ml.? $\qquad$ *Ans.* 0.325 *l.*

4.4. How many millimeters are there in 15.0 in.? $\qquad$ *Ans.* 381 mm.

4.5. How many feet are there in 1000 mm.? $\qquad$ *Ans.* 3.28 ft.

4.6. Given that there are $30.5 \frac{\text{cm.}}{\text{ft.}}$, determine the number of feet per

centimeter $\left(\frac{\text{ft.}}{\text{cm.}}\right)$.          *Ans.* $3.28 \times 10^{-2} \frac{\text{ft.}}{\text{cm.}}$.

4.7. Convert 1.56 kilograms to milligrams.      *Ans.* $1.56 \times 10^6$ mg.

4.8. Convert 1.25 meters to angstroms.      *Ans.* $1.25 \times 10^{10}$ A.

4.9. A car is traveling $50.0 \frac{\text{ft.}}{\text{sec.}}$. What is the speed of the car in miles

per hour $\left(\frac{\text{mi.}}{\text{hr.}}\right)$?          *Ans.* $34.1 \frac{\text{mi.}}{\text{hr.}}$.

4.10. Show that $15 \frac{\text{mi.}}{\text{hr.}} = 22 \frac{\text{ft.}}{\text{sec.}}$.

4.11. In each of the following derive the dimensional formula for the conversion of the given dimensions to the desired dimensions; then determine the value of the constant relating the two dimensions.

a. mi.³ to ft.³          *Ans.* $1.47 \times 10^{11}$.

b. mm. to km.          *Ans.* $10^{-6}$.

c. $\frac{\text{ft.}^3}{\text{sec.}}$ to $\frac{\text{gal.}}{\text{min.}}$          *Ans.* 449.

d. mm. to m.          *Ans.* $10^{-3}$.

e. lb. to mg.          *Ans.* $4.54 \times 10^5$.

4.12. What is the weight in grams of 25.0 in.³ of water, given that 1.00 cm.³ of water weighs 1.00 g.?          *Ans.* 410 g.

## Part II

4.13. Convert 5000 A. to in.      *Ans.* $1.97 \times 10^{-5}$ in.

4.14. How many ft.³ are there in 1.00 mi.³?      *Ans.* $1.47 \times 10^{11}$ ft.³

4.15. How many mi.³ are there in 1.00 in.³?      *Ans.* $3.93 \times 10^{-15}$ mi.³

4.16. How many m.³ are there in 1.00 mi.³?      *Ans.* $4.17 \times 10^9$ m.³

4.17. How many in.³ are there in 1.00 mi.³?      *Ans.* $2.54 \times 10^{14}$ in.³

4.18. How many $\mu$ are there in 3.17 m.?      *Ans.* $3.17 \times 10^6 \, \mu$.

4.19. How many kilograms are there in 15.0 lb.?      *Ans.* 6.82 kg.

4.20. How many pounds are there in 15.0 kg.?      *Ans.* 33.0 lb.

4.21. How many gallons are there in 1.00 yd.³?      *Ans.* 202 gal.

4.22. What is the weight in ounces of 25.0 in.³ of water, given that 1.00 ft.³ of water weighs 62.4 lb.?          *Ans.* 14.4 oz.

4.23. What is the numerical constant when converting yards to miles?

         *Ans.* $5.68 \times 10^{-4}$.

4.24. How many A.³ are there in 1.00 cm.³?      *Ans.* $10^{24}$ A.³

4.25. How many pounds are there in 5.0 gallons of water?      *Ans.* 41.7 lb.

4.26. How many liters are there in 5.0 gallons of gasoline?      *Ans.* 18.9 *l*.

4.27. A car is traveling $60 \frac{\text{mi.}}{\text{hr.}}$. What is its speed in $\frac{\text{hr.}}{\text{mi.}}$?

         *Ans.* $1.67 \times 10^{-2} \frac{\text{hr.}}{\text{mi.}}$.

4.28. Classify each of the following as representing length, area, or volume:

   a. m.$^2$        *Ans.* Area.

   b. $\dfrac{cm.^3}{cm.^2}$        *Ans.* Length.

   c. ft.$^3$        *Ans.* Volume.

   d. $\dfrac{mi.}{hr.} \times \dfrac{min.}{sec.} \times \dfrac{hr.}{min.} \times sec.$        *Ans.* Length.

   e. gal. $\times \dfrac{in.^3}{gal.} \times \left(\dfrac{cm.}{in.}\right)^3$        *Ans.* Volume.

4.29. In each of the following derive the dimensional formula for the conversion of the given dimensions to the desired dimensions; then determine the value of the constant relating the two dimensions.

   a. $\dfrac{ft.}{sec.}$ to $\dfrac{mi.}{hr.}$        *Ans.* 0.682.

   b. mg. to kg.        *Ans.* $10^{-6}$.

   c. A. to mm.        *Ans.* $10^{-7}$.

   d. ft.$^3$ to gal.        *Ans.* 7.48.

   e. $\dfrac{gal.}{min.}$ to $\dfrac{yd.^3}{hr.}$        *Ans.* 0.297.

   f. yd. to $\mu$.        *Ans.* $9.14 \times 10^5$.

   g. ft.$^3$ to ml.        *Ans.* $2.83 \times 10^4$.

   h. in. to A.        *Ans.* $2.54 \times 10^8$.

4.30. The volume, V, of a sphere is given by the formula $V = \frac{4}{3}\pi r^3$, where r is the radius of the sphere.

   a. What is the numerical value of the constant relating V and r?

          *Ans.* 4.1888.

   b. What is the numerical value of the constant relating the volume and diameter of a sphere?        *Ans.* 0.5236.

   c. The diameter of sphere A is twice that of sphere B. How many times greater is the volume of A than that of B?        *Ans.* 8.

   d. What is the volume of a sphere the radius of which is 5.00 cm.?

          *Ans.* 524 cm.$^3$

# 5

# Density and Specific Gravity

Density and specific gravity are concepts which are useful in inter-relating mass and volume for any given substance. The substance may be in the solid, liquid, or gaseous state. Dimensional analysis is essential in order to understand and distinguish between the two concepts.

**5.1. Density.** *Density* is defined as the mass of a unit volume of a substance. That is:

$$\text{Density} = \frac{\text{mass}}{\text{volume}} \quad \text{or} \quad D = \frac{M}{V}.$$

Any unit of weight and any unit of volume may be chosen. However, in scientific work the densities of solids and liquids are usually given as grams per cubic centimeter $\left(\frac{g.}{cm.^3}\right)$, or as grams per milliliter $\left(\frac{g.}{ml.}\right)$, and the densities of gases are given as grams per liter $\left(\frac{g.}{l.}\right)$. English units are commonly used by engineers. In engineering work, therefore, densities are given as pounds per cubic foot $\left(\frac{lb.}{ft.^3}\right)$. For example, the density of silver is 10.5 $\frac{g.}{cm.^3}$, or 655 $\frac{lb.}{ft.^3}$. Since the numerical value of density depends upon the units of weight and volume chosen, it is essential that the dimensions be given when expressing density.

Table 5.1, p. 40, gives the densities of a number of substances.

**Example 5.1.** Calculate the density of a liquid 17.45 ml. of which weighs 16.3 g.

**Solution.** By definition the density of the liquid is the weight in grams of one milliliter. Therefore:

$$\text{density} = \frac{16.3 \text{ g.}}{17.45 \text{ ml.}} = 0.934 \frac{g.}{ml.}.$$

36

**Example 5.2.** How many milliliters are there in 500 g. of mercury, given that the density of mercury is $13.6 \frac{g.}{ml.}$?

**Solution.** Since 1.00 ml. of mercury weighs 13.6 g., then the number of milliliters in 500 g. is:

$$\frac{500 \text{ g.}}{13.6 \frac{g.}{ml.}} = \frac{500}{13.6} \text{ g.} \times \frac{ml.}{g.} = 36.8 \text{ ml.}$$

**Example 5.3.** Given that 140 ml. of chlorine gas weighs 0.450 g.; find the density of chlorine in grams per liter $\left(\frac{g.}{l.}\right)$.

**Solution.** By definition the density of chlorine is the weight in grams of 1.00 liter. Therefore:

$$\frac{140 \text{ ml.}}{0.450 \text{ g.}} = \frac{1000 \text{ ml.}}{x \text{ g.}}$$

or                $x = 3.21$ g. = weight of one liter of chlorine.

**Example 5.4.** A solution of hydrochloric acid has a density of $1.20 \frac{g.}{ml.}$ and contains 35.0 per cent HCl by weight. How many grams of HCl are there in 250 ml. of the solution?

**Solution.** Since the per cent by weight of HCl is given, the first step is to find the weight of the 250 ml. of solution.

$$250 \text{ ml.} \times 1.20 \frac{g.}{ml.} = 300 \text{ g. of solution.}$$

Then 300 g. $\times$ 0.35 = 105 g. of HCl.

**Example 5.5.** What is the weight in grams of a block of silver measuring 2.50 cm. by 8.00 cm. by 4.00 cm., given that the density of silver is $10.5 \frac{g.}{cm.^3}$?

**Solution.** Since 1.00 cm.³ of silver weighs 10.5 g., the first step is to find the number of cm.³ of silver in the block.

$$2.50 \text{ cm.} \times 8.00 \text{ cm.} \times 4.00 \text{ cm.} = 80.0 \text{ cm.}^3$$

Then          $80.0 \text{ cm.}^3 \times 10.5 \frac{g.}{cm.^3} = 840$ g. = weight of block.

### Problems

#### Part I

5.1. What is the density of ether, given that 300 ml. weighs 217.5 g.?

*Ans.* $0.725 \frac{g.}{ml.}$.

5.2. How many milliliters are there per gram of ether $\left(\dfrac{ml.}{g.}\right)$? (See problem 5.1.)

*Ans.* 1.38 $\dfrac{ml.}{g.}$.

5.3. How many grams of glycerine, density 1.25 $\dfrac{g.}{cm.^3}$, will a 125 ml. flask hold?

*Ans.* 156 g.

5.4. What is the density of cork if a cube measuring 1.50 cm. on a side weighs 1.00 g.?

*Ans.* 0.296 $\dfrac{g.}{cm.^3}$.

5.5. Calculate the density of carbon dioxide gas, given that 450 ml. weighs 0.891 g.

*Ans.* 1.98 $\dfrac{g.}{l.}$.

5.6. A carboy contains 41.3 kg. of hydrochloric acid, density 1.18 $\dfrac{g.}{ml.}$. What is the volume of the carboy in liters?

*Ans.* 35.0 $l.$

5.7. A solution of hydrochloric acid has a density of 1.12 $\dfrac{g.}{ml.}$. Calculate:

a. The weight of 750 ml. of the solution.          *Ans.* 840 g.
b. The volume occupied by 750 g. of the solution.  *Ans.* 670 ml.

5.8. A solution of sulfuric acid has a density of 1.84 $\dfrac{g.}{ml.}$ and contains 98.0 per cent acid by weight. What volume of solution would contain 360 grams of acid?

*Ans.* 200 ml.

## Part II

5.9. What would be the dimensions of a cube of copper weighing 7920 g.?

*Ans.* 10 cm.

5.10. What is the weight in grams of 1.00 quart of water?          *Ans.* 946 g.

5.11. A cubic foot of iron weighs 428 pounds. What is the density of iron in ounces per cubic inch $\left(\dfrac{oz.}{in.^3}\right)$?

*Ans.* 3.96 $\dfrac{oz.}{in.^3}$.

5.12. What volume of aluminum would be equal in weight to 100 cm.³ of lead?

*Ans.* 420 cm.³

5.13. Calculate the weight of a block of an alloy measuring 3.62 cm. by 1.23 m. by 1.00 mm., given that the density of the alloy is 9.63 $\dfrac{g.}{cm.^3}$.

*Ans.* 429 g.

5.14. A block of stone has a density of 428 $\dfrac{lb.}{ft.^3}$. What is the density in $\dfrac{g.}{cm.^3}$?

*Ans.* 6.86 $\dfrac{g.}{cm.^3}$.

5.15. A bottle weighs 13.45 g. empty and 16.72 g. filled with water. The same bottle when filled with a sugar solution weighs 19.01 g. What is the density of the sugar solution?                    *Ans.* 1.70 $\frac{g.}{ml.}$.

5.16. A graduated cylinder contained 20.0 ml. of water. When 100 g. of brass shot were added to the cylinder the water level read 32.6 ml.

What is the density of the brass?                    *Ans.* 7.94 $\frac{g.}{ml.}$.

5.17. What is the weight in grams of 1.00 in.$^3$ of mercury?        *Ans.* 222 g.

5.18. A 100 ml. bulb weighs 67.423 g. when filled with air, and 67.879 g. when filled with xenon gas. What is the density of xenon, given that

air weighs 1.29 $\frac{g.}{l.}$?                    *Ans.* 5.85 $\frac{g.}{l.}$.

5.19. A cube of wood measuring 20.0 cm. on a side is placed in water. How much of the wood will extend above the water, given that the

density of the wood is 0.80 $\frac{g.}{cm.^3}$?                    *Ans.* 1600 cm.$^3$

5.20. Given that the density of air is 1.29 $\frac{g.}{l.}$, hydrogen 0.09 $\frac{g.}{l.}$, and helium

0.18 $\frac{g.}{l.}$; what per cent of the lifting power of hydrogen is helium

capable of exerting?                    *Ans.* 93 per cent.

5.21. Five hundred grams of mercury were poured into a 100 ml. graduated cylinder. How much water would have to be added to bring the water up to the 100 ml. mark?                    *Ans.* 63.1 ml.

5.22. Show how the weight of one cubic foot of gold, as given in Table 5.1,

p. 40, could be calculated from the density as given in $\frac{g.}{cm.^3}$.

5.23. A 1.00 in.$^3$ of metal weighs 87.7 g. when suspended in mercury. What is the metal?                    *Ans.* Uranium.

5.24. Gold costs approximately $1.12 per gram. What would be the cost of 1.00 in.$^3$ of gold?                    *Ans.* $354.

5.25. What is the constant which, when multiplied by $\frac{lb.}{ft.^3}$, will give $\frac{g.}{cm.^3}$?

*Ans.* 0.0160.

**5.2. Specific Gravity.** *Specific gravity* is defined as the *ratio* between the weight of an object and the weight of an equal volume of some substance taken as a standard. Solids and liquids are usually referred to water as a standard, and gases are referred to air. Since density represents the weight of a unit volume of a substance, it follows that density may be used to calculate specific gravity. That is:

$$\text{Sp. gr.} = \frac{\text{weight of object}}{\text{weight of equal volume of standard}} = \frac{\text{density of substance}}{\text{density of standard}}.$$

TABLE 5.1

THE DENSITIES AND SPECIFIC GRAVITIES OF A NUMBER OF SUBSTANCES

| Substance | Density | | | Specific Gravity |
| --- | --- | --- | --- | --- |
| | $\frac{g.}{cm.^3}$ | $\frac{g.}{l.}$ | $\frac{lb.}{ft.^3}$ | |
| Air | — | 1.29 | — | 1.00 |
| Aluminum | 2.70 | — | 168 | 2.70 |
| Bromine | 2.93 | — | 183 | 2.93 |
| Carbon dioxide | — | 1.98 | — | 1.53 |
| Carbon tetrachloride | 1.60 | — | 100 | 1.60 |
| Copper | 7.92 | — | 494 | 7.92 |
| Gold | 19.30 | — | 1204 | 19.30 |
| Lead | 11.34 | — | 708 | 11.34 |
| Mercury | 13.55 | — | 846 | 13.55 |
| Oxygen | — | 1.43 | — | 1.11 |
| Sulfur | 2.06 | — | 129 | 2.06 |
| Sulfur dioxide | — | 2.93 | — | 2.27 |
| Uranium | 18.90 | — | 1189 | 18.90 |
| Water | 1.00 | — | 62.4 | 1.00 |

**Example 5.6.** The density of iron is 493 $\frac{lb.}{ft.^3}$, and that of water 62.4 $\frac{lb.}{ft.^3}$. What is the specific gravity of iron?

**Solution.** The above represents the weight in pounds of 1.00 ft.³ each of iron and water. Therefore:

$$\text{Sp. gr. of iron} = \frac{493 \; \frac{lb.}{ft.^3}}{62.4 \; \frac{lb.}{ft.^3}} = 7.9.$$

**Example 5.7.** Given that the density of iron is 7.9 $\frac{g.}{cm.^3}$; determine the specific gravity of iron.

**Solution.** As in Example 5.6:

$$\text{Sp. gr. of iron} = \frac{7.9 \; \frac{g.}{cm.^3}}{1.0 \; \frac{g.}{cm.^3}} = 7.9.$$

Several important facts are illustrated in Examples 5.6 and 5.7.

(1) Specific gravity has no dimensions since, as shown above, all dimensions cancel. (2) Specific gravity represents the number of times heavier a substance is than an equal volume of the substance taken as a standard. (3) Density and specific gravity are numerically the same when density is expressed in metric units and referred to water as a standard. This is because water weighs $1.00 \frac{g.}{cm.^3}$ (Example 5.7).

**Example 5.8.** A block of metal measuring 3.60 cm. by 4.50 cm. by 8.40 cm. weighs 1122 g. What is the specific gravity of the metal?

**Solution.** First find the volume of the block in cm.³ Since 1.00 cm.³ of water weighs 1.00 g., this volume will be the weight in grams of an equal volume of water.

3.60 cm. × 4.50 cm. × 8.40 cm. = 136 cm.³ = volume of block.

Then

$$\textbf{Sp. gr. of metal} = \frac{1122 \, g.}{136 \, g.} = \textbf{8.25.}$$

## Problems

### Part I

5.26. A liquid has a specific gravity of 0.784. What is the density?

*Ans.* $0.784 \frac{g.}{cm.^3}$.

5.27. The specific gravity of mercury is 13.55. What is the weight of 250 ml. of mercury? *Ans.* 3388 g.

5.28. Calculate the weight of a block of stone, the dimensions of which are 15.0 cm. by 20.0 cm. by 25.0 cm., given that the specific gravity of the stone is 4.23. *Ans.* 31.7 kg.

5.29. The density of a metal is $624 \frac{lb.}{ft.^3}$. What is the specific gravity of the metal? *Ans.* 10.0.

5.30. The density of a stone is $5.90 \frac{g.}{cm.^3}$. What is the weight in pounds of one cubic foot of the stone? *Ans.* 368 lb.

### Part II

5.31. Calculate the weight of a block of sulfur measuring 24.0 in. by 18.0 in. by 12.0 in. *Ans.* 387 lb.

5.32. The specific gravity of mercury is 13.55. What is the density of mercury in both English and metric units?

*Ans.* $846 \frac{lb.}{ft.^3}$; $13.55 \frac{g.}{cm.^3}$.

5.33. From the following data determine the specific gravity of the liquid:
   1. Weight of a dry volumetric flask      = 36.22 g.
   2. Weight of flask filled with water     = 46.22 g.

   3. Weight of flask filled with the liquid = 44.82 g.      *Ans.* $0.86 \frac{g.}{ml.}$ .

5.34. A bar of metal weighs 16.354 g. in air and 15.507 g. when suspended in water.  Is the metal copper or gold?      *Ans.* Gold.

5.35. A sample of cast iron has a specific gravity of 7.20.  What is the weight of one cubic foot of the cast iron?      *Ans.* 449 lb.

5.36. A can holds 200 lb. of water or 130 lb. of gasoline.  (a) What is the specific gravity of the gasoline, and (b) what is the ft.$^3$ capacity of the can?      *Ans.* (a) 0.65;  (b) 3.21 ft.$^3$

5.37. What volume ratio of copper : gold would represent equal weights of the metals?      *Ans.* 1 : 2.44.

5.38. A block of metal weighs 68.4 g. and has a volume of 0.95 in.$^3$  What is the specific gravity of the metal?      *Ans.* 4.4.

5.39. Osmium is the heaviest metal known, having a specific gravity of 22.5.  What is the weight of one cubic inch of osmium?      *Ans.* 369 g.

5.40. What is the volume in gallons of 1000 pounds of cottonseed oil, specific gravity 0.926?      *Ans.* 129 gal.

# 6

# Chemical Units of Mass

The establishment of fundamental units is essential in order to solve problems. The chemist and physicist have devised certain fundamental units of mass based upon the actual masses of atoms and molecules. The student must be familiar with the meaning and usage of such units in order to solve problems in chemistry. In this chapter, several of the more common units are defined and their use is explained.

## Relative Units of Mass

**6.1. Atomic and Formula Weights.** An atom or molecule is too small to weigh, even on the most sensitive balance made. However, scientists are able to weigh masses containing a known number of atoms or molecules, thus making it possible to actually determine the weight of a single atom or molecule.

Since the weight in grams of an atom or molecule is extremely small, a system of relative weights, called *atomic weights*, has been devised. The atomic weights of the elements are based upon the oxygen atom as having a relative weight of 16.0000 units. For example, the atomic weight of sulfur is 32.066, which means that an atom of sulfur is $32.066 \div 16.000 = 2.004$ times heavier than an oxygen atom. An atom of uranium is $238.07 \div 16.00 = 14.88$ times heavier than an oxygen atom.

The atoms of the elements are the building units of all substances, always combining in the same ratio under similar conditions to form the same substance. Since substances are made up of definite ratios of atoms, the sum of the weights of the atoms as designated in the formula represents the *formula weight* of the substance. Following are the formula weights of two substances:

43

Water, $H_2O = (2 \times 1.008) + 16.000 = 18.016$;

                                                      formula weight

                                      contribution of oxygen atom

                       contribution of hydrogen atoms

Salt, $NaCl = 22.997 + 35.457 = 58.454$.

In the case of nonionic compounds such as water the formula weight represents a true *molecular weight*. However, with ionic compounds such as sodium chloride the formula merely represents the ratio of ions in the substance, there being no entity such as a molecule. The term molecular weight, therefore, has no significance in the case of ionic compounds.

**Example 6.1.** What is the formula weight of $Fe_2(SO_4)_3$?

**Solution.** The formula weight is the sum of the weights of the atoms making up the formula. Therefore:

$$\begin{array}{ll}
\text{iron contributes } 2 \times 55.85 & = 111.70 \text{ units} \\
\text{sulfur contributes } 3 \times 32.066 & = \phantom{0}96.20 \text{ units} \\
\text{oxygen contributes } 12 \times 16.00 & = \underline{192.00 \text{ units}} \\
\text{formula weight} & = 399.90 \text{ units}
\end{array}$$

## Arbitrarily Established Chemical Units of Mass

**6.2. The Gram-Atom as a Chemical Unit of Mass.** Even though the atomic weights of the elements are relative weights, they may be expressed in absolute weights such as grams, pounds, and tons. When expressed as grams, the *atomic weight* becomes the *gram-atomic weight* or, for convenience, the *gram-atom*. For example, one gram-atom of oxygen would be 16.0000 grams, and two gram-atoms of sulfur would be $2 \times 32.066 = 64.132$ grams. Also, 32.066 pounds of sulfur would be one *pound-atom*.

**Example 6.2.** How many gram-atoms would there be in a bottle containing 1000 grams of mercury?

**Solution.** One gram-atom of mercury is 200.61 grams. Therefore, 1000 grams of mercury would represent:

$$\frac{1000}{200.61} = 4.98 \text{ gram-atoms.}$$

**6.3. The Mole as a Chemical Unit of Mass.** Just as the atomic weight of an element may be expressed in grams to become the gram-atomic weight, so the *formula weight* of a substance may be designated in grams to become the *gram-molecular weight,* abbreviated *mole* for convenience. Similarly, we may have a *pound-molecular weight* or *ton-molecular weight.* Note that the quantity is called the gram-molecular weight whether it originates from the formula weight of ionic compounds or from the true molecular weight of nonionic compounds.

**Example 6.3.** How many grams of $Fe_2(SO_4)_3$ would there be in 2.75 moles of the compound?

**Solution.** From Example 6.1 we see that one mole of the compound is equal to 399.90 grams. Therefore, 2.75 moles of $Fe_2(SO_4)_3$ would be:

$$2.75 \times 399.90 = 1100 \text{ g.}$$

**Example 6.4.** How many moles are there in one pound of sugar?

**Solution.** One pound is equal to 454 grams. From the formula, $C_{12}H_{22}O_{11}$, one mole of sugar is equal to 342.30 grams. Therefore, 454 grams of sugar would be:

$$\frac{454}{342.30} = 1.33 \text{ moles.}$$

**6.4. The Avogadro Number.** Evidently there is some fundamental reason for the use of the gram-atom and the mole as chemical units of mass. The atomic weights of the elements are in the same ratio as the absolute weights of the atoms in grams. For example:

$$\frac{\text{weight of one atom of He}}{\text{weight of one atom of O}_2} = \frac{\text{atomic weight of He}}{\text{atomic weight of O}_2}$$

or

$$\frac{6.65 \times 10^{-24} \text{ g.}}{26.58 \times 10^{-24} \text{ g.}} = \frac{4.003}{16.000}.$$

It follows, therefore, that one gram-atom of each of the elements contains the same number of atoms. For example, 16.0000 g. of oxygen contains the same number of atoms as 32.066 g. of sulfur. This number has been determined experimentally and found to be $6.024 \times 10^{23}$ atoms per gram-atom. It is called the *Avogadro number* in honor of the Italian scientist Amedeo Avogadro (1776–1856). For convenience the number is commonly designated by the letter "N." Similarly, one mole of a substance contains N molecules of that substance.

**Example 6.5.** Show that one mole of water contains N molecules.

**Solution.** One mole of water contains:

$$2.00 \text{ gram-atoms of hydrogen} = 2 \text{ N atoms}$$
$$1.00 \text{ gram-atom of oxygen} = \text{N atoms}$$

Therefore, $1.00$ mole of $H_2O$ $= 3 \text{ N atoms.}$

However there are 3 atoms per molecule of water. Therefore,

$$1.00 \text{ mole of } H_2O = \frac{3 \text{ N \cancel{atoms}}}{3 \frac{\cancel{atoms}}{molecule}} = N \text{ molecules.}$$

The one fact of basic importance to the scientist is that the gram-atom and the mole represent units of mass containing a known number of atoms or molecules — the fundamental units involved in chemical reactions.

**Example 6.6.** How many atoms of oxygen are there in 1.000 g. of oxygen?

**Solution.** 1.00 gram-atom of oxygen, or 16.000 g., contains N atoms of oxygen. Therefore:

$$\frac{1.000}{16.000} \times N = 0.0625 \text{ N atoms in } 1.000 \text{ g. of oxygen.}$$

Since $N = 6.024 \times 10^{23}$, then:

$$(0.0625)(6.024 \times 10^{23}) = 3.77 \times 10^{22} \text{ atoms of oxygen.}$$

## Problems

### Part I

**6.1.** How many atoms are represented by each of the following formulas: (a) $Fe_2O_3$, (b) $Fe(OH)_3$, (c) $Ca(HCO_3)_2$, (d) $Mg_3(PO_4)_2$, (e) $(NH_4)_2Cr_2O_7$? *Ans.* (a) 5, (b) 7, (c) 11, (d) 13, (e) 19.

**6.2.** What is the total number of atoms represented in each of the following expressions: (a) $2 Fe_2O_3$, (b) $5 Ca(HCO_3)_2$, (c) $10 (NH_4)_2SO_4$, (d) $5 (NH_4)_2Cr_2O_7$, (e) $6 H_2$? *Ans.* (a) 10, (b) 55, (c) 150, (d) 95, (e) 12.

**6.3.** Determine the formula weight of each of the following: (a) $Fe_2O_3$, (b) $Fe(OH)_3$, (c) $Ca(HCO_3)_2$, (d) $Mg_3(PO_4)_2$, (e) $(NH_4)_2Cr_2O_7$. *Ans.* (a) 159.70, (b) 106.88, (c) 162.12, (d) 262.91, (e) 252.10.

**6.4.** How many gram-atoms of sulfur are there in 100 g. of sulfur? *Ans.* 3.12.

**6.5.** How many grams are there in 2.75 gram-atoms of iron? *Ans.* 154 g.

**6.6.** How many gram-atoms of iron are there in a rectangular block of iron measuring 4.00 cm. by 2.50 cm. by 10.00 cm., the density of the iron being $7.90 \frac{g.}{cm.^3}$? *Ans.* 14.1.

**6.7.** How many moles are there in each of the following quantities: (a) 250 g. of $SO_2$, (b) 250 g. of $Fe_2O_3$, (c) 250 g. of $O_2$? *Ans.* (a) 3.90, (b) 1.57, (c) 7.81.

**6.8.** How many grams are there in each of the following quantities:

(a) 2.65 moles of NaCl, (b) 1.50 moles of sulfur, (c) 5.00 moles of nitrogen? *Ans.* (a) 155 g., (b) 48.10 g., (c) 140 g.

6.9. How many grams are there in 100 millimoles of sugar, $C_{12}H_{22}O_{11}$?

*Ans.* 34.2 g.

6.10. What is the weight in grams of one atom of lead?

*Ans.* $344 \times 10^{-24}$ g.

6.11. What is the weight in grams of 2 N atoms of aluminum?

*Ans.* 53.96 g.

6.12. How many times heavier is an atom of silver than an atom of iron?

*Ans.* 1.93 times.

6.13. How many molecules are there in 0.75 mole of $CO_2$? *Ans.* 0.75 N.

6.14. How many molecules are there in 0.75 mole of Fe? *Ans.* 0.75 N.

6.15. How many atoms are there in 2.50 moles of oxygen? *Ans.* 5 N.

## Part II

6.16. Determine the formula weight of (a) oxygen, (b) copper, (c) sugar, $C_{12}H_{22}O_{11}$. *Ans.* (a) 32, (b) 63.54, (c) 342.30.

6.17. How many moles are there in one liter of water? *Ans.* 55.5 moles.

6.18. How many moles are there in a cube of aluminum 10.0 cm. on a side?

*Ans.* 100.

6.19. How many moles are there in 1.00 kg. of iron rust, $Fe_2O_3$?

*Ans.* 6.26.

6.20. How many moles are there in 1.00 kg. of iron? *Ans.* 17.9.

6.21. How many moles are there in 1.00 in.$^3$ of water? *Ans.* 0.91 mole.

6.22. How many millimoles are there in 1.00 mole of any substance?

*Ans.* 1000.

6.23. How many millimoles are there in 1.00 g. of water? *Ans.* 55.5.

6.24. How many gram-atoms are there in a cube of platinum 10.0 cm. on a side? *Ans.* 110.

6.25. How many gram-atoms are there in 1.00 kg. of iron? *Ans.* 17.9.

6.26. How many gram-atoms each of chemically combined hydrogen and oxygen are there in 1.00 mole of water? *Ans.* 2.00 $H_2$, 1.00 $O_2$.

6.27. How many moles each of chemically combined hydrogen and oxygen are there in 1.00 mole of water? *Ans.* 1.00 $H_2$, 0.50 $O_2$.

6.28. How many grams are there in 1.65 gram-atoms of copper?

*Ans.* 105 g.

6.29. What is the weight in grams of 0.35 gram-atom of sodium?

*Ans.* 8.0 g.

6.30. A mixture contains 0.25 gram-atom of iron and 1.25 gram-atoms of sulfur. What is the weight of the mixture? *Ans.* 54.1 g.

6.31. An experiment calls for one-half mole of zinc. How many grams would be required? *Ans.* 32.69 g.

6.32. How many moles of $H_2SO_4$ would be contained in 250 ml. of a 95 per cent solution of sulfuric acid, density 1.84 $\frac{g.}{ml.}$? *Ans.* 4.5 moles.

**6.33.** One liter of hydrogen chloride gas weighs 1.63 grams. How many liters are there in one mole of hydrogen chloride?     *Ans.* 22.4 *l.*

**6.34.** How many grams are there in one pound-molecular weight of zinc sulfate, $ZnSO_4$?     *Ans.* $7.3 \times 10^4$ g.

**6.35.** What is the weight in milligrams of one atom of uranium?
    *Ans.* $4 \times 10^{-19}$ mg.

**6.36.** What is the weight in micrograms of 1,000,000 atoms of gold?
    *Ans.* $3.3 \times 10^{-10}$ µg.

**6.37.** What is the weight in grams of 0.5 N atoms of chlorine?    *Ans.* 17.73 g.

**6.38.** What is the weight in grams of 0.5 N molecules of chlorine?
    *Ans.* 35.46 g.

**6.39.** Given that an atom of mercury weighs $333 \times 10^{-24}$ g.; calculate the atomic weight of mercury by means of N.     *Ans.* 200.6.

**6.40.** How many atoms are there in one cm.³ of lead, density 11.3 g. per cm.³?
    *Ans.* $3.28 \times 10^{22}$.

**6.41.** What is the weight in grams of one molecule of water?
    *Ans.* $3.0 \times 10^{-23}$ g.

**6.42.** How many times heavier is a molecule of oxygen than a molecule of hydrogen?     *Ans.* 15.9 times.

**6.43.** How many times heavier is an atom of oxygen than an atom of hydrogen?     *Ans.* 15.9 times.

**6.44.** How many times heavier is an atom of oxygen than a molecule of hydrogen?     *Ans.* 7.94 times.

**6.45.** How many times heavier is a molecule of $CO_2$ than a molecule of $CH_4$?
    *Ans.* 2.75 times.

**6.46.** What is the weight in grams of $10^{30}$ atoms of oxygen?
    *Ans.* $2.66 \times 10^7$ g.

**6.47.** How many atoms of sulfur are there in 1.00 g. of sulfur?
    *Ans.* $1.9 \times 10^{22}$.

**6.48.** How many atoms of oxygen would be required to weigh 8.00 g.?
    *Ans.* 0.5 N atoms.

# 7

# The Physical Behavior of Gases

Under suitable conditions most substances may exist either as a gas, liquid, or solid. Many chemical reactions occur involving substances in the gaseous state, both as reactants and as products. It is important, therefore, that the physical laws relating to the gaseous state be understood before discussing problems involving chemical changes of substances existing in the gaseous state. Such physical laws relating to gases may usually be explained in terms of the kinetic energy of molecules.

## The Energy of Molecules in the Gaseous State

**7.1. The Kinetic-Molecular Theory of Matter.** The principal difference between substances in the solid, liquid, and gaseous states lies in the freedom of movement of their molecules. The kinetic-molecular theory of matter deals with the energy associated with molecules due to their motion, the word *kinetic* coming from a Greek word meaning *motion*. Molecules in the liquid and solid states have a somewhat limited freedom of movement, whereas those in the gaseous state are limited in movement only by the walls of the containing vessel.

The kinetic energy of a particle in motion, whether it be a molecule or an aggregate of molecules, is given by the expression:

$$\text{Kinetic energy in ergs} = \tfrac{1}{2} \, mv^2$$

$$\begin{array}{c} \text{velocity in cm. per sec.} \\ \text{mass in grams} \end{array}$$

Since $10^7$ ergs = 0.24 cal., the above expression becomes:

$$\text{Kinetic energy in calories} = (1.2 \times 10^{-8}) \, mv^2$$

The kinetic energy of all molecules is the same at any given temperature. This means that light molecules, such as hydrogen, must be moving at a greater velocity at any given temperature than are

49

heavier molecules, such as oxygen, in order to compensate for the difference in mass.

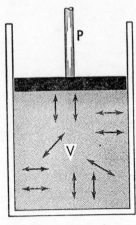

Fig. 7.1. Pressure is produced by the impact of molecules on the walls of the containing vessel.

**7.2. The Pressure Exerted by Gaseous Molecules.** Gases are composed of molecules which are vibrating in all directions within the container, as shown in Fig. 7.1.

Gas pressure is the result of the impacts of the molecules on the walls of the containing vessel. The pressure exerted by the gas may be determined by measuring the force necessary to hold the piston, P, in a given position in the cylinder.

Pressure is defined as the *force* acting on a *unit surface area*, and may be expressed in any one of several conventional units. Steam pressure is usually measured in pounds per square inch. In scientific work a unit called the *atmosphere* is commonly used. One atmosphere is the pressure exerted by the air on a unit surface area at sea level and is equal to:

1033 grams per square centimeter,

or             14.7 pounds per square inch.

The equivalent of one atmosphere pressure is commonly used in the solution of problems involving gases, and should not be confused with the above absolute values. Considering equal cross-sectional areas, one atmosphere is equivalent to the pressure exerted by:

760 millimeters of mercury,

29.9 inches of mercury,

or             33.9 feet of water.

In the solution of problems involving gas pressure, any of the above absolute or equivalent values may be used, provided the same units are used consistently throughout the problem.

**Problems**

Part I

7.1. Two bullets weighing 4.0 g. and 8.0 g., respectively, are traveling at a velocity of 100 m. per second. What is the kinetic energy of each (a) in ergs, and (b) in calories?

*Ans.* (a) $2.0 \times 10^8$ ergs, $4.0 \times 10^8$ ergs;    (b) 4.8 cal., 9.6 cal.

7.2. Two bullets weighing 8.0 g. each are traveling at velocities of 100 m. per second and 200 m. per second, respectively. What is the kinetic energy of each (a) in ergs, and (b) in calories?

*Ans.* (a) $4.0 \times 10^8$ ergs, $16.0 \times 10^8$ ergs; (b) 9.6 cal., 38.4 cal.

7.3. The mass of an oxygen molecule is approximately 16 times that of a hydrogen molecule. At room temperature a hydrogen molecule has a velocity of about one mile per second. What is the velocity of an oxygen molecule in feet per second under the same conditions?

*Ans.* $1320 \frac{\text{ft.}}{\text{sec.}}$

7.4. A pressure of $450 \frac{\text{lb.}}{\text{in.}^2}$ was recorded on a pressure gauge of an oxygen tank. What would this be in terms of atmospheres?

*Ans.* 30.6 atm.

7.5. A barometer registered 520 mm. of Hg on the top of Pikes Peak, Colo. This would be equivalent to how many atmospheres?

*Ans.* 0.684 atm.

## Part II

7.6. What is the kinetic energy in (a) ergs, and (b) calories, of a 16.0 lb. shot traveling at a velocity of $20.0 \frac{\text{ft.}}{\text{sec.}}$?

*Ans.* (a) $1.35 \times 10^9$ ergs; (b) 32.4 cal.

7.7. Under similar conditions, what would be the ratio of velocities of an oxygen molecule and a molecule of sulfur dioxide? A sulfur dioxide molecule has twice the mass of an oxygen molecule. *Ans.* 1.4 : 1.

7.8. What type of variation exists between the kinetic energy of a particle in motion and (a) its mass, and (b) its velocity?

*Ans.* (a) varies directly; (b) varies as velocity squared.

7.9. How many mm. of Hg are equivalent to 0.760 atm.?

*Ans.* 578 mm. of Hg.

7.10. A pressure of 2.36 atm. would be equivalent to how many pounds per square inch? *Ans.* $34.7 \frac{\text{lb.}}{\text{in.}^2}$

## Laws Relating to Substances in the Gaseous State

**7.3. Introduction.** The volume of a given mass of gas is dependent upon the temperature and pressure under which the gas exists. It is, therefore, possible to describe the physical behavior of gases in terms of the three variables: *temperature*, T; *pressure*, P; and *volume*, V. For a given volume of gas under given conditions of temperature and pressure, a change in any one or more of the three variables will result in a change in the remaining variables according to definitely established laws called the *gas laws*. The relationship between any two of the variables may be studied, provided the remaining variable is maintained constant, as shown in Fig. 7.2.

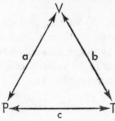

**7.4. The Law of Charles.** The law of Charles expresses the relationship between the two variables, *temperature* and *volume*, for a given mass of gas, the pressure remaining constant. The pressure must remain constant in order that the observed change in volume may be attributed solely to the change in temperature. The relationship is expressed in the law of Charles: pressure constant, the volume of a given mass of gas varies *directly* with the *absolute temperature*. That is:

Fig. 7.2. Relationship among the variables pressure, temperature, and volume, for substances in the gaseous state: (a) law of Boyle; (b) law of Charles; (c) law of Gay-Lussac.

$V \propto T$ (pressure and mass of gas constant).

The above proportionality indicates that although V and T may not be equal numerically, they vary proportionately with each other. This is shown in Table 7.1.

TABLE 7.1

THE VARIATION IN THE VOLUME OF A GIVEN MASS OF GAS WITH TEMPERATURE, PRESSURE CONSTANT

| Temperature (T) | Volume (V) |
|---|---|
| 274° K. | 500 ml. |
| 548° K. | 1000 ml. |
| 137° K. | 250 ml. |

From Table 7.1 we see that:

$$\frac{V}{T} = \frac{500 \text{ ml.}}{274° \text{ K.}} = \frac{1000 \text{ ml.}}{548° \text{ K.}} = \frac{250 \text{ ml.}}{137° \text{ K.}} = 1.82.$$

That is, for a given mass of gas at constant pressure:

$$\frac{V_1}{T_1} = \frac{V_2}{T_2} = \frac{V_3}{T_3} = K,$$

where K is a constant. The value of the constant for the data given in Table 7.1 is 1.82.

Things equal to the same thing are equal to each other. Therefore:

$$\frac{V_1}{T_1} = \frac{V_2}{T_2}$$

or
$$V_2 = V_1 \times \frac{T_2}{T_1}.$$

temperature correction fraction

original volume at $T_1$

corrected volume at $T_2$

**Example 7.1.** A cylinder contained 600 ml. of air at 20° C. What would be the volume of the air at 40° C., pressure constant?

**Solution.** The four quantities involved are:

Original conditions:    $V_1 = 600$ ml.

$T_1 = 20 + 273 = 293°$ K.

Corrected conditions:   $V_2 = x$ ml.

$T_2 = 40 + 273 = 313°$ K.

The 600 ml. volume will increase proportionately with the temperature. The temperature correction fraction must, therefore, be greater than unity. That is:

$$\frac{T_2}{T_1} = \frac{313° \text{ K.}}{293° \text{ K.}}.$$

Then:

$$V_2 = 600 \text{ ml.} \times \frac{313° \text{ K.}}{293° \text{ K.}}$$

$$= 641 \text{ ml.}$$

**7.5. The Law of Boyle.** The law of Boyle deals with the relationship existing between the two variables, *pressure* and *volume*, for a given mass of gas at constant temperature. The relationship is expressed in the law of Boyle: temperature constant, the volume of a given mass of gas varies *inversely* with the *pressure*. That is:

$$V \propto \frac{1}{P} \text{ (temperature and mass of gas constant).}$$

The variation of volume with pressure, as expressed in the law of Boyle, is shown in Table 7.2, p. 54.

From Table 7.2 we see that:

$$PV = (760)(500) = (1520)(250) = (380)(1000) = 380,000.$$

That is, for a given mass of gas at constant temperature:

$$P_1V_1 = P_2V_2 = P_3V_3 = K,$$

where K is a constant. The value of the constant for the data given in Table 7.2 is 380,000.

Since things equal to the same thing are equal to each other, then:

$$P_1V_1 = P_2V_2$$

or

$$V_2 = V_1 \times \frac{P_1}{P_2}.$$

$$\begin{array}{l} \quad\quad\quad\quad\quad \text{pressure correction fraction} \\ \quad\quad\quad \text{original volume at } P_1 \\ \text{corrected volume at } P_2 \end{array}$$

TABLE 7.2

THE VARIATION IN THE VOLUME OF A GIVEN MASS OF GAS
WITH PRESSURE, TEMPERATURE CONSTANT

| Pressure (P) | Volume (V) |
|---|---|
| 760 mm. of Hg | 500 ml. |
| 1520 mm. of Hg | 250 ml. |
| 380 mm. of Hg | 1000 ml. |

**Example 7.2.** A volume of air measuring 380 ml. was collected at a pressure of 640 mm. of Hg. Calculate the volume the air would occupy at a pressure of 760 mm. of Hg, temperature constant.

**Solution.** The four quantities involved are:

Original conditions: $V_1 = 380$ ml.
$P_1 = 640$ mm. of Hg.

Corrected conditions: $V_2 = x$ ml.
$P_2 = 760$ mm. of Hg.

Since the pressure increases, the volume will decrease. This means that the pressure correction fraction is less than unity. That is:

$$\frac{P_1}{P_2} = \frac{640 \text{ mm. of Hg}}{760 \text{ mm. of Hg}}.$$

Then

$$V_2 = 380 \text{ ml.} \times \frac{640 \text{ mm. of Hg}}{760 \text{ mm. of Hg}}.$$

$$= 320 \text{ ml.}$$

**7.6. The Law of Gay-Lussac.** The law of Gay-Lussac deals with the relationship existing between the two variables, *pressure* and *temperature*, for a given mass of gas at constant volume. The relationship is expressed in the law of Gay-Lussac: volume constant, the pressure exerted by a given mass of gas varies *directly* with the *absolute temperature*. That is:

$$P \propto T \text{ (volume and mass of gas constant)}.$$

It will be observed that the same type of variation exists between pressure and temperature as exists between volume and temperature (Sec. 7.4). Then:

$$\frac{P_1}{T_1} = \frac{P_2}{T_2}$$

or

$$P_2 = P_1 \times \frac{T_2}{T_1}.$$

temperature correction fraction

original pressure at $T_1$

corrected pressure at $T_2$

**Example 7.3.** The air in a tank was at a pressure of 640 mm. of Hg at 23° C. When placed in sunlight the temperature rose to 48° C. What was the pressure in the tank?

**Solution.** A rise in temperature would result in a rise in pressure. Therefore, the temperature correction fraction must be greater than unity. That is:

$$P_2 = 640 \text{ mm. of Hg} \times \frac{(273 + 48)°K}{(273 + 23)°K}$$

$$= 694 \text{ mm. of Hg.}$$

**7.7. A General Gas Law.** A general gas law would involve the three variables, temperature, pressure, and volume, simultaneously. Such a general gas law may be obtained by combining any two of the three gas laws discussed previously, since the three variables would be involved. For example, consider the laws of Charles and Boyle combined to give one equation.

$$V_1 \propto T_1, \quad \text{and} \quad V_1 \propto \frac{1}{P_1}.$$

Then $\quad V_1 \propto \frac{T_1}{P_1} \quad \text{or} \quad V_1 = K \frac{T_1}{P_1}, \quad \text{and} \quad K = \frac{P_1 V_1}{T_1}.$

For a second set of conditions $V_2$, $T_2$, and $P_2$:

$$K = \frac{P_2 V_2}{T_2}.$$

Therefore,    $\dfrac{P_1V_1}{T_1} = \dfrac{P_2V_2}{T_2}$ (for a given mass of gas)

and              $V_2 = V_1 \times \dfrac{T_2}{T_1} \times \dfrac{P_1}{P_2}.$

                                          pressure correction fraction

                               temperature correction fraction

                     original volume at $T_1$ and $P_1$

               corrected volume at $T_2$ and $P_2$

**Example 7.4.**  A volume of 250 ml. of oxygen was collected at 20° C. and 785 mm. of Hg.  The next day the temperature was 37° C. and the pressure 770 mm. of Hg.  Calculate the resultant volume of the oxygen.

**Solution.**  The quantities involved are:

Original conditions:    $P_1 = 785$ mm. of Hg.
                                  $V_1 = 250$ ml.
                                  $T_1 = 293°$ K.

Corrected conditions:  $P_2 = 770$ mm. of Hg.
                                  $V_2 = x$ ml.
                                  $T_2 = 310°$ K.

Both the increase in temperature and the decrease in pressure will result in an increase in volume of the oxygen.  Therefore:

$$V_2 = 250 \text{ ml.} \times \frac{310°\text{ K}}{293°\text{ K}} \times \frac{785 \text{ mm. of Hg}}{770 \text{ mm. of Hg}}$$

$$= 270 \text{ ml.}$$

## 7.8. The Change in Density of a Gas with Changes in Temperature and Pressure.

Since the volume of a given mass of gas is dependent upon the temperature and pressure under which it exists, it is apparent that the density of a gas will be dependent upon these same variables.

From Fig. 7.3 we see that the density of a gas varies directly with the pressure.  That is, $d \propto P$.

From Fig. 7.4 we see that the density of a gas varies inversely with the absolute temperature.  That is, $d \propto \dfrac{1}{T}$.  From the relationship that $d \propto P$ and that $d \propto \dfrac{1}{T}$, for a given mass of gas, it can be shown that (Secs. 7.4 and 7.5):

$$\frac{d_1T_1}{P_1} = \frac{d_2T_2}{P_2}$$

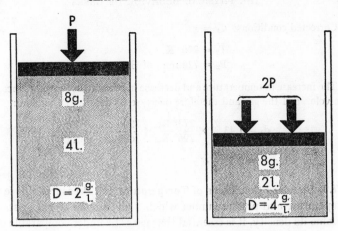

Fig. 7.3. Variation in the density of a gas with pressure.

or $$d_2 = d_1 \times \frac{T_1}{T_2} \times \frac{P_2}{P_1}.$$

**Example 7.5.** A liter of oxygen weighs 1.43 grams at 0° C. and 760 mm. of Hg. Calculate the weight of one liter of oxygen at 23° C. and 720 mm. of Hg.

**Solution.** The quantities involved are:

Original conditions:    $d_1 = 1.43 \frac{g.}{l.}$

                         $T_1 = 273°$ K.

                         $P_1 = 760$ mm. of Hg.

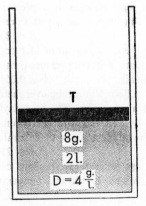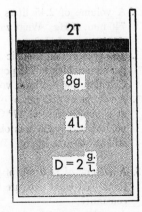

Fig. 7.4. Variation in the density of a gas with temperature.

Corrected conditions: $d_2 = x \dfrac{g.}{l.}$

$\qquad\qquad\qquad T_2 = 296°$ K.

$\qquad\qquad\qquad P_2 = 720$ mm. of Hg.

The increase in temperature and decrease in pressure both tend to increase the volume of the gas and therefore decrease its density. Therefore:

$$d_2 = 1.43 \frac{g.}{l.} \times \frac{273°\,\cancel{K.}}{296°\,\cancel{K.}} \times \frac{720\,\cancel{\text{mm. of Hg}}}{760\,\cancel{\text{mm. of Hg}}}$$

$$= 1.25 \frac{g.}{l.}.$$

**7.9. Standard Conditions of Temperature and Pressure.** Since the temperature and pressure under which a given mass of gas exists determine its density, it is essential that gases be under comparable conditions when comparing their densities. Such reference conditions have been arbitrarily established as 0° C. and 760 mm. of Hg. These are termed *standard conditions*, S.C., or *normal temperature and pressure*, N.T.P. Standard conditions may be assumed to be implied when densities of gases are given without stating the conditions under which they exist.

### Problems

Part I

**7.11.** A volume of 473 ml. of oxygen was collected at 27° C. What volume would the oxygen occupy at 173° C., pressure constant?

*Ans.* 703 ml.

**7.12.** A volume of 2.45 liters of oxygen was collected at a pressure of 740 mm. of Hg. What volume would the oxygen occupy at a pressure of 765 mm. of Hg? *Ans.* 2.37 *l.*

**7.13.** The pressure on a cubic foot of air was increased from 14.7 pounds per square inch to 231 pounds per square inch, temperature constant. Calculate the resultant volume of the air. *Ans.* 0.064 ft.$^3$

**7.14.** A volume of 21.5 ml. of oxygen was collected in a tube over mercury at a temperature of 17° C. and 740 mm. of Hg. The next day the volume of oxygen was observed to be 22.1 ml. with the barometer still at 740 mm. of Hg. What was the temperature of the laboratory?

*Ans.* 25° C.

**7.15.** A volume of 84.0 ml. of hydrogen was collected at standard conditions. At what pressure would the volume be 100 ml., temperature constant? *Ans.* 638 mm. of Hg.

**7.16.** A gas occupies a volume of 50 ml. at 30° C. and 680 mm. of Hg. Calculate the volume the gas would occupy at standard conditions.

*Ans.* 40 ml.

7.17. Air weighs 1.29 grams per liter at S.C.   Calculate the density of the air on Pikes Peak when the pressure is 450 mm. of Hg and the temperature 17° C.                                    *Ans.* 0.719 $\frac{g.}{l.}$·

7.18. One liter of nitrogen weighs 1.25 grams at S.C.   At what temperature would the density be one-half this value, pressure constant?
                                                        *Ans.* 273° C.

7.19. A closed metal cylinder contains air at a pressure of 930 mm. of Hg and a temperature of 27° C.   To what temperature would the air in the cylinder have to be raised in order to exert a pressure of 1500 mm. of Hg?                             *Ans.* 211° C.

7.20. At standard conditions one liter of ammonia, $NH_3$, weighs 0.771 g. What is the density of ammonia at 640 mm. of Hg and 27° C.?

                                                    *Ans.* 0.591 $\frac{g.}{l.}$·

## Part II

7.21. A room is 16 ft. by 12 ft. by 12 ft.   Would air enter or leave the room and how much if the temperature changed from 27° C. to −3° C., pressure remaining constant?               *Ans.* 230 ft.³ entering.

7.22. A bottle of nitrogen was collected at 0° C.   Assuming the pressure to remain constant, at what temperature would the volume be doubled?                                          *Ans.* 273° C.

7.23. An automobile tire contains air at 38 lb. per in.²   How many times the original volume would the air in the tire occupy if released at 15 lb. per in.², temperature constant?   Note: a tire gauge registers excess over atmospheric pressure.        *Ans.* 3.5 times.

7.24. The temperature of a tire rose from 50° F. to 120° F. as the result of traveling on a hot pavement.   Assuming the volume of the tire to be constant, what was the resulting pressure in the tire if the initial pressure was 40 lb. per in.²?        *Ans.* 46 $\frac{lb.}{in.^2}$·

7.25. A volume of 385 ml. of air at 760 mm. of Hg and 27° C. was carried to a mountaintop where the temperature was −23° C. and the pressure 470 mm. of Hg.   Calculate the resultant volume of the air.
                                                        *Ans.* 519 ml.

7.26. At the place Piccard started his ascent in the stratosphere balloon, the temperature was 17° C. and the pressure 640 mm. of Hg.   At the highest altitude reached, the temperature was −48° C. and the pressure 310 mm. of Hg.   To what fractional part of its total capacity was the balloon filled before ascending in order that it would be fully expanded at the highest altitude reached?        *Ans.* 0.62.

7.27. A given mass of chlorine occupies a volume of 130 ft.³ at 726 mm. of Hg.   Calculate the volume the chlorine would occupy at 2.00 atmospheres, temperature constant.        *Ans.* 62.1 ft.³

7.28. What pressure would be required to compress 250 $l$. of carbon dioxide at 1.00 atmosphere into a 15.0 $l$. cylinder, temperature constant?

*Ans.* 16.7 atm.

7.29. A given mass of nitrogen occupies a volume of 25.0 ft.³ at 70° F. At constant pressure, what will be the volume of the nitrogen at 212° F.? *Ans.* 31.7 ft.³

7.30. In a laboratory experiment a student collected 186 ml. of carbon dioxide over mercury. The barometer registered 74.5 cm. and the thermometer 68° F. What would be the volume of the carbon dioxide collected when reduced to standard conditions? *Ans.* 170 ml.

7.31. A sealed glass bulb contained helium at a pressure of 750 mm. of Hg and 27° C. The bulb was packed in dry ice at −73° C. What was the resultant pressure of the helium? *Ans.* 500 mm. of Hg.

7.32. A 2.00 ft.³ cylinder of nitrogen is under a pressure of 2000 $\frac{lb.}{in.^2}$. What volume would the nitrogen occupy if released in a room in which the pressure was 745 mm. of Hg, there being no change in temperature? *Ans.* 278 ft.³

7.33. By means of a vacuum pump it is possible to obtain a pressure of $10^{-6}$ mm. of Hg. What would this be equivalent to in pounds per square inch? *Ans.* $2 \times 10^{-8} \frac{lb.}{in.^2}$.

7.34. At standard conditions nitrogen weighs 1.25 $\frac{g.}{l.}$. What is the weight of 650 ml. of nitrogen at 725 mm. of Hg and 23° C.? *Ans.* 0.72 $\frac{g.}{l.}$.

7.35. What weight of oxygen would be contained in a 2.00 ft.³ cylinder at a pressure of 2000 $\frac{lb.}{in.^2}$ and 68° F.? At S.C. one liter of oxygen weighs 1.43 g. *Ans.* 10.3 kg.

7.36. The temperature of a given mass of gas is changed from 23° C. to 319° C., and the pressure from 420 mm. of Hg to 840 mm. of Hg. What is the resultant volume? *Ans.* No change.

7.37. At standard conditions 1.00 $l$. of carbon dioxide weighs 1.98 g. What is the weight per liter at 15° C. and 675 mm. of Hg? *Ans.* 1.67 $\frac{g.}{l.}$.

7.38. A given mass of neon occupies a volume of 125 ml. at 75.0 cm. of Hg and 68° F. What volume would the neon occupy at 3.75 atmospheres and 300° K.? *Ans.* 33.7 ml.

7.39. A given quantity of gas occupies a volume of 875 ml. at 68° F. and 73 cm. of Hg. Calculate the volume the gas would occupy at 350° K. and 12 atmospheres pressure. *Ans.* 84 ml.

7.40. A tank containing 4 ft.³ of butane gas at 15 atm. pressure is connected to a tank containing 6 ft.³ of the gas at 5 atm. pressure. Calculate

the resultant pressure in the connected tanks, assuming no temperature change.        *Ans.* 9 atm.

7.41. One liter of a gas weighs 1.33 grams at 750 mm. of Hg and 17° C.
Calculate the weight of 500 ml. of the gas at 640 mm. of Hg and
37° C.        *Ans.* 0.53 g.

7.42. An automobile tire gauge registered 40 lb. with the barometer reading
760 mm. of Hg and the temperature 23° C. After driving on a hot
pavement the gauge registered 43 lb. What was the temperature
of the tire, assuming its volume to remain constant?        *Ans.* 39° C.

## Laws Relating to Mixtures of Gases

**7.10. Dalton's Law of Partial Pressures.** Dalton's law states that
the total pressure exerted by a mixture of gases is equal to the sum of
the partial pressures of each of the gases constituting the mixture. By
*partial pressure* is meant the pressure each gas would exert if it alone
occupied the volume occupied by the mixture of gases. For example,
if one liter of hydrogen and one liter of oxygen, each at 0° C. and
380 mm. of Hg, are forced into a third container of one liter capacity
as shown in Fig. 7.5, then the resultant pressure of the mixture would
be:

$$380 \text{ mm. of Hg} + 380 \text{ mm. of Hg} = 760 \text{ mm. of Hg.}$$

total pressure

partial pressure of oxygen

partial pressure of hydrogen

Dalton's law finds its most useful application in general chemistry
to calculations involving the collection of gases over water, where
water vapor is always present with the collected gas. In such calcula-

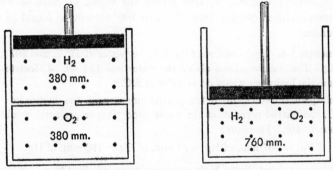

Fig. 7.5. Illustrating Dalton's law of partial pressures.

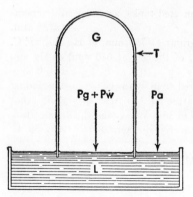

Fig. 7.6. Dalton's law of partial pressures applied to gases collected over water.

tions a correction must be made for the water vapor present. The higher the temperature of the water over which the gas is collected, the greater the amount of water vapor present. The actual amount of gas collected is therefore less than the measured volume. In Fig. 7.6 the gas, G, has been collected over the water, L. The space G therefore contains both water vapor and gas. If the level of the liquid is the same inside and outside the tube, T, then the pressure of the gases in the tube is equal to the barometric pressure of the room in which the gas is collected. Then, from Dalton's law:

$$P_g + P_w = P_a.$$

$$
\begin{array}{ccc}
| & | & | \\
| & | & \text{atmospheric pressure} \\
| & \text{partial pressure of water vapor} & \\
\text{partial pressure of the collected gas} & &
\end{array}
$$

Solving the above for $P_g$ gives:

$$P_g = P_a - P_w.$$

Therefore, to find the pressure, $P_g$, under which the collected gas would exist if it alone occupied the total volume in the tube, subtract the vapor pressure of the water at the given temperature from the atmospheric pressure. A table giving the vapor pressure of water for temperatures ranging from 0° C. to 100° C. will be found in the Appendix.

**Example 7.6.** Hydrogen was collected over water at 27° C. and 807 mm. of Hg. The volume of gas above the water was 124 ml. Calculate the volume the hydrogen would occupy dry at S.C.

**Solution.** First calculate the partial pressure of the hydrogen. At 27° C. the partial pressure of the water vapor (vapor pressure) would be 27 mm. of Hg. Therefore:

$$P_{H_2} = 807 \text{ mm. of Hg} - 27 \text{ mm. of Hg} = 780 \text{ mm. of Hg}.$$

This means that, if the hydrogen alone occupied the 124 ml., it would exert a pressure of 780 mm. of Hg. We may now apply the general gas law

(Sec. 7.7) to change the hydrogen to standard conditions (Sec. 7.9). Then:

$$V_{H_2} = 124 \text{ ml.} \times \frac{273° \text{ K.}}{300° \text{ K.}} \times \frac{780 \text{ mm. of Hg}}{760 \text{ mm. of Hg}}$$

$$= 116 \text{ ml. at S.C.}$$

**7.11. Graham's Law of Gaseous Diffusion.** The law of Graham deals with the relationship existing between the *rates of diffusion*, **D**, of gases, and their *densities*, d. By diffusion is meant the ability of gaseous molecules to pass through small openings, such as in the fabric of balloons or unglazed porcelain; or the intermingling of molecules in a mixture. On the basis of the kinetic-molecular theory it is evident that increasing the temperature of a gas will increase its rate of diffusion, since increasing the temperature increases the velocity of the molecules, thus producing a greater number of impacts on the walls of the containing vessel in any given unit of time. It is also apparent that increasing the pressure of a gas will produce more impacts on the walls of the vessel, thus increasing the rate of diffusion.

TABLE 7.3

DIFFUSION OF GASES AS RELATED TO THEIR DENSITIES

| Gas | $d\left(\frac{g.}{l.}\right)$ | $\sqrt{d}$ | $D\left(\frac{ml.}{hr.}\right)$ |
|---|---|---|---|
| $H_2$ | 0.09 | 0.3 | 400 |
| $O_2$ | 1.43 | 1.2 | 100 |

From Table 7.3 we see that the greater the density of the gas, the slower the rate of diffusion of the gas. This is in accord with the law of Graham: under similar conditions such as temperature, pressure, and the size of the openings through which the gases diffuse, the rates of diffusion of gases vary *inversely* as the *square roots* of their *densities*. That is:

$$D \propto \frac{1}{\sqrt{d}}.$$

Treating the above variables in the same manner as the variables pressure and volume in Sec. 7.5, we have:

$$D_1\sqrt{d_1} = D_2\sqrt{d_2}$$

or

$$D_2 = D_1 \times \frac{\sqrt{d_1}}{\sqrt{d_2}} = D_1 \times \sqrt{\frac{d_1}{d_2}}.$$

When one considers that light molecules are moving with a greater velocity than are heavier molecules (Sec. 7.1), it becomes evident why the lighter molecules will diffuse the faster.

**Example 7.7.** Two balloons of the same size and like material are filled respectively with hydrogen and oxygen at the same temperature and pressure. If the oxygen escapes at the rate of 65 ml. per hour, calculate the rate of escape of the hydrogen.

**Solution.** Using the values of the densities given in Table 7.3, we have:

$$D_{H_2} = 65 \frac{ml.}{hr.} \times \sqrt{\frac{1.43}{0.09}}$$

$$= 260 \frac{ml.}{hr.}$$

Since the hydrogen is the lighter of the two gases it will diffuse the faster. Also, the quantity $\sqrt{\frac{1.43}{0.09}} = 4$ tells us that hydrogen will diffuse four times faster than oxygen.

The densities of gases are proportional to their molecular weights. For example, in the case of oxygen and hydrogen, we have:

$$\frac{1.43 \frac{g.}{l.}}{0.09 \frac{g.}{l.}} = \frac{32.00}{2.016} = 15.9.$$

It is therefore possible to substitute the molecular weights of the gases, M, for their densities in the above formula. That is:

$$D_2 = D_1 \times \sqrt{\frac{M_1}{M_2}}.$$

**Example 7.8.** Compare the rates of diffusion of methane, $CH_4$, and sulfur dioxide, $SO_2$.

**Solution.** The molecular weight of $CH_4 = 16$ and of $SO_2 = 64$. Therefore the $CH_4$ will diffuse the faster. Let the rate of diffusion of $SO_2$ be unity. Then:

$$\text{Rate of diffusion of } CH_4 = 1 \times \sqrt{\tfrac{64}{16}} = 2.$$

That is, $CH_4$ diffuses twice as fast as $SO_2$.

### Problems

#### Part I

7.43. Hydrogen was collected over water, the volume of hydrogen and water vapor being one liter at 25° C. and 640 mm. of Hg.

a. What is the partial pressure of the hydrogen?  *Ans.* 616 mm. of Hg.

b. Calculate the volume the hydrogen would occupy dry under the given conditions.  *Ans.* 0.963 $l$.

c. Calculate the volume the hydrogen would occupy dry at standard conditions.  *Ans.* 0.742 $l$.

d. What fractional part of the original liter was water vapor?  *Ans.* 0.037.

7.44. A volume of 1.43 liters of dry hydrogen at 27° C. and 760 mm. of Hg was bubbled through water. What was the volume of the mixture of hydrogen and water vapor, temperature and pressure constant?

*Ans.* 1.48 $l$.

7.45. Nitrogen weighs 1.25 g. per $l$. and chlorine 3.21 g. per $l$. at standard conditions. Which will escape the faster and by how much if enclosed in an unglazed porcelain container in equal amounts?

*Ans.* $N_2$, 1.6 times faster.

7.46. Chlorine will escape through a small opening one-sixth as fast as hydrogen under similar conditions. Given that one liter of hydrogen weighs 0.0899 g., calculate the density of chlorine.

*Ans.* 3.24 g. per $l$.

7.47. Two porous containers were filled respectively with hydrogen and oxygen at S.C. At the end of one hour 880 ml. of hydrogen had escaped. How much oxygen had escaped during this same period of time?  *Ans.* 220 ml.

7.48. Calculate the partial pressures of oxygen and nitrogen in the atmosphere, given that air contains 21 per cent oxygen and 78 per cent nitrogen by volume. Barometric pressure, 746 mm. of Hg.

*Ans.* $O_2 = 157$ mm.; $N_2 = 582$ mm.

7.49. Arrange the following gases in order of their increasing rates of diffusion: $N_2$, He, $H_2$, $CH_4$, $CO_2$, $O_2$.  *Ans.* $CO_2$, $O_2$, $N_2$, $CH_4$, He, $H_2$.

7.50. It required 16 sec. for 250 ml. of $CH_4$ to diffuse through a small opening. Under the same conditions of temperature and pressure, how long would be required for 1500 ml. of $SO_2$ to diffuse through the same opening?  *Ans.* 192 sec.

## Part II

7.51. In a laboratory experiment 763 ml. of gas was collected over water at 35° C. and 748 mm. of Hg. Calculate the volume the gas would occupy dry at standard conditions.  *Ans.* 628 ml.

7.52. In an experiment hydrogen was collected over water at 27° C. and 725 mm. of Hg. The volume of hydrogen and water vapor measured 350 ml. Upon standing the temperature changed to 17° C. and the pressure to 750 mm. of Hg. What was the resultant volume?

*Ans.* 332 ml.

7.53. What volume will 2.500 g. of oxygen occupy at 27° C. and 760 mm. of Hg, when collected over (a) mercury, and (b) water?

*Ans.* (a) 1.92 $l$.  (b) 1.99 $l$.

**7.54.** A mixture of gases consists of 20% $N_2$, 30% $O_2$, and 50% He at 760 mm. of Hg. What is the partial pressure of each gas?

*Ans.* $N_2$ = 152 mm.; $O_2$ = 228 mm.; He = 380 mm.

**7.55.** Two liters of oxygen and eight liters of nitrogen, at S.C., are mixed in a 25.0 *l.* tank. At 0° C. (a) what is the pressure in the tank, and (b) what is the partial pressure of each gas?

*Ans.* (a) 304 mm.; (b) $O_2$ = 61 mm., $N_2$ = 243 mm.

**7.56.** Three similar balloons were filled respectively with $O_2$, $CO_2$, and $Cl_2$ under similar conditions. In ten hours one-half the $CO_2$ had escaped. How much of each of the other gases escaped during the same period of time? *Ans.* $O_2$ = 0.6; $Cl_2$ = 0.4.

**7.57.** A porous container was filled with equal amounts of oxygen and a gas of unknown molecular weight. The oxygen escaped 1.77 times faster than the unknown gas. Calculate the molecular weight of the unknown gas. *Ans.* 99.

**7.58.** What are the relative rates of diffusion of the gases $H_2$ and $COCl_2$ under similar conditions? *Ans.* 7 : 1.

**7.59.** Methane, $CH_4$, diffuses through an opening at the rate of 135 ml. per sec. At what rate will argon diffuse through the same opening under similar conditions? *Ans.* 85.4 ml. per sec.

**7.60.** Arrange the following in order of increasing time required to diffuse through a given opening under similar conditions: 150 ml. $COCl_2$, 500 ml. $H_2$, 375 ml. $CO_2$. *Ans.* $H_2$, $COCl_2$, $CO_2$.

# 8

# Chemical Equations

Chemistry is a study of the behavior of atoms, and the laws underlying such behavior. The chemist expresses such behavior of atoms in the form of a chemical equation. In order to write a chemical equation one must know the reactants and products involved. One may predict the course of a chemical change. However, experimental methods must be used to determine accurately the products of a chemical change. Most chemical changes fall into one of four categories — combination, decomposition, displacement, and metathesis.

In writing a chemical equation, first classify the reaction as to type; then determine the products of the reaction; and finally write the balanced expression which represents the chemical equation. The reactants and products in an equation must contain the same number of each kind of atom.

**8.1. Combination.** Any chemical change in which two or more substances combine to form a single product is a *combination* reaction. The simplest form of combination reactions are those in which elements are the reactants. For example, one atom of sulfur will combine with two atoms of oxygen to form one molecule of sulfur dioxide. That is:

$$S + O_2 \rightarrow SO_2.$$

Every chemical change occurs under certain specified conditions. The above reaction takes place under ordinary room conditions. Under suitable conditions sulfur and oxygen combine to form sulfur trioxide. That is:

$$S + O_2 \rightarrow SO_3.$$

The above expression does not represent an equation since the reactants contain two atoms of oxygen and the product three atoms of oxygen. By trial and error one may obtain the equation:

$$2\,S \;+\; 3\,O_2 \;\rightarrow\; 2\,SO_3.$$

$$\underset{\substack{| \\ | \\ 2\ \text{atoms}}}{\phantom{2S}} \qquad \underset{\substack{| \\ 6\ \text{atoms}}}{\phantom{3O_2}} \qquad \underset{\substack{|| \\ 6\ \text{atoms} \\ 2\ \text{atoms}}}{\phantom{2SO_3}}$$

It is apparent that a knowledge of the conditions under which a chemical change takes place is necessary in order to write the chemical equation for the reaction. Unless otherwise specified, room conditions are usually implied.

Combination reactions may involve compounds as shown below.

$$SO_2 + H_2O \rightarrow H_2SO_3.$$
$$CaO + H_2O \rightarrow Ca(OH)_2.$$
$$P_2O_5 + 3\,H_2O \rightarrow 2\,H_3PO_4.$$
$$CaCO_3 + CO_2 + H_2O \rightarrow Ca(HCO_3)_2.$$

**8.2. Decomposition.** Decomposition is the reverse of combination. That is, a single reactant is broken down into two or more products. The simplest decomposition type of reaction is one in which a binary compound is broken down into its constituent elements. When mercuric oxide is heated, mercury and oxygen are the products.

$$2\,HgO \rightarrow 2\,Hg + O_2.$$

When potassium chlorate is heated the products are potassium chloride and oxygen.

$$2\,KClO_3 \rightarrow 2\,KCl + 3\,O_2.$$

Decomposition reactions may be quite complex. For example, the reaction occurring when ammonium dichromate is heated is:

$$2(NH_4)_2Cr_2O_7 \rightarrow 4\,NH_3 \uparrow \;+\; 2\,H_2O + 2\,Cr_2O_3 + 3\,O_2 \uparrow.$$

**8.3. Displacement.** Displacement reactions are those in which the atoms of an element displace the atoms of a second element in a compound. That is:

$$A + BC \rightarrow AC + B,$$

where A and B are elements. Some examples follow.

$$Zn + H_2SO_4 \rightarrow ZnSO_4 + H_2.$$
$$Fe + CuSO_4 \rightarrow FeSO_4 + Cu.$$
$$Cl_2 + 2\,NaI \rightarrow 2\,NaCl + I_2.$$

**8.4. Metathesis.** Most reactions of the metathetic type occur in water solution, and are therefore characteristic of ionic compounds.

Metathesis is essentially a double displacement involving ions. That is:

$$AB + CD \rightarrow AD + CB.$$

In order to have any appreciable degree of completion of such reactions, one or both of the products must become unavailable for the reverse reaction. Otherwise, an equilibrium would result with essentially no chemical change having taken place. That is:

$$A^+ + B^- + C^+ + D^- \rightarrow A^+ + D^+ + C^+ + B^-.$$

The principal conditions which result in a product being unavailable for the reverse reaction are (1) insolubility, (2) gaseous state, and (3) nonionizability. For example:

(1)   $AgNO_3 + NaCl \rightarrow NaNO_3 + AgCl \downarrow$

or      $Ag^+ + NO_3^- + Na^+ + Cl^- \rightarrow Na^+ + NO_3^- + AgCl \downarrow$ .

(2)   $Na_2S + H_2SO_4 \rightarrow Na_2SO_4 + H_2S \uparrow$

or      $2\,Na^+ + S^{-2} + 2\,H^+ + SO_4^{-2} \rightarrow 2\,Na^+ + SO_4^{-2} + H_2S \uparrow$ .

(3)   $HCl + NaOH \rightarrow NaCl + H_2O$

or      $H^+ + Cl^- + Na^+ + OH^- \rightarrow Na^+ + Cl^- + H_2O.$

In the above reactions silver chloride, $AgCl$, is removed as a precipitate; hydrogen sulfide, $H_2S$, as a gas; and water, $H_2O$, as a nonionizable product.

**8.5. Combustion Reactions.** Reactions which take place with the emission of *heat* and *light* are called combustion reactions. Most combustion reactions involve burning with atmospheric oxygen, such as the burning of coal, wood, natural gas, and oils. In reactions of this type the carbon of the fuel is burned to carbon dioxide and the hydrogen to water.

$$C + O_2 \rightarrow CO_2.$$
$$2\,H_2 + O_2 \rightarrow 2\,H_2O.$$

Natural gas is principally methane, $CH_4$.

$$CH_4 + 2\,O_2 \rightarrow CO_2 + 2\,H_2O.$$

One of the principal constituents of gasoline is heptane, $C_7H_{16}$.

$$C_7H_{16} + 11\,O_2 \rightarrow 7\,CO_2 + 8\,H_2O.$$

Alcohol is $C_2H_5OH$.

$$2\,C_2H_5OH + 7\,O_2 \rightarrow 4\,CO_2 + 6\,H_2O.$$

## Problems

### Part I

8.1. Balance the following combination reactions:

a. $P + O_2 \rightarrow P_2O_5$.

b. $Mg + N_2 \rightarrow Mg_3N_2$.

c. $Na + O_2 \rightarrow Na_2O_2$.

d. $Al + N_2 \rightarrow AlN$.

e. $Fe + O_2 \rightarrow Fe_3O_4$.

8.2. Balance the following decomposition reactions:

a. $KNO_3 \rightarrow KNO_2 + O_2$.

b. $Pb(NO_3)_2 \rightarrow PbO + NO_2 + O_2$.

c. $Fe_2(C_2O_4)_3 \rightarrow FeC_2O_4 + CO_2$.

d. $Fe(OH)_3 \rightarrow Fe_2O_3 + H_2O$.

e. $HNO_2 \rightarrow HNO_3 + NO + H_2O$.

8.3. Balance each of the following displacement reactions:

a. $Al + CuSO_4 \rightarrow Al_2(SO_4)_3 + Cu$.

b. $Al + HCl \rightarrow AlCl_3 + H_2$.

c. $Zn + AgNO_3 \rightarrow Zn(NO_3)_2 + Ag$.

d. $Na + HOH \rightarrow NaOH + H_2$.

e. $Cl_2 + NaBr \rightarrow NaCl + Br_2$.

8.4. Balance each of the following metathesis reactions in both the non-ionic and ionic forms:

a. $Al(OH)_3 + HCl \rightarrow AlCl_3 + H_2O$.

b. $Ca(OH)_2 + H_3PO_4 \rightarrow Ca_3(PO_4)_2 + H_2O$.

c. $AgNO_3 + H_2S \rightarrow Ag_2S \downarrow + HNO_3$.

d. $NaCl + H_2SO_4 \rightarrow Na_2SO_4 + HCl \uparrow$.

e. $FeCl_3 + Ca(OH)_2 \rightarrow Fe(OH)_3 \downarrow + CaCl_2$.

8.5. Write the equations for the combustion of:

a. Benzene, $C_6H_6$.

b. Propane, $C_5H_{12}$.

c. Methyl alcohol, $CH_3OH$.

d. Sugar, $C_{12}H_{22}O_{11}$.

e. Carbon monoxide, CO.

8.6. Balance each of the following miscellaneous types of reactions:

a. $Fe_3O_4 + H_2 \rightarrow Fe + H_2O$.

b. $MnO_2 + HCl \rightarrow MnCl_2 + H_2O + Cl_2 \uparrow$.

c. $Cu + HNO_3 \rightarrow Cu(NO_3)_2 + NO \uparrow + H_2O$.

d. $FeCl_2 + HCl + HNO_3 \rightarrow FeCl_3 + NO \uparrow + H_2O$.

e. $Al(NO_3)_3 + NaOH \rightarrow NaAlO_2 + NaNO_3 + H_2O$.

### Part II

8.7. Classify each of the following as to type, predict the products, and then write the equations:

a. $Al + Br_2$.

b. $Al + Fe_2O_3$.

c. $AlCl_3 + KOH$.

d. $BaCl_2 + Na_2CO_3$.

e. $BaCl_2 + AgNO_3$.

f. $BaO + SO_3$.

g. $Ba(OH)_2 + H_2CO_3$.

h. $Br_2 + H_2$.

i. $Cd(NO_3)_2 + (NH_4)_2S$.

j. $Ca + H_2O$.

k. $BaO + H_2O$.

l. $CaO + HCl$.

m. $CaO + CO_2$.

n. $Ca(OH)_2 + HNO_3$.

o. $CaO + HNO_3$.

p. $CO_2 + H_2O$.

q. $CS_2 + O_2$.

r. $C_{10}H_{16} + O_2$.

s. $Cl_2 + FeCl_2$.

t. $Cl_2 + KI$.

u. $HCl + Al$.

v. $H_2O + Li_2O$.

w. $Ba(OH)_2 + H_3PO_4$.

x. $N_2 + H_2$.

y. $Al(OH)_3 + H_2SO_4$.

8.8. Balance the following miscellaneous reactions:

a. $AgCl + NH_4OH \rightarrow Ag(NH_3)_2Cl + H_2O$.

b. $Ca(OH)_2 + H_2SO_4 \rightarrow Ca(HSO_4)_2 + H_2O$.

c. $Ca(OH)_2 + (NH_4)_2CO_3 \rightarrow NH_3 + CaCO_3 \downarrow + H_2O$.

d. $Ca(PO_3)_2 + C \rightarrow Ca_3(PO_4)_2 + CO \uparrow + P_4$.

e. $CaSO_3 + H_2SO_4 \rightarrow CaSO_4 + H_2O + SO_2 \uparrow$.

f. $C + BaSO_4 \rightarrow CO \uparrow + BaS$.

g. $C + HNO_3 \rightarrow NO_2 \uparrow + CO_2 \uparrow + H_2O$.

h. $CO + Fe_2O_3 \rightarrow Fe + CO_2 \uparrow$.

i. $Cu + H_2SO_4 \rightarrow CuSO_4 + H_2SO_3 + H_2O$.

j. $CuS + HNO_3 \rightarrow Cu(NO_3)_2 + H_2O + NO \uparrow + S$.

k. $HCl + HClO_3 \rightarrow H_2O + Cl_2 \uparrow$.

l. $HCl + HNO_3 \rightarrow H_2O + NO \uparrow + Cl_2 \uparrow$.

m. $HCl + Fe_2O_3 \rightarrow FeCl_3 + H_2O$.

n. $HNO_3 + H_2S \rightarrow H_2O + NO \uparrow + S \downarrow$.

o. $FeCl_3 + H_2S \rightarrow FeCl_2 + HCl + S \downarrow$.

p. $Fe(NO_3)_3 + Ba(OH)_2 \rightarrow Fe(OH)_3 \downarrow + Ba(NO_3)_2$.

q. $H_2SO_4 + Na_2SO_3 \rightarrow Na_2SO_4 + H_2O + SO_2 \uparrow$.

r. $Pb(NO_3)_2 + K_2CrO_4 \rightarrow PbCrO_4 \downarrow + KNO_3$.

s. $Hg + HNO_3 \rightarrow Hg(NO_3)_2 + NO_2 \uparrow + H_2O$.

t. $KBr + KOH + Cl_2 \rightarrow KBrO_3 + KCl + H_2O$.

u. $KCN + Fe(OH)_2 \rightarrow K_4Fe(CN)_6 + KOH$.

v. $KI + H_2O \rightarrow KOH + I_2 \downarrow$.

w. $SiF_4 + H_2O \rightarrow HF \uparrow + Si(OH)_4$.

x. $SO_3 + HNO_3 \rightarrow H_2SO_4 + N_2O_5 \uparrow$.

8.9. Balance the following as ionic equations:

a. $HCl + Pb(NO_3)_2 \rightarrow PbCl_2 \downarrow + HNO_3$.

b. $Ca(OH)_2 + Na_3PO_4 \rightarrow Ca_3(PO_4)_2 \downarrow + NaOH$.

c. $BaCl_2 + K_2CO_3 \rightarrow BaCO_3 \downarrow + KCl$.

d. $KCl + H_3PO_4 \rightarrow K_3PO_4 + HCl \uparrow$.

e. $KOH + H_2SO_4 \rightarrow K_2SO_4 + H_2O$.

f. $CaS + HCl \rightarrow CaCl_2 + H_2S \uparrow$.

g. $AgNO_3 + K_2CrO_4 \rightarrow KNO_3 + Ag_2CrO_4 \downarrow$.

h. $BaCl_2 + Na_2SO_4 \rightarrow NaCl + BaSO_4 \downarrow$.

i. $CdSO_4 + H_2S \rightarrow CdS \downarrow + H_2SO_4$.

j. $FeCl_3 + NaOH \rightarrow Fe(OH)_3 \downarrow + NaCl$.

8.10. Transcribe the following word equations into the conventional symbol equations:

a. Aluminum + magnesium oxide → magnesium + aluminum oxide.

b. Aluminum chloride + ammonium hydroxide → aluminum hydroxide ↓ + ammonium chloride.

c. Silver nitrate + sodium phosphate → silver phosphate ↓ + sodium nitrate.

d. Chlorine + potassium iodide → potassium chloride + iodine ↓ .

e. Ferric sulfate + calcium hydroxide → ferric hydroxide ↓ + calcium sulfate ↓ .

f. Barium nitrate + ammonium carbonate → barium carbonate ↓ + ammonium nitrate.

g. Potassium hydroxide + sulfuric acid → potassium sulfate + water.

h. Ferrous hydroxide + hydrochloric acid → ferrous chloride + water.

i. Cupric sulfate + hydrogen sulfide → cupric sulfide ↓ + sulfuric acid.

j. Silver nitrate + potassium chromate → silver chromate ↓ + potassium nitrate.

# 9

# Equivalent Weights of the Elements

The previous chapters have dealt with fundamentals which the student must understand in order to speak the language of the chemist. We are now ready to use some of these fundamental ideas in studying the mass relationships involved when the various elements combine to form compounds. In order for the chemist to explain quantitatively the laws controlling the formation of compounds from elements, a unit of mass called the *gram-equivalent weight* has been devised. This represents the third unit of mass discussed, based upon the actual masses of atoms and molecules, the gram-atom and the mole having been presented in Chapter 6.

## Combining Proportions among the Elements

**9.1. Introduction.** Under similar conditions, such as temperature and pressure, the atoms of two or more elements which react to form a compound will always combine in the same ratio. For example, when hydrogen burns in oxygen the product is $H_2O$, indicating that two atoms of hydrogen combine with one of oxygen. Also, excluding variations due to isotopes, the atoms of a given element all possess the same mass. The above facts account for the *law of constant composition:* the proportions by weight of the elements constituting a compound are always the same.

It has been shown experimentally that definite combining proportions by weight exist among the elements. This is shown diagrammatically in Fig. 9.1. Such a diagram could be extended to include all the known elements.

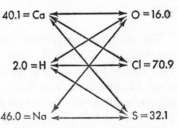

Fig. 9.1. Combining proportions among several of the elements.

73

Any two of the elements shown in Fig. 9.1 which combine to form a compound will do so in the ratio by weight as given. That is, 40.1 grams of calcium will combine with 16.0 grams of oxygen to form 56.1 grams of calcium oxide; 46.0 grams of sodium will combine with 32.1 grams of sulfur to form 78.1 grams of sodium sulfide; and 2.0 grams of hydrogen will combine with 70.9 grams of chlorine to form 72.9 grams of hydrogen chloride. Observe that these combining proportions of the elements are either their atomic weights, as in the case of calcium, oxygen, and sulfur, or a multiple of their atomic weights, as with sodium, hydrogen, and chlorine.

The above may be summarized as follows. Under given conditions, elements combine in a definite ratio by weight, the ratio being represented by the atomic weights of the elements or some multiple thereof.

**Example 9.1.** A piece of calcium weighing 2.16 grams was exposed to the air until oxidation was complete. (a) How much oxygen combined with the calcium? (b) What was the weight of the calcium oxide formed?

**Solution.** (a) From Fig. 9.1 we see that 40.1 g. of calcium combines with 16.0 g. of oxygen. Therefore:

$$\frac{16.0 \text{ g. O}_2}{40.1 \text{ g. Ca}} = \frac{x \text{ g. O}_2}{2.16 \text{ g. Ca}}$$

or
$$x = 0.862 \text{ g. O}_2.$$

(b) The weight of the calcium oxide is the sum of the weights of the calcium and oxygen reacting. That is:

Weight of calcium oxide formed = 2.16 g. + 0.862 g. = 3.02 g.

The weight of the oxide formed could have been obtained from the relationship that 40.1 grams of calcium combine with 16.0 grams of oxygen to form 56.1 grams of oxide. Then:

$$\frac{40.1 \text{ g. Ca}}{56.1 \text{ g. CaO}} = \frac{2.16 \text{ g. Ca}}{x \text{ g. CaO}}$$

or
$$x = 3.02 \text{ g. CaO.}$$

The combining proportions of the elements are related directly to the Avogadro number N. For example, 40.1 grams of calcium and 16.0 grams of oxygen each contain N atoms (Sec. 6.4). This means that one atom of calcium combines with one atom of oxygen to form calcium oxide, CaO. On the other hand 46.0 grams of sodium contain 2 N atoms, and 32.1 grams of sulfur contain N atoms. Therefore, two atoms of sodium must combine with one atom of sulfur. This is shown in the formula $Na_2S$ for sodium sulfide.

## Equivalent Weight

**9.2. Gram-equivalent Weight.** Since definite combining proportions have been shown to exist among the elements, it is evident that a standard of reference for combining power would be convenient. The standard adopted is 8.0000 grams of oxygen. The *gram-equivalent weight* is defined, therefore, as the number of grams of an element which will combine with 8.0000 grams of oxygen. Since the combining proportions in Fig. 9.1 involve 16.0000 grams of oxygen, the gram-equivalent weights of the six elements shown would be one-half the combining proportions given. The concept is important since any two elements which react chemically will combine in amounts proportional to their gram-equivalent weights. The gram-equivalent weights of the elements are determined experimentally.

**Example 9.2.** The gram-equivalent weight of aluminum is 9.0 g. and of chlorine, 35.5 g. How many grams of aluminum will combine with 7.63 grams of chlorine?

**Solution.** The two elements will combine in amounts proportional to their gram-equivalent weights. Therefore:

$$\frac{9.0 \text{ g. Al}}{35.5 \text{ g. Cl}_2} = \frac{x \text{ g. Al}}{7.63 \text{ g. Cl}_2}$$

or
$$x = 1.93 \text{ g. Al.}$$

**Example 9.3.** An analysis of magnesium oxide showed that 2.099 g. of the oxide contained 0.833 g. of oxygen and 1.266 g. of magnesium. From the above data calculate the gram-equivalent weight of magnesium.

**Solution.** By definition the gram-equivalent weight of magnesium is the amount combined with 8.0000 g. of oxygen. Therefore:

$$\frac{1.266 \text{ g. Mg}}{0.833 \text{ g. O}_2} = \frac{x \text{ g. Mg}}{8.000 \text{ g. O}_2}$$

or
$$x = 12.16 \text{ g.} = \text{gram-equivalent weight of Mg.}$$

The gram-equivalent weight of any element has the same combining power as 8.0000 grams of oxygen. The gram-equivalent weight of hydrogen is 1.008 g. or 11,200 ml. at standard conditions. Use may be made of this fact to determine the gram-equivalent weight of a metal by displacement of hydrogen from acid solution. The amount of metal required to displace 1.008 g. of hydrogen or 11,200 ml. at standard conditions from an acid solution is the gram-equivalent weight of the metal.

**Example 9.4.** When 0.684 g. of zinc reacted with sulfuric acid there was liberated 234 ml. of hydrogen, measured at standard conditions. Determine the gram-equivalent weight of zinc.

**Solution.** By definition, the gram-equivalent weight of zinc is the number of grams required to liberate 11,200 ml. of $H_2$ at S.C. Therefore:

$$\frac{0.684 \text{ g. Zn}}{234 \text{ ml. } H_2} = \frac{x \text{ g. Zn}}{11,200 \text{ ml. } H_2}$$

or $\qquad\qquad x = 32.7$ g. = gram-equivalent weight of Zn.

**Example 9.5.** It was found that 0.450 g. of Al liberated 760 ml. of hydrogen from a solution of sulfuric acid, the gas being collected over water at 27° C. and 640 mm. of Hg. Calculate the gram-equivalent weight of aluminum from the data given in the problem.

**Solution.** One gram-equivalent weight of aluminum will displace 11,200 ml. of hydrogen at standard conditions. Evidently the first step in the solution will be to convert the collected gas to the volume it would occupy at standard conditions. Then:

$$V_{\text{S.C.}} = 760 \text{ ml.} \times \frac{273° \text{K}}{300° \text{K}} \times \frac{(640 - 27) \text{ mm. of Hg}}{760 \text{ mm. of Hg}}$$

$$= 558 \text{ ml. of } H_2, \text{ dry, at standard conditions.}$$

The amount of aluminum required to liberate 11,200 ml. of hydrogen can now be calculated.

$$\frac{0.450 \text{ g. Al}}{558 \text{ ml. } H_2} = \frac{x \text{ g. Al}}{11,200 \text{ ml. } H_2}$$

or $\qquad\qquad x = 9.0$ g. = gram-equivalent weight of aluminum.

**9.3. The Gram-equivalent Weight of an Element as Related to Oxidation Number.** The gram-equivalent weight of an element may be determined from the oxidation number (or valence) of the element as it exists in a given compound. The oxidation number of the free element is, of course, zero. The following formula expresses the relationship between *gram-equivalent weight*, *atomic weight*, and *oxidation number:*

$$\text{Gram-equivalent weight} = \frac{\text{gram-atomic weight}}{\text{oxidation number}}.$$

**Example 9.6.** Determine the gram-equivalent weight of the metal as given in each of the following formulas: (a) NaCl, (b) $CaCl_2$, (c) $Fe_2O_3$.

**Solution.** First determine the oxidation number of the metal; then use the formula given above.

(a) NaCl. Oxidation number of Na = +1. Therefore:

$$\text{Gram-equivalent weight of Na} = \frac{22.997 \text{ g.}}{1} = 22.997 \text{ g.}$$

(b) $CaCl_2$. Oxidation number of Ca = +2. Therefore:

$$\text{Gram-equivalent weight of Ca} = \frac{40.08 \text{ g.}}{2} = 20.04 \text{ g.}$$

(c) $Fe_2O_3$. Oxidation number of Fe = +3. Therefore:

$$\text{Gram-equivalent weight of Fe} = \frac{55.85 \text{ g.}}{3} = 18.62 \text{ g.}$$

In each of the metals in Example 9.6, one gram-equivalent weight of the metal loses N electrons as the result of the formation of the compound from the elements. That is:

22.997 g. Na = N atoms, each of which loses 1 electron.

20.04 g. Ca = $\frac{N}{2}$ atoms, each of which loses 2 electrons.

18.62 g. Fe = $\frac{N}{3}$ atoms, each of which loses 3 electrons.

The above may be summarized by the statement that N electrons of an element are involved when one gram-equivalent weight of that element enters into chemical combination with another element.

**9.4. The Gram-equivalent Weights of Elements of Variable Oxidation States.** It so happens that the atoms of two or more elements sometimes combine in more than one ratio, each combination occurring only under certain specified conditions. That is, some elements exhibit more than one oxidation state. For example, iron may exist in either the ferrous state, $Fe^{+2}$, or the ferric state, $Fe^{+3}$. It follows, therefore, that an element will have a gram-equivalent weight for each oxidation state it assumes.

**Example 9.7.** Determine the equivalent weight of iron in (a) $FeCl_2$, and in (b) $FeCl_3$.

**Solution.** Following the same procedure as in Example 9.6, we have:

(a) Gram-equivalent weight of Fe in $FeCl_2 = \dfrac{55.85 \text{ g.}}{2} = 27.93 \text{ g.}$

(b) Gram-equivalent weight of Fe in $FeCl_3 = \dfrac{55.85 \text{ g.}}{3} = 18.62 \text{ g.}$

Observe that the gram-equivalent weights for an element in its various oxidation states are in a ratio of small integer values. For example, for iron, as calculated in Example 9.7:

$$\frac{18.62}{27.93} = \frac{2}{3}.$$

The above small-integer ratio relationship is sometimes referred to as the *law of multiple proportions:* when two elements combine to form more than one compound, the weights of one combined with a fixed weight of the other element are in a ratio of small whole numbers. In Example 9.7 a fixed weight of chlorine, 35.457 g., is combined with 18.62 g. of Fe in $FeCl_3$, and with 27.93 g. of Fe in $FeCl_2$.

**Example 9.8.** Tin and oxygen combine to form two different oxides. One contains 78.77 per cent tin, and the other 88.12 per cent tin. Determine the equivalent weight of tin in each of the two oxides and show that the values are in accord with the law of multiple proportions.

**Solution.** By definition the gram-equivalent weight is the number of grams of tin which will combine with 8.0000 g. of oxygen.

Then, for oxide No. 1:

$$\frac{78.77 \text{ g. Sn}}{21.23 \text{ g. } O_2} = \frac{x \text{ g. Sn}}{8.000 \text{ g. } O_2}$$

or $\qquad\qquad x = 29.68$ g. $=$ gram-equivalent weight of Sn.

And, for oxide No. 2:

$$\frac{88.12 \text{ g. Sn}}{11.88 \text{ g. } O_2} = \frac{x \text{ g. Sn}}{8.000 \text{ g. } O_2}$$

or $\qquad\qquad x = 59.34$ g. $=$ gram-equivalent weight of Sn.

The ratio 29.68 : 59.34 is as 1 : 2, which is in agreement with the law of multiple proportions.

## Problems

### Part I

**9.1.** How much oxygen will combine with 1.00 g. of calcium?

*Ans.* 0.400 g.

**9.2.** How much calcium will combine with 1.00 g. of oxygen? *Ans.* 2.50 g.

**9.3.** How much sulfur will combine with 15.0 g. of sodium? *Ans.* 10.5 g.

**9.4.** In a laboratory experiment it was found that 0.562 g. of aluminum combined with 0.500 g. of oxygen. Calculate the equivalent weight of aluminum. *Ans.* 8.99 g.

**9.5.** Zinc oxide contains 80.3 per cent zinc. Calculate the gram-equivalent weight of zinc. *Ans.* 32.6 g.

**9.6.** When 1.391 g. of mercuric oxide was heated, 71.8 ml. of oxygen was liberated, measured at standard conditions. Calculate the gram-equivalent weight of mercury. *Ans.* 100 g.

**9.7.** Calculate the gram-equivalent weight of bismuth if 3.96 g. of the element forms 4.71 g. of oxide. *Ans.* 42.2 g.

9.8. What is the (a) oxidation number, and (b) gram-equivalent weight of tin in $SnCl_4$? *Ans.* (a) 4; (b) 29.68 g.

9.9. The oxidation number of an element is $+3$ and the gram-equivalent weight 69.67 g. (a) What is the atomic weight of the element, and (b) what is the symbol of the element? *Ans.* (a) 209.0; (b) Bi.

9.10. How many electrons are lost by 1.00 g. of Mg when the element combines with chlorine? *Ans.* $4.95 \times 10^{22}$.

9.11. How many liters of hydrogen at S.C. would be liberated by the action of 0.100 gram-equivalent weight of a metal with acid? *Ans.* 1.12 $l$.

9.12. When 0.723 g. of iron reacted with a solution of $H_2SO_4$, there was liberated 340 ml. of hydrogen which was collected over water at 27° C. and 740 mm. of Hg. Calculate the gram-equivalent weight of iron.
*Ans.* 27.9 g.

9.13. Two oxides of copper contain respectively 20.1 per cent and 11.2 per cent oxygen. (a) What is the gram-equivalent weight of copper in each of the two oxides? (b) Show that the data are in accord with the law of multiple proportions. *Ans.* (a) 31.8 g., 63.4 g.; (b) 1 : 2.

9.14. Nitrogen forms five oxides: $N_2O$, NO, $N_2O_3$, $NO_2$, and $N_2O_5$. (a) What is the equivalent weight of nitrogen in each of the oxides? (b) Which oxide contains 53.3 per cent oxygen?
*Ans.* (a) 14.0 g., 7.00 g., 4.67 g., 3.50 g., 2.80 g.; (b) NO.

### Part II

9.15. When 5.81 g. of silver oxide was heated, 0.401 g. of oxygen was liberated. Calculate the gram-equivalent weight of silver.
*Ans.* 108 g.

9.16. It was found that 4.90 g. of a monovalent element combined with 1.00 g. of oxygen. What was the element? *Ans.* K.

9.17. A metallic oxide contains 52.9 per cent metal. What is the gram-equivalent weight of the metal? *Ans.* 9.0.

9.18. A mass of metallic oxide weighing 2.59 g. contained 0.401 g. of oxygen. Calculate the gram-equivalent weight of the metal. *Ans.* 43.8.

9.19. The gram-equivalent weight of a trivalent metal is 17.34 g. What is the metal? *Ans.* Cr.

9.20. The mole weight of $R_2O_3$ is 326. What is the equivalent weight of R?
*Ans.* 46.3.

9.21. When 0.590 g. of sodium reacted with water, there was liberated 314 ml. of hydrogen collected over water at 17° C. and 755 mm. of Hg. Calculate the gram-equivalent weight of sodium. *Ans.* 23 g.

9.22. A 4.00 g. sample of cupric oxide, CuO, was reduced to free copper by passing hydrogen over the hot oxide. The reduced copper weighed 3.20 g. Calculate the gram-equivalent weight of copper.
*Ans.* 32.0 g.

9.23. An iron nail weighs 6.34 grams. What weight of rust, $Fe_2O_3$, would be formed by the nail? *Ans.* 9.06 g.

**9.24.** How much sodium and chlorine could be obtained by the decomposition of 12.0 grams of salt, NaCl?  *Ans.* 7.28 g. $Cl_2$; 4.72 g. Na.

**9.25.** Calculate the gram-equivalent weight of copper in $Cu_3(PO_4)_2$.

*Ans.* 31.77 g.

**9.26.** How many liters of hydrogen, measured over water at 24° C. and 720 mm. of Hg, would be obtained by the action of 2.50 g. of calcium on an acid?  *Ans.* 1.65 *l.*

**9.27.** How many electrons would be liberated by 1.00 g. of the element in the process of formation of the following ions: (a) $Cs^+$, (b) $Ca^{+2}$, (c) $Al^{+3}$?  *Ans.* (a) $4.5 \times 10^{21}$; (b) $3.0 \times 10^{22}$; (c) $6.7 \times 10^{22}$.

**9.28.** How many grams of magnesium would have to react in order to liberate 4 N electrons?  *Ans.* 48.64 g.

**9.29.** Mercury and chlorine form two compounds. In one compound 0.669 g. of mercury combines with 0.118 g. of chlorine; in the other compound 1.00 g. of mercury combines with 0.355 g. of chlorine. What is the gram-equivalent weight of mercury in each compound?

*Ans.* 201; 100.

**9.30.** Iron exists in two possible oxidation states, $+2$ and $+3$. How many grams of iron will combine with 25.0 g. of iodine?

*Ans.* 5.50 g.; 3.67 g.

# 10

# The Quantitative Significance
# of Chemical Formulas

Formulas are the fundamental expressions used by chemists to designate substances. The quantitative interpretation of formulas is the most basic and therefore the most important aspect of the study of chemistry. Such quantitative knowledge gives one a better appreciation of the science of chemistry. The quantitative interpretation of formulas is presented for substances existing in the solid, liquid, and gaseous states.

## Some Quantitative Relationships Involving
## Molecules in the Gaseous State

**10.1. The Mole Volume of Substances in the Gaseous State.** An interesting relationship is shown when we compare the volumes occupied by one mole of gaseous substances under the same conditions of temperature and pressure. This relationship is shown for five gases in Table 10.1.

TABLE 10.1

THE MOLE VOLUME OF A NUMBER OF GASEOUS SUBSTANCES
AT STANDARD CONDITIONS

| Gas | One Mole | Weight of One Liter | Mole Volume at S.C. | | |
|-----|----------|---------------------|------|------|------|
| $O_2$ | 32.00 g. | 1.43 g. | 32.00 | ÷ 1.43 | = 22.4 $l$. |
| $N_2$ | 28.02 g. | 1.25 g. | 28.02 | ÷ 1.25 | = 22.4 $l$. |
| $H_2$ | 2.016 g. | 0.0899 g. | 2.016 | ÷ 0.0899 | = 22.4 $l$. |
| HCl | 36.47 g. | 1.63 g. | 36.47 | ÷ 1.63 | = 22.4 $l$. |
| $CO_2$ | 44.01 g. | 1.965 g. | 44.01 | ÷ 1.965 | = 22.4 $l$. |

From the table we see that the volume occupied by one mole of each of the five gases at standard conditions is 22.4 liters, or 22,400 ml.

The quantity 22.4 liters is called the *gram-molecular volume* (G.M.V.), and represents the volume occupied by one mole of any gas at standard conditions. Since one mole represents the weight in grams of $6.024 \times 10^{23}$ molecules (Sec. 6.4), it follows that use may be made of the gram-molecular volume principle to determine the molecular weight of substances when in the gaseous state.

**Example 10.1.** It was found that 326 ml. of a gas weighed 0.492 g. at standard conditions. Calculate the molecular weight of the gas.

**Solution.** The molecular weight of the gas is the weight in grams of 22,400 ml. at standard conditions. Then:

$$\frac{326 \text{ ml.}}{0.492 \text{ g.}} = \frac{22,400 \text{ ml.}}{x \text{ g.}}$$

or    $x = 33.8 =$ molecular weight of the gas.

**Example 10.2.** It was found that 426 ml. of a gas weighed 0.492 g. at 27° C. and 640 mm. of Hg. Calculate the molecular weight of the gas.

**Solution.** Again, the molecular weight of the gas is the weight of 22,400 ml. at standard conditions. However, the given volume of gas is not at standard conditions. We must, therefore, reduce the given volume to standard conditions. Then:

$$V_{\text{s.c.}} = 426 \text{ ml.} \times \frac{273° \text{ K.}}{300° \text{ K.}} \times \frac{640 \text{ mm. of Hg}}{760 \text{ mm. of Hg}}$$

$$= 326 \text{ ml.}$$

The problem is now identical to Example 10.1. Compressing the 426 ml. of gas to 326 ml. volume would not change the weight of the given mass of gas. The molecular weight of the gas is, therefore, 33.8 as in Example 10.1.

The gram-molecular volume principle may also be used to determine the weight of any given volume of a gaseous substance, providing its molecular weight is known.

**Example 10.3.** Determine the weight of one liter of hydrogen sulfide, $H_2S$, at standard conditions.

**Solution.** We know that one mole of $H_2S$, or

$$(2 \times 1.008) + 32.066 = 34.082 \text{ g.,}$$

occupies a volume of 22.4 liters at standard conditions. Therefore:

$$H_2S = \frac{34.082 \text{ g.}}{22.4 \text{ } l.} = 1.52 \frac{\text{g.}}{l.}$$

**Example 10.4.** Determine the weight of 375 ml. of oxygen at 23° C. and 740 mm. of Hg.

**Solution.** Since the gram-molecular volume principle applies only to standard conditions, it will be necessary to reduce the given volume of oxygen to the volume it would occupy at standard conditions. Then:

$$V_{\text{s.c.}} = 375 \text{ ml.} \times \frac{273° \text{K}}{296° \text{K}} \times \frac{740 \text{ mm. of Hg}}{760 \text{ mm. of Hg}}$$

$$= 337 \text{ ml.}$$

We know that 22,400 ml. of oxygen weighs 32.00 g. at S.C. Therefore:

$$\frac{22,400 \text{ ml.}}{32.00 \text{ g.}} = \frac{337 \text{ ml.}}{x \text{ g.}}$$

or                $x = 0.481 \text{ g.} = $ weight of 337 ml. of $O_2$ at S.C.

## Problems

### Part I

10.1. One liter of chlorine gas at standard conditions weighs 3.214 g. Calculate the molecular weight of chlorine.     *Ans.* 72.0.

10.2. Calculate the molecular weight of a gas, 225 ml. of which weighs 0.281 g. at standard conditions.     *Ans.* 28.0.

10.3. Calculate the molecular weight of a gas, 642 ml. of which weighs 1.61 g. at 100° C. and 740 mm. of Hg.     *Ans.* 78.8.

10.4. Calculate the weight of one liter of (a) ammonia, and (b) helium at standard conditions.     *Ans.* (a) 0.76 g.; (b) 0.18 g.

10.5. Calculate the weight of one liter of carbon dioxide at (a) standard conditions, and (b) 27° C. and 730 mm. of Hg.

*Ans.* (a) 1.96 g.; (b) 1.71 g.

10.6. A compound has the formula $COCl_2$. Calculate the weight of one liter of the gas at standard conditions.     *Ans.* 4.42 g.

10.7. The molecular weight of a gaseous substance is 80. Calculate the volume occupied by one gram of the substance at standard conditions.     *Ans.* 280 ml.

10.8. Calculate the weight of 350 ml. of $CO_2$ at S.C.     *Ans.* 0.687 g.

### Part II

10.9. When 0.700 g. of a substance was heated to 300° C., it formed 350 ml. of gaseous vapor. The barometric pressure was 72.4 cm. Calculate the molecular weight of the substance.     *Ans.* 98.7.

10.10. Calculate the molecular weight of a substance, 2.810 g. of which formed 850 ml. of vapor at 200° C. and a reduced pressure of 60 mm. of Hg.     *Ans.* 163.

10.11. What is the weight of 1500 ml. of argon at S.C.?     *Ans.* 2.67 g.

10.12. What volume would 12.0 g. of neon occupy at standard conditions?

*Ans.* 13.3 *l.*

10.13. What volume would 12.0 g. of neon occupy when collected over water at 22° C. and 720 mm. of Hg?     *Ans.* 15.6 *l.*

10.14. A mass of gas weighing 22.50 g. occupies a volume of 17.5 $l$. at 23° C. and 740 mm. of Hg. What would be the weight of 1.00 liter of the gas at 100° C. and 780 mm. of Hg?       *Ans.* 1.08 $\frac{g.}{l.}$.

10.15. The substance in problem 10.14 is an element. What is the element?
                                           *Ans.* Oxygen.

10.16. A mass 0.475 g. of a gaseous substance occupied a volume of 131.5 ml. at 40° C. and 740 mm. of Hg. Calculate the molecular weight of the substance.                               *Ans.* 95.

10.17. How many molecules are there in one liter of oxygen at S.C.?
                                     *Ans.* $2.69 \times 10^{22}$.

10.18. How many molecules are there in 1.00 ml. of hydrogen at 27° C. and 640 mm. of Hg?                 *Ans.* $2.06 \times 10^{19}$.

10.19. Which of the three gases — $CO_2$, $NH_3$, $N_2$ — has the smallest weight per liter under similar conditions?         *Ans.* $NH_3$.

10.20. A tank has a volume of 100 $l$. How many grams of oxygen will the tank hold at S.C.?                       *Ans.* 143 g.

10.21. How many grams of oxygen will the tank given in problem 10.20 hold at 27° C. and 720 mm. of Hg?        *Ans.* 123 g.

10.22. It was found that 0.336 $l$. of a gas weighed 0.240 g. at S.C. Was the gas $CH_4$, $O_2$, $NH_3$, or $F_2$?          *Ans.* $CH_4$.

10.23. What is the difference in weight between 50.0 $l$. each of the gases $PH_3$ and $CH_4$ at S.C.?           *Ans.* 40.2 g.

10.24. What is the density of oxygen at 86° F. and 64 cm. of Hg?

                                   *Ans.* 1.09 $\frac{g.}{l.}$

10.25. One of the principal constituents of gasoline is heptane, $C_7H_{16}$, the density of which is 0.68 g. per cm.³ What volume would one liter of heptane occupy if vaporized at 200° C. and 740 mm. of Hg?
                                     *Ans.* 271 $l$.

## Some Quantitative Relationships Involving Formulas

**10.2. Determination of the Formula of a Compound.** In order to determine the molecular formula of a compound, the following information must be available: (1) the elements constituting the compound; (2) the atomic weights of the constituent elements; (3) the percentage composition of the compound; and (4) the molecular weight of the compound. The above information must be obtained experimentally. However, details of the experimental procedure need not be known in order to understand the calculations involved.

**Example 10.5.** A compound upon analysis was found to have the following percentage composition: carbon, 81.82 per cent; and hydrogen, 18.18

per cent. The molecular weight was found to be 44. Determine the formula of the compound.

**Solution.** The solution lies in finding the values of A and B in the expression $C_A H_B$. Since 81.82 per cent of the molecular weight is contributed by carbon and 18.18 per cent by hydrogen, then:

$$0.8182 \times 44 = 36 \text{ units contributed by carbon}$$
and $$0.1818 \times 44 = \phantom{0}8 \text{ units contributed by hydrogen.}$$

Next we must find how many carbon atoms are required to contribute 36 units to the molecular weight. This will be the value of A. Since one carbon atom contributes 12 units, its atomic weight, then:

$$36 \div 12 = 3 \text{ atoms of carbon} = A.$$

Each atom of hydrogen in the molecule contributes 1 unit to the molecular weight. Therefore:

$$8 \div 1 = 8 \text{ atoms of hydrogen} = B.$$

The formula for the compound is, therefore, $C_3 H_8$.

**Example 10.6.** A compound was found to contain 40.01 per cent carbon, 6.67 per cent hydrogen, and 53.32 per cent oxygen. The molecular weight was found to be 178. What is the formula of the compound?

**Solution.** Following the same procedure as in Example 10.5, we will first determine the contribution of each element to the molecular weight, 178. Then:

Carbon    = $0.4001 \times 178 = 71.2$ units of molecular weight;
Hydrogen = $0.0667 \times 178 = 11.9$ units of molecular weight;
Oxygen   = $0.5332 \times 178 = 94.9$ units of molecular weight.

The number of atoms of each in a molecule would be:

$$71.2 \div 12 = \phantom{0}6 \text{ carbon atoms;}$$
$$11.9 \div \phantom{0}1 = 12 \text{ hydrogen atoms;}$$
$$94.9 \div 16 = \phantom{0}6 \text{ oxygen atoms.}$$

The formula of the compound is, therefore, $C_6 H_{12} O_6$.

As will be observed later, most methods for the determination of the molecular weight of a compound give only approximate values. The correct molecular weight of $C_6 H_{12} O_6$ would be 180.16. This means that the contribution of each atom as calculated above may be somewhat in error and may, therefore, not represent an exact multiple of the atomic weight of the element. However, since a molecule must contain an integer number of atoms of each of the elements constituting the molecule, the inherent error in the experimental value must be taken into consideration. Observe that the nearest integer value was used in the second step above. On the other hand, methods of analysis have enabled chemists to determine percentage composition and atomic weights with a high degree of accuracy.

The term molecular weight has no significance when referred to ionic compounds (Sec. 6.1). The formulas for such compounds must, therefore, be determined without this information.

**Example 10.7.** A compound was found to contain 88.80 per cent copper and 11.20 per cent oxygen. What is the formula of the compound?

**Solution.** Since the molecular weight has no meaning, the contribution of each atom to the molecular weight cannot be determined. It is possible, however, to determine the simplest ratio of atoms in the substance. First, divide the percentages given by the respective atomic weights of the elements. Then:

$$\left. \begin{array}{l} \text{Copper} = \dfrac{88.80}{63.54} = 1.40 \\[2ex] \text{Oxygen} = \dfrac{11.20}{16.00} = 0.70 \end{array} \right\} \begin{array}{l} \text{Ratio of copper to} \\ \text{oxygen atoms.} \end{array}$$

Next, reduce the above ratio to the simplest integer ratio of atoms. These values represent the number of atoms of each element as expressed in the formula. Then:

$$1.40 : 0.70 = 2 : 1.$$

oxygen
copper

The formula is, therefore, $Cu_2O$.

**Example 10.8.** Red lead is composed of 90.65 per cent lead and 9.35 per cent oxygen. What is the formula for red lead?

**Solution.** The ratio of atoms would be:

$$\left. \begin{array}{l} \text{Lead} \ \ = \dfrac{90.65}{207.21} = 0.437 \\[2ex] \text{Oxygen} = \dfrac{9.35}{16.00} \ = 0.584 \end{array} \right\} \begin{array}{l} \text{Ratio of lead to} \\ \text{oxygen atoms.} \end{array}$$

Reducing the ratio $0.437 : 0.584$ to small integer values will evidently require more careful consideration than in Example 10.7. In this case trial and error is the best method. Evidently, one of the following integer ratios is the correct one:

$$\frac{0.437}{0.584} = \frac{1}{2} = \frac{1}{3} = \frac{2}{3} = \frac{1}{4} = \frac{3}{4} = \frac{4}{5} = \frac{5}{6}.$$

A few moments' inspection will show that:

$$\left.\begin{array}{l} \dfrac{0.437}{0.584} = \dfrac{3}{4} \\[2mm] \text{or} \quad\quad 0.437 \times 4 = 0.584 \times 3 \\[1mm] \text{and} \quad\quad 1748 = 1752. \end{array}\right\} \begin{array}{l}\text{Proof for the validity} \\ \text{of a proportion.}\end{array}$$

The formula for red lead is, therefore, $Pb_3O_4$.

**10.3. Determination of the Percentage Composition of a Compound from the Formula.** The percentage composition of a compound for which the formula is not known must be determined experimentally by standard methods of chemical analysis. If the formula is known, then the percentage composition may be calculated.

**Example 10.9.** Calculate the percentage composition of water.

**Solution.**

$$\text{One mole of water} = (2 \times 1.008) + 16.000 = 18.016 \text{ g.}$$

That is, in 18.016 grams of water there are 2.016 grams of hydrogen and 16.000 grams of oxygen. Therefore:

$$\frac{2.016 \text{ g.}}{18.016 \text{ g.}} \times 100 = 11.19 \text{ per cent hydrogen}$$

and

$$\frac{16.000 \text{ g.}}{18.016 \text{ g.}} \times 100 = 88.81 \text{ per cent oxygen.}$$

**Example 10.10.** What is the per cent of water in washing soda, $Na_2CO_3 \cdot 10 \ H_2O$?

**Solution.** First calculate the weight of one mole. Then:

$$\begin{array}{ccccc} Na_2 & C & O_3 & \cdot \ 10 & H_2O \\ (2 \times 22.997) & + \ 12.01 & + \ (3 \times 16.000) & + \ (10 \times 18.016) & = 286.16 \text{ g.} \end{array}$$

The weight of one mole is 286.16 grams, of which 180.16 grams is water. Therefore:

$$\frac{180.16 \text{ g.}}{286.16 \text{ g.}} \times 100 = 62.96 \text{ per cent water.}$$

### Problems

#### Part I

**10.26.** A compound was found to contain 32.00 per cent carbon, 42.66 per cent oxygen, 18.67 per cent nitrogen, and 6.67 per cent hydrogen. Calculate the formula if the molecular weight is known to be about 75.       *Ans.* $C_2O_2NH_5$.

**10.27.** A compound was found to contain 42.11 per cent carbon, 51.46 per cent oxygen, and 6.43 per cent hydrogen. The molecular weight was found to be approximately 340. What is the formula of the compound?                                                    *Ans.* $C_{12}H_{22}O_{11}$.

10.28. An oxide of iron contained 30.0 per cent oxygen. What was the formula of the oxide?                                    *Ans.* $Fe_2O_3$.

10.29. Calculate the formula of a compound which contains 31.80 per cent potassium, 29.00 per cent chlorine, and 39.20 per cent oxygen.

*Ans.* $KClO_3$.

10.30. A gaseous compound was found to contain 75 per cent carbon and 25 per cent hydrogen. It was found that 22.4 liters of the gas at standard conditions weighed 16 grams. What is the formula of the compound?                                    *Ans.* $CH_4$.

10.31. A compound was found to have the formula $CH_2O$, as calculated without knowledge of the molecular weight. Later the molecular weight was found to be approximately 177. What was the formula of the compound?                                    *Ans.* $C_6H_{12}O_6$.

10.32. A compound was found to contain 20.00 per cent hydrogen and 80.00 per cent carbon. It was found that 250 ml. of the gas weighed 0.256 g. at 27° C. and 640 mm. of Hg. What was the formula of the compound?                                    *Ans.* $C_2H_6$.

10.33. What is the per cent of aluminum in $Al_2O_3$?    *Ans.* 52.9%.

10.34. Determine the percentage composition of formaldehyde, $CH_2O$, and glucose, $C_6H_{12}O_6$.    *Ans.* C = 40%; H = 6.7%; O = 53.3%.

10.35. What is the per cent of water in borax, $Na_2B_4O_7 \cdot 10\ H_2O$?

*Ans.* 47.2%.

## Part II

10.36. One liter of a gas was found to weigh 1.25 grams at standard conditions. Analysis showed it to contain 42.85 per cent carbon and 57.15 per cent oxygen. What is the formula of the compound?

*Ans.* CO.

10.37. A sample of iron weighing 0.763 g. was burned in oxygen. The product weighed 0.982 g. What was the formula of the oxide formed?                                    *Ans.* FeO.

10.38. A compound A upon analysis showed the following composition: potassium 38.67 per cent; nitrogen, 13.85 per cent; and oxygen, 47.48 per cent. When heated, a compound B was formed having the composition: potassium 45.85 per cent; nitrogen 16.47 per cent; and oxygen 37.66 per cent. Write the equation for the reaction.

*Ans.* $2\ KNO_3 \rightarrow 2\ KNO_2 + O_2$.

10.39. Calculate the formulas of the following inorganic compounds:
  (a) Na = 39.3%; Cl = 60.7%.
  (b) Al = 15.8%; S = 28.1%; $O_2$ = 56.1%.

*Ans.* (a) NaCl; (b) $Al_2(SO_4)_3$.

10.40. A gas is known to be one of the five oxides of nitrogen. Upon analysis it was found to contain 36.8 per cent nitrogen. What is the formula for the oxide?                                                           *Ans.* $N_2O_3$.

10.41. A gas had the composition 71.72 per cent chlorine, 16.16 per cent oxygen, and 12.12 per cent carbon. Oxygen diffused through a small opening 1.76 times faster than the gas analyzed. What is the formula of the gas?                                           *Ans.* $COCl_2$.

10.42. The molecular weight of chlorine, as determined experimentally, is 72. What is the formula for chlorine?            *Ans.* $Cl_2$.

10.43. The molecular weight of argon has been found to be 40. What is the formula for argon?                                      *Ans.* A.

10.44. What is the per cent of CaO in $CaCO_3$?               *Ans.* 56%.

10.45. The bones of an adult person weigh about 24 pounds and they are 50 per cent calcium phosphate, $Ca_3(PO_4)_2$. How many pounds of phosphorus are there in the bones of the average adult?
*Ans.* 2.4 lb.

10.46. Washing soda is sold in two forms, as the anhydrous salt $Na_2CO_3$, and as the hydrated salt $Na_2CO_3 \cdot 10\ H_2O$. Considering that the active constituent in washing soda is $Na_2CO_3$, which would be the cheaper to the consumer, the anhydrous salt at ten cents per pound or the hydrated salt at five cents per pound?    *Ans.* Anhydrous salt.

10.47. How much iron is there in one ton of iron ore containing 80 per cent hematite, $Fe_2O_3$?                                  *Ans.* 1100 lb.

10.48. What is the per cent of copper in an ore containing 5.0 per cent of malachite, $CuCO_3 \cdot Cu(OH)_2$?                        *Ans.* 2.88%.

10.49. Calculate the per cent of available chlorine in bleaching powder, $CaOCl_2$, assuming that only one of the two chlorine atoms in the formula is liberated as free chlorine.              *Ans.* 28%.

10.50. A compound was known to be either $CuCl_2$ or $CuBr_2$. A 5.00 g. sample yielded 2.36 g. of copper upon reduction. What was the compound?                                             *Ans.* $CuCl_2$.

10.51. Lead dioxide, $PbO_2$, liberates one-half the oxygen atoms as free oxygen when heated. How much $PbO_2$ would be required to produce 10.0 g. of oxygen?                              *Ans.* 150 g.

10.52. How much oxygen could be obtained from one pound of mercuric oxide, HgO, assuming all the oxygen to be liberated upon heating?
*Ans.* 0.074 lb.

10.53. Calculate the formula of a compound, given that 55.85 g. of iron combines with 32.07 g. of sulfur.                    *Ans.* FeS.

10.54. A sample of copper weighing 3.18 g. formed 3.98 g. of oxide when made to react with oxygen. What is the formula of the oxide?
*Ans.* CuO.

10.55. How many gram-atoms of oxygen are there in 500 g. of $Fe_2O_3$?
*Ans.* 9.40.

**10.56.** Blood hemoglobin contains 0.33 per cent iron. Assuming that there are two atoms of iron per molecule of hemoglobin, calculate the approximate molecular weight of hemoglobin.                *Ans.* 34,000.

**10.57.** One liter of a gas weighs 1.34 g. at S.C. The simplest formula for the substance is known to be $CH_3$. What is the correct molecular formula of the substance?                          *Ans.* $C_2H_6$.

**10.58.** Upon analysis an organic compound was found to consist of carbon and hydrogen. When 0.781 g. of the compound was burned there was formed 2.64 g. of $CO_2$ and 0.540 g. of $H_2O$. The molecular weight was found to be approximately 78. Determine the formula of the substance.                               *Ans.* $C_6H_6$.

**10.59.** A compound upon analysis was found to contain potassium, chromium, and oxygen. There was present in the compound 26.57 per cent potassium and 35.36 per cent chromium. Determine the formula of the compound.                     *Ans.* $K_2Cr_2O_7$.

**10.60.** How much iron could be obtained from one ton of iron ore containing 45.0 per cent $Fe_2O_3$?                     *Ans.* 630 lb.

# 11

# The Quantitative Significance of Chemical Equations

Chemical equations show the rearrangement of atoms during the course of a chemical change. A quantitative interpretation of an equation is a summation of the interpretation of the formulas making up the equation. The quantitative study of equations may involve substances in the solid, liquid, or gaseous state. In any given chemical reaction definite quantities of reactants produce predictable amounts of products. The economy of the chemical industry of the world is based upon this consistency involving chemical changes.

**11.1. Introduction.** Chemical equations express a definite weight relationship among the reactants and products in a reaction. Also, an equation indicates the manner in which the atoms of the reactants are rearranged to form the products. The above statements are supported by two fundamental facts: (1) atoms are the smallest parts of the elements involved in a chemical change, and (2) the atoms of each of the elements have fixed weights, excluding the variation due to isotopes, and always combine in the same ratio under similar conditions.

Since a symbol of an element represents a definite weight of that element, an equation can be interpreted in terms of definite amounts of reactants and products. In an equation the reactants and products contain the same number and kind of atoms. An equation also expresses volume relationships between reactants and products which are in the gaseous state. The preceding statements are summarized below.

|  | Zn | + | $H_2SO_4$ | → | $ZnSO_4$ | + | $H_2 \uparrow$ |
|---|---|---|---|---|---|---|---|
| Atoms | 1 | | 7 | | 6 | | 2 |
| Moles | 1 | | 1 | | 1 | | 1 |
| Grams | 65.38 | | 98.09 | | 161.45 | | 2.02 |
| Liters (S.C.) | — | | — | | — | | 22.4 |
| Pounds | 65.38 | | 98.09 | | 161.45 | | 2.02 |

Observe that the weight of the reactants, 163.47 g., is equal to the weight of the products, 163.47 g.

Since chemical equations indicate weight and volume relationships, three types of problems will be discussed:

1. Problems involving weight;
2. Problems involving volume;
3. Problems involving both weight and volume.

## 11.2. Problems Involving Weight Relationships among the Reactants and Products.

**Example 11.1.** How many grams of zinc sulfate, $ZnSO_4$, would be formed by the action of 4.31 grams of zinc on sulfuric acid?

**Solution.** Observe the following procedure in solving problems based upon chemical equations. (1) Write the equation involved. (2) Underscore the substances about which the problem is concerned. (3) Designate the quantities of these substances as expressed in the equation. That is:

$$\underset{65.38 \text{ g.}}{Zn} + H_2SO_4 \rightarrow \underset{161.45 \text{ g.}}{ZnSO_4} + H_2.$$

The problem designates the gram as the unit of weight to be used.

The above equation tells us that 65.38 g. of Zn will react with $H_2SO_4$ to produce 161.45 g. of $ZnSO_4$. From the law of definite composition we know that the ratio **g. of Zn : g. of $ZnSO_4$** must be a constant. The next step is to set up the proportion, one ratio of which is given in the equation and the other in the problem. Then:

$$\frac{65.38 \text{ g. Zn}}{161.45 \text{ g. } ZnSO_4} = \frac{4.31 \text{ g. Zn}}{x \text{ g. } ZnSO_4}$$

or $$x = 10.6 \text{ g. } ZnSO_4.$$

**Example 11.2.** How many moles of $Fe_2O_3$ would be formed by the action of oxygen on one kilogram of iron?

**Solution.** The solution to the problem is based upon the equation:

$$\underset{223.4 \text{ g.}}{4 \text{ Fe}} + 3 \text{ O}_2 \rightarrow \underset{2 \text{ moles}}{2 \text{ Fe}_2O_3}.$$

Observe that the problem requires the use of grams for iron and moles for $Fe_2O_3$. Then:

$$\frac{223.4 \text{ g. Fe}}{2 \text{ moles } Fe_2O_3} = \frac{1000 \text{ g. Fe}}{x \text{ moles } Fe_2O_3}$$

or $$x = 8.95 \text{ moles of } Fe_2O_3.$$

**Example 11.3.** The decomposition of 2000 pounds of limestone, $CaCO_3$, by heating would produce how much (a) quicklime, CaO, and (b) carbon dioxide, $CO_2$?

**Solution.** The unit of weight involved is the pound. Therefore:

$$CaCO_3 \rightarrow CaO + CO_2$$
$$100.09 \text{ lb.} \quad 56.08 \text{ lb.} \quad 44.01 \text{ lb.}$$

(a) Only two different substances may be involved in a given proportion. The two substances involved in this part of the problem are $CaCO_3$ and CaO. Therefore:

$$\frac{100.09 \text{ lb. } CaCO_3}{56.08 \text{ lb. CaO}} = \frac{2000 \text{ lb. } CaCO_3}{x \text{ lb. CaO}}$$

or
$$x = 1121 \text{ lb. CaO.}$$

(b) The two substances involved in this part of the problem are $CaCO_3$ and $CO_2$. Therefore:

$$\frac{100.09 \text{ lb. } CaCO_3}{44.01 \text{ lb. } CO_2} = \frac{2000 \text{ lb. } CaCO_3}{x \text{ lb. } CO_2}$$

or
$$x = 879 \text{ lb. } CO_2.$$

It is not always necessary to write the complete equation to solve a problem. For example, when silver reacts with nitric acid the silver is converted to silver nitrate, $AgNO_3$, with a number of other products, the reaction being somewhat complex. The products other than silver nitrate need not be indicated, provided they are not involved in the problem.

**Example 11.4.** Wire silver weighing 3.48 g. was dissolved in nitric acid. What weight of silver nitrate was formed?

**Solution.** Since the silver was converted to silver nitrate, we are interested only in the fact that one gram-atom of silver, 107.88 g., will form one mole of $AgNO_3$, 169.89 g.
That is:

$$Ag \rightarrow AgNO_3$$
$$107.88 \text{ g.} \quad 169.89 \text{ g.}$$

Therefore:

$$\frac{107.88 \text{ g. Ag}}{169.89 \text{ g. } AgNO_3} = \frac{3.48 \text{ g. Ag}}{x \text{ g. } AgNO_3}$$

or
$$x = 5.48 \text{ g. } AgNO_3.$$

**Example 11.5.** How many pounds of water of hydration are there in 100 pounds of washing soda, $Na_2CO_3 \cdot 10 \, H_2O$?

**Solution.** One pound-mole of washing soda contains 10 pound-moles of water. That is:

$$\frac{Na_2CO_3 \cdot 10\ H_2O}{\text{1 pound-mole}} \rightarrow \frac{10\ H_2O}{\text{10 pound-moles}}$$
$$= 286\ lb.\qquad\qquad = 180\ lb.$$

Therefore:

$$\frac{286\ lb.\ Na_2CO_3 \cdot 10\ H_2O}{180\ lb.\ H_2O} = \frac{100\ lb.\ Na_2CO_3 \cdot 10\ H_2O}{x\ lb.\ H_2O}$$

or
$$x = 63.0\ lb.\ H_2O.$$

**Example 11.6.** Iodic acid, $HIO_3$, is converted to iodine pentoxide, $I_2O_5$, by heat. Assuming that $I_2O_5$ is the only product of the reaction containing iodine, how much $I_2O_5$ could be obtained from 250 g. of $HIO_3$?

**Solution.** Only iodine need be balanced. Therefore:

$$\frac{2\ HIO_3}{351.8\ g.} \rightarrow \frac{I_2O_5}{333.8\ g.}$$

and
$$\frac{351.8\ g.\ HIO_3}{333.8\ g.\ I_2O_5} = \frac{250\ g.\ HIO_3}{x\ g.\ I_2O_5}$$

or
$$x = 237\ g.\ I_2O_5.$$

**11.3. Problems Involving Volume Relationships among the Reactants and Products.** One mole of a gaseous compound at standard conditions occupies a volume of 22.4 liters. Since an equation involves mole quantities of reactants and products, it follows that reactants or products existing in the gaseous state under the given conditions may be interpreted in terms of volumes. For example:

|  | $N_2$ | $+$ | $3\ H_2$ | $\rightarrow$ | $2\ NH_3$ |
|---|---|---|---|---|---|
| Molecules | 1 |  | 3 |  | 2 |
| Moles | 1 |  | 3 |  | 2 |
| Liters (S.C.) | 22.4 |  | 67.2 |  | 44.8 |

Observe that the ratio 22.4 $l$. $N_2$ : 67.2 $l$. $H_2$ : 44.8 $l$. $NH_3$ is the same as that of the number of molecules entering into the reaction, 1 $N_2$ : 3 $H_2$ : 2 $NH_3$.

**Example 11.7.** How many liters of ammonia, $NH_3$, could be prepared from 750 liters of nitrogen, all gases being measured at standard conditions?

**Solution.** From the above equation we see that 22.4 liters of nitrogen will form 44.8 liters of ammonia. Therefore:

$$\frac{22.4\ l.\ N_2}{44.8\ l.\ NH_3} = \frac{750\ l.\ N_2}{x\ l.\ NH_3}$$

or
$$x = 1500\ l.\ NH_3.$$

One could have obtained the above answer by inspection since, from the equation, we see that 2 volumes of $NH_3$ are formed for each volume of $N_2$ involved. Therefore $2 \times 750 = 1500$ $l.$ $NH_3$.

**Example 11.8.** How many milliliters of $CO_2$ would be formed at standard conditions by burning 120 milliliters of ethane, $C_2H_6$?

**Solution.** First write the equation for the reaction.

$$\underset{\substack{\text{2 volumes} \\ 44.8\ l. \\ 44,800\ \text{ml.}}}{2\ C_2H_6} + 7\ O_2 \rightarrow 6\ H_2O + \underset{\substack{\text{4 volumes} \\ 89.6\ l. \\ 89,600\ \text{ml.}}}{4\ CO_2}$$

By inspection we see that twice the volume of $CO_2$ is formed as $C_2H_6$ burned. Therefore, 240 ml. of $CO_2$ will be formed. Solving by proportion, we have:

$$\frac{44,800\ \text{ml. } C_2H_6}{89,600\ \text{ml. } CO_2} = \frac{120\ \text{ml. } C_2H_6}{x\ \text{ml. } CO_2}$$

or $$x = 240\ \text{ml. } CO_2.$$

**11.4. Problems Involving Both Weight and Volume Relationships among the Reactants and Products.** This type of problem is a combination of the types discussed in Secs. 11.2 and 11.3.

**Example 11.9.** What volume of oxygen at standard conditions could be obtained by heating 8.66 grams of potassium chlorate, $KClO_3$?

**Solution.** The equation for the reaction would be:

$$\underset{245.2\ \text{g.}}{2\ KClO_3} \rightarrow 2\ KCl + \underset{67.2\ l.}{3\ O_2}.$$

Note that the problem requires the use of grams for $KClO_3$ and liters for oxygen. Therefore:

$$\frac{245.2\ \text{g. } KClO_3}{67.2\ l.\ O_2} = \frac{8.66\ \text{g. } KClO_3}{x\ l.\ O_2}$$

or $$x = 2.37\ l.\ \text{of oxygen at S.C.}$$

**Example 11.10.** What volume of oxygen, collected at 27° C. and 740 mm of Hg, could be obtained by heating 8.66 g. of $KClO_3$?

**Solution.** Note that this problem differs from Example 11.9 in that the oxygen is collected at other than standard conditions. Therefore, the value 2.37 $l.$, obtained in Example 11.9, must be changed to the volume it would occupy under the conditions given in the problem. Then:

$$V_2 = 2.37\ l. \times \frac{300°\ \text{K}}{273°\ \text{K}} \times \frac{760\ \text{m. of Hg}}{740\ \text{mm. of Hg}}$$

$$= 2.68\ l.\ \text{of } O_2 \text{ at } 27°\ \text{C. and 740 mm. of Hg.}$$

**Example 11.11.** What volume of phosphine, $PH_3$, could be obtained at 43° C. and 725 mm. of Hg by the action of 5.28 g. of phosphorus on an excess of a strong solution of sodium hydroxide? Assume 100 per cent conversion of phosphorus to $PH_3$.

**Solution.** Only phosphorus need be balanced. Therefore:

$$\underset{31.0 \text{ g.}}{P} \rightarrow \underset{22.4 \ l. \text{ (S.C.)}}{PH_3}$$

and

$$\frac{31.0 \text{ g. P}}{22.4 \ l. \text{ PH}_3} = \frac{5.28 \text{ g. P}}{x \ l. \text{ PH}_3}$$

or

$$x = 3.82 \ l. \text{ at S.C.}$$

At 43° C. and 725 mm. of Hg the $PH_3$ would occupy:

$$V_2 = 3.82 \ l. \times \frac{316° \text{ K.}}{273° \text{ K.}} \times \frac{760 \text{ mm. of Hg}}{725 \text{ mm. of Hg}}$$

$$= 4.64 \ l. \text{ at 43° C. and 725 mm. of Hg.}$$

**Example 11.12.** A mass of zinc weighing 1.635 g. was dissolved in dilute sulfuric acid. The hydrogen liberated measured 636 ml. collected by downward displacement of water at 24° C. and 750 mm. of Hg. Calculate:

(a) The volume the hydrogen would occupy dry at standard conditions.

(b) The gram-equivalent weight of zinc.

**Solution.**

(a)

$$V_{H_2} = 636 \text{ ml.} \times \frac{273° \text{ K.}}{297° \text{ K.}} \times \frac{(750-22) \text{ mm. of Hg}}{760 \text{ mm. of Hg}}$$

$$= 560 \text{ ml. at S.C.}$$

(b) The gram-equivalent weight of zinc is that weight which will displace 1.00 gram-equivalent weight of hydrogen. Since 1.00 gram-equivalent weight of hydrogen is 1.008 g. or 11,200 ml. at S.C., it follows that the answer would be based on the equation:

$$\underset{1.635 \text{ g.}}{Zn} + H_2SO_4 \rightarrow ZnSO_4 + \underset{x \text{ ml.}}{H_2} \uparrow$$

or

$$\frac{1.635 \text{ g. Zn}}{560 \text{ ml. H}_2} = \frac{x \text{ g. Zn}}{11,200 \text{ ml. H}_2}$$

and

$$x = 32.69 \text{ g.}$$

That is, 1.00 gram-equivalent weight of zinc is equal to 32.69 g.

## Problems

### Part I

11.1. When limestone, $CaCO_3$, is heated to a sufficiently high temperature it decomposes into lime, CaO, and carbon dioxide. How much lime could be obtained from 150 g. of limestone?     *Ans.* 84.1 g.

11.2. How many moles of zinc would be required to prepare 12 moles of zinc chloride by the action of zinc on hydrochloric acid?

*Ans.* 12 moles.

11.3. How many moles of ferrous sulfate would be formed by the action of 100 g. of iron on sulfuric acid? *Ans.* 1.79 moles.

11.4. What weight of aluminum sulfate could be obtained by the action of 25.0 g. of aluminum on an excess of sulfuric acid? *Ans.* 158 g.

11.5. Given the equation $2 Fe + 3 H_2O \rightarrow Fe_2O_3 + 3 H_2 \uparrow$ :

a. How many grams of water will react with one mole of iron?

*Ans.* 27 g.

b. How many grams of $Fe_2O_3$ would be formed from one mole of water?

*Ans.* 53.2 g.

11.6. Given the equation:

$$Cu + 2 H_2SO_4 \rightarrow CuSO_4 + SO_2 + 2 H_2O:$$

a. How many grams of copper sulfate would be formed for each mole of copper reacting? *Ans.* 159.6 g.

b. How many grams of copper would be required to produce 100 g. of copper sulfate? *Ans.* 39.8 g.

c. How many moles of sulfur dioxide would be found for each mole of acid reacting? *Ans.* 0.50 mole.

d. How many grams of water would be formed for each mole of copper sulfate formed? *Ans.* 36 g.

11.7. How many grams of sulfur will combine with 3.5 g. of copper to form CuS? *Ans.* 1.8 g.

11.8. How many grams of iron would be required to replace the copper in 3.96 g. of copper sulfate, $CuSO_4$? *Ans.* 1.39 g.

11.9. How many grams of iron would be required to replace one-half gram-atom of copper from a solution of copper sulfate, $CuSO_4$?

*Ans.* 27.9 g.

11.10. Calculate the volume of oxygen required to burn 60 liters of propane, $C_3H_8$, to $CO_2$ and $H_2O$, all gases being measured under standard conditions. *Ans.* 300 *l.*

11.11. Given the equation:

$$2 Al + 3 H_2SO_4 \rightarrow Al_2(SO_4)_3 + 3 H_2 \uparrow, \text{ calculate:}$$

a. The number of grams of $Al_2(SO_4)_3$ formed for each gram-atom of aluminum reacting. *Ans.* 171.07 g.

b. The number of grams of $Al_2(SO_4)_3$ formed for each mole of hydrogen formed. *Ans.* 114.05 g.

c. The number of moles of $H_2SO_4$ required for each mole of $Al_2(SO_4)_3$ formed. *Ans.* 3 moles.

d. The number of grams of aluminum required for each liter of hydrogen formed at standard conditions. *Ans.* 0.803 g.

11.12. Given the equation:

$$6\,FeCl_2 + 14\,HCl + K_2Cr_2O_7 \rightarrow 6\,FeCl_3 + 2\,KCl + 2\,CrCl_3 + 7\,H_2O:$$

    a. Indicate the weight relationships expressed in the products.

        *Ans.* 973.3 g. $FeCl_3$, 149.2 g. $KCl$, 316.8 g. $CrCl_3$, 126.1 g. $H_2O$.

    b. How many grams of $CrCl_3$ would have been formed from 0.78 g. of $K_2Cr_2O_7$?     *Ans.* 0.84 g.

    c. How many grams of $FeCl_3$ would be formed from 5.00 g. of $FeCl_2$?

        *Ans.* 6.40 g.

11.13. A portion of a silver coin weighing 2.44 g. and containing 90 per cent silver was dissolved in nitric acid. What weight of silver nitrate was formed?     *Ans.* 3.46 g.

11.14. How many moles of water will be liberated by the conversion of 500 g. of $CuSO_4 \cdot 5\,H_2O$ to the anhydrous salt?     *Ans.* 10.0 moles.

11.15. Calculate the gram-equivalent weight of magnesium, given that 1.10 g. of magnesium will liberate one liter of hydrogen at standard conditions.     *Ans.* 12.3 g.

11.16. Given that the gram-equivalent weight of calcium is 20.04 g.:

    a. With how many grams of bromine will 1.00 g. of calcium combine?

        *Ans.* 3.99 g.

    b. How many liters of hydrogen, at 27° C. and 725 mm. of Hg, could be obtained by the action of 1.00 g. of calcium on water?

        *Ans.* 0.645 *l.*

11.17. A mass of 1.00 g. of sodium was made to react with water. The hydrogen measured 663 ml. collected over water at 27° C. and 640 mm. of Hg. Calculate the gram-equivalent weight of sodium.

        *Ans.* 23.0 g.

11.18. In an experiment it was found that 1.365 g. of sulfur combined with 9.188 g. of silver. The gram-equivalent weight of silver is 107.9 g. Determine the gram-equivalent weight of sulfur.

        *Ans.* 16.03 g.

## Part II

11.19. Given the equation $N_2 + 3\,H_2 \rightarrow 2\,NH_3$:

    a. How many grams of ammonia would be prepared from 1000 g. of nitrogen?     *Ans.* 1214 g.

    b. How many liters of hydrogen at standard conditions would react with 1000 g. of nitrogen?     *Ans.* 2400 *l.*

    c. Under similar conditions, how many cubic feet of ammonia would be formed from 1000 ft.³ of nitrogen?     *Ans.* 2000 ft.³

    d. Under similar conditions, how many cubic feet of hydrogen will combine with 1000 ft.³ of nitrogen?     *Ans.* 3000 ft.³

11.20. How many grams of $Ca(OH)_2$ would be formed by the reaction of 25.0 g. of CaO with water?     *Ans.* 33.1 g.

11.21. Given the equation for the burning of acetylene in air:

$$2 C_2H_2 + 5 O_2 \rightarrow 4 CO_2 \uparrow + 2 H_2O:$$

a. How many grams of water would be formed from 2.5 moles of $C_2H_2$?
    *Ans.* 45 g.

b. At S.C., how many liters of carbon dioxide would be formed from 1.00 g. of $C_2H_2$?    *Ans.* 1.72 *l*.

11.22. Rust may be removed from linen by the action of dilute hydrochloric acid, $Fe_2O_3 + 6 HCl \rightarrow 2 FeCl_3 + 3 H_2O$. The $FeCl_3$ is soluble in water. How many grams of rust could be removed by the action of 100 ml. of acid of density 1.018 g. per ml. and containing 4.00 per cent acid by weight?    *Ans.* 2.97 g.

11.23. How many grams of copper would be precipitated by one gram of iron from a cupric salt in solution?    *Ans.* 1.14 g.

11.24. Calculate the number of grams of NaCl required to react with 100 ml. of 95 per cent $H_2SO_4$, density 1.84 g. per ml., according to the equation:

$$2 NaCl + H_2SO_4 \rightarrow 2 HCl + Na_2SO_4.$$

*Ans.* 209 g.

11.25. How many pounds of $Fe_2O_3$ could be obtained from 800 pounds of $Fe(OH)_3$?    *Ans.* 598 lb.

11.26. How many grams of $BaSO_4$ would be precipitated by the action of $H_2SO_4$ on 2.68 g. of $BaCl_2$?    *Ans.* 3.00 g.

11.27. How many pounds of water would be required to slake 50 pounds of CaO?    *Ans.* 16 lb.

11.28. How many pounds of limestone, 80 per cent $CaCO_3$, would be required to make one ton of CaO?    *Ans.* 4460 lb.

11.29. How many milliliters of nitric acid, density 1.21 g. per ml., and containing 34.3 per cent acid by weight, would be required to dissolve 25.0 g. of silver? Note: the products of the reaction are $AgNO_3$, $H_2O$, and $NO_2$.    *Ans.* 70.4 ml.

11.30. Phosphorus is prepared according to the equation:

$$Ca_3(PO_4)_2 + 3 SiO_2 + 5 C \rightarrow 3 CaSiO_3 + 5 CO \uparrow + 2 P.$$

a. How many pounds of phosphorus could be obtained from 2000 lb. of phosphate rock containing 70.5 per cent $Ca_3(PO_4)_2$?
    *Ans.* 282 lb.

b. How many pounds of sand, $SiO_2$, would be required to react with 500 lb. of $Ca_3(PO_4)_2$?    *Ans.* 290 lb.

c. How many pounds of carbon would be required for each ton of $Ca_3(PO_4)_2$?    *Ans.* 387 lb.

d. What volume of CO, reduced to standard conditions, would be formed for each 100 lb. of carbon used?    *Ans.* $8.47 \times 10^4$ *l*.

11.31. How many pounds of lime, CaO, could be obtained from 500 lb. of limestone containing 95 per cent $CaCO_3$?    *Ans.* 266 lb.

11.32. A sample of zinc weighing 10.93 g. reacted with 22.5 ml. of hydrochloric acid of density 1.18 g. per ml. and containing 35 per cent HCl by weight. Assuming the impurities in the zinc to be nonreactive toward HCl, what is the per cent of zinc in the sample?

*Ans.* 76.2%.

11.33. How much sodium hydroxide could be prepared from 2500 g. of calcium hydroxide on the basis of the reaction:

$$Na_2CO_3 + Ca(OH)_2 \rightarrow CaCO_3 + 2\,NaOH?$$    *Ans.* 2700 g.

11.34. A tank holding 25.0 *l.* of butane, $C_4H_{10}$, at 27° C. and 5 atmospheres pressure, would require what volume of oxygen, measured at 27° C. and 770 mm. of Hg, for complete combustion?    *Ans.* 802 *l.*

11.35. What weight of oxygen would be required to roast one ton of pyrite, $FeS_2$, on the basis of the reaction:

$$4\,FeS_2 + 11\,O_2 \rightarrow 2\,Fe_2O_3 + 8\,SO_2?$$    *Ans.* 1467 lb.

11.36. Commercial HCl is prepared according to the equation:

$$NaCl + H_2SO_4 \rightarrow NaHSO_4 + HCl.$$

How many liters of $H_2SO_4$, density 1.84 g. per ml. and containing 95 per cent acid by weight, would be required to prepare 25 *l.* of hydrochloric acid of density 1.18 g. per ml. and containing 36 per cent HCl by weight?    *Ans.* 16.3 *l.*

11.37. How many moles of $NH_4Cl$ would be required to prepare 0.10 mole of nitrogen, given the reaction:

$$NH_4Cl + NaNO_2 \rightarrow NaCl + 2\,H_2O + N_2?$$

*Ans.* 0.10 mole.

11.38. Chlorine is to be prepared according to the reaction:

$$MnO_2 + 4\,HCl \rightarrow MnCl_2 + 2\,H_2O + Cl_2.$$

What volume of concentrated hydrochloric acid, density 1.18 g. per ml. and containing 36 per cent HCl by weight, and what weight of pyrolusite ore containing 75 per cent by weight $MnO_2$, would be required to prepare 100 g. of chlorine?    *Ans.* 484 ml., 164 g.

11.39. How many cubic feet of chlorine will combine with 25.0 ft.³ of hydrogen, all gases measured at S.C.?    *Ans.* 25.0 ft.³

11.40. How many tons of 95 per cent $H_2SO_4$ could be prepared from one ton of pyrite containing 90 per cent $FeS_2$, assuming all the sulfur to be converted to acid?    *Ans.* 1.5 tons.

11.41. How many grams of 68 per cent $HNO_3$ could be prepared from 25 grams of $NaNO_3$ by the action of $H_2SO_4$?    *Ans.* 27.2 g.

11.42. The $CO_2$ resulting from the burning of 0.325 g. of a compound in oxygen was passed through lime water, resulting in the formation of 1.08 g. of $CaCO_3$ as a precipitate. What was the per cent of carbon in the compound?    *Ans.* 39.9%.

**11.43.** What volume of $CO_2$ would be formed at standard conditions when one cubic foot of $CH_4$ burns to $CO_2$ and water? *Ans.* 1 ft.$^3$

**11.44.** What volume of ozone would be formed from 960 ml. of oxygen, temperature and pressure being constant? *Ans.* 640 ml.

**11.45.** Twelve liters of oxygen were partially converted to ozone. The resultant volume of the oxygen-ozone mixture was 11.8 liters. What volume of ozone was formed? *Ans.* 0.4 $l$.

**11.46.** What volume of oxygen, measured at 15° C. and 720 mm. of Hg, could be obtained from 18 g. of HgO? *Ans.* 1.04 $l$.

**11.47.** How many grams of $KClO_3$ would be required to produce 480 ml. of oxygen at 21° C. and 640 mm. of Hg? *Ans.* 1.37 g.

**11.48.** How many liters of hydrogen could be obtained by the action of steam on 100 g. of iron at 200° C. and 760 mm. of Hg? *Ans.* 92.7 $l$.

**11.49.** How many liters of hydrogen at S.C. would be required to reduce 80 g. of CuO to free Cu? *Ans.* 22.5 $l$.

**11.50.** How much zinc would be required to prepare 500 ml. of hydrogen at 20° C. and 720 mm. of Hg? *Ans.* 1.29 g.

**11.51.** Calculate the weight of 39 per cent HCl required to prepare sufficient chlorine by action with $MnO_2$ to fill a cylinder of 3500 ml. capacity under a pressure of 20 atmospheres at 0° C. *Ans.* 1170 g.

**11.52.** How many grams of $(NH_4)_2SO_4$ reacting with $Ca(OH)_2$ would be required to prepare sufficient ammonia to react with 10 liters of HCl at S.C.? *Ans.* 29.4 g.

**11.53.** How many moles of $CO_2$ would be formed by burning 500 pounds of coal containing 96 per cent carbon? *Ans.* $1.8 \times 10^4$ moles.

**11.54.** What volume of hydrogen at 27° C. and 760 mm. of Hg will contain the same number of molecules as one liter of oxygen at standard conditions? *Ans.* 1.1 $l$.

**11.55.** How many moles of hydrogen could be obtained by the action of steam on 1.00 kg. of iron? *Ans.* 23.9 moles.

**11.56.** What weight of nitrogen will contain the same number of molecules as 2500 ml. of hydrogen at S.C.? *Ans.* 3.13 g.

**11.57.** What weight of lead will contain the same number of atoms as 1.00 g. of sulfur? *Ans.* 6.46 g.

**11.58.** How many grams of zinc reacting with $H_2SO_4$ will liberate the same amount of hydrogen as 2.30 g. of sodium reacting with water?

*Ans.* 3.27 g.

**11.59.** At standard conditions, how many cubic feet of hydrogen will unite with 6.0 ft.$^3$ of nitrogen to form ammonia? *Ans.* 18 ft.$^3$

**11.60.** How many cubic feet of ammonia will be formed in problem 11.59? *Ans.* 12 ft.$^3$

**11.61.** The following equation represents a commercial method for the preparation of nitric oxide, NO:

$$4 NH_3 + 5 O_2 \rightarrow 6 H_2O + 4 NO.$$

How many liters each of ammonia and oxygen would be required to produce 80.0 $l$. of NO at S.C.?          *Ans.* 80 $l$., 100 $l$.

11.62. Sodium chloride weighing 1.225 g. was dissolved in 500 ml. of water. To this solution was added 1.700 g. of $AgNO_3$ in solution. How much AgCl precipitated?          *Ans.* 1.43 g.

11.63. How many grams of iron can be oxidized to $Fe_2O_3$ by one mole of oxygen?          *Ans.* 74.5 g.

11.64. What volume of hydrogen at standard conditions would be liberated by the action of 3.22 g. of zinc on 50 ml. of 40 per cent $H_2SO_4$, specific gravity 1.30?          *Ans.* 1100 ml.

11.65. How many moles of $CO_2$, measured at 21° C. and 740 mm. of Hg, would be liberated by the action of 25.0 ml. of 20 per cent HCl, density 1.10 g. per ml., on 30.0 g. of marble containing 90 per cent $CaCO_3$?          *Ans.* 0.075 mole.

11.66. How much $SO_2$ could be obtained from 16.033 g. of sulfur?

*Ans.* 32.033 g.

11.67. How many moles of $SO_2$ could be obtained from 25.0 g. of sulfur?

*Ans.* 0.78 mole.

11.68. How much zinc must react with sulfuric acid in order to obtain 750 ml. of hydrogen collected at 33° C. and 680 mm. of Hg?

*Ans.* 1.75 g.

11.69. How many pounds of zinc oxide, ZnO, could be obtained by roasting 100 pounds of zinc blende, ZnS, given the equation:

$$2 \, ZnS + 3 \, O_2 \rightarrow 2 \, ZnO + 2 \, SO_2?$$          *Ans.* 83.5 lb.

11.70. How many moles of $CO_2$ would be formed by burning 120.1 g. of carbon?          *Ans.* 10 moles.

11.71. How many grams of oxygen must be contained in a flash bulb to oxidize 0.25 g. of aluminum?          *Ans.* 0.22 g.

11.72. How many gram-atoms of iron would be required to prepare five moles of $Fe_2O_3$?          *Ans.* 10 gram-atoms.

11.73. Given the equation, $2 \, Fe + 3 \, H_2O \rightarrow Fe_2O_3 + 3 \, H_2$, calculate the following:

    a. 1.00 g. of Fe combines with ____ mole of $H_2O$.          *Ans.* 0.0268 mole.

    b. 1.00 mole of Fe combines with ____ g. of $H_2O$.          *Ans.* 27.0 g.

    c. 1.00 mole of Fe forms ____ g. of $Fe_2O_3$.          *Ans.* 79.85 g.

11.74. How many grams of oxygen are required to prepare 100 g. of $P_2O_5$?

*Ans.* 56.3 g.

11.75. A sulfuric acid plant uses 2500 tons of $SO_2$ daily. How many tons of sulfur must be burned to produce this amount of $SO_2$ gas?

*Ans.* 1250 tons.

11.76. How many grams of carbon could be oxidized to $CO_2$ by the oxygen liberated from 231.76 g. of silver oxide, $Ag_2O$?          *Ans.* 6.0 g.

11.77. When 25.0 g. of Al was dissolved in HCl, the hydrogen was collected over water at 0° C. and 765 mm. of Hg. What was the volume of gas collected? *Ans.* 31.1 *l.*

**11.78.** How many moles of aluminum oxide, $Al_2O_3$, could be obtained from 100 g. of aluminum? *Ans.* 1.85 moles.

**11.79.** Two moles of hydrochloric acid and 100 g. of sodium hydroxide were placed in a beaker containing water. Which reactant was in excess and by how much? *Ans.* NaOH, 0.5 mole.

**11.80.** Ferric oxide may be reduced with carbon according to the equation:

$$2 \ Fe_2O_3 + 6 \ C \rightarrow 6 \ CO + 4 \ Fe.$$

a. How many liters of carbon monoxide will be produced at S.C. for each mole of ferric oxide reduced? *Ans.* 67.2 *l.*

b. How many grams of carbon will be required for each mole of ferric oxide? *Ans.* 36 g.

c. How many pounds of ferric oxide would be required for each 100 lb. of iron produced? *Ans.* 143 lb.

**11.81.** When 0.850 g. of calcium reacted with hydrochloric acid, there was liberated 476 ml. of hydrogen measured at S.C. From these data calculate the gram-equivalent weight of calcium. *Ans.* 20.0 g.

**11.82.** When 1.215 g. of cadmium reacted with hydrochloric acid, 283 ml. of gas was collected over water at 27° C. and 740 mm. of Hg. Calculate the gram-equivalent weight of cadmium. *Ans.* 56.2 g.

**11.83.** Water gas is produced from carbon and water according to the equation, $C + H_2O \rightarrow CO + H_2$. A furnace burns 100 ft.$^3$ of water gas per hour. What volume of carbon dioxide, at S.C., would be formed each 24 hr. period the furnace operates? *Ans.* 1200 ft.$^3$

**11.84.** How many pounds of water would be produced by the furnace in problem 11.83 for each 24 hr. period of operation? *Ans.* 60 lb.

**11.85.** How many kilograms each of hydrogen and oxygen could be obtained by the electrolysis of one ton of water? *Ans.* 101 kg., 807 kg.

**11.86.** A grocer bought 100 lb. of washing soda, $Na_2CO_3 \cdot 10 \ H_2O$, at five cents per pound. During the period of storage the water of hydration was lost. The grocer then sold the washing soda at eight cents per pound. Did the grocer gain or lose in the transaction and how much? *Ans.* Lost $2.04.

**11.87.** How much weight would be lost by 2.614 g. of $BaCl_2 \cdot 2 \ H_2O$ if heated until the water of hydration had been liberated? *Ans.* 0.385 g.

**11.88.** A hydrate of strontium chloride contains 40.54 per cent water. What is the formula for the hydrate? *Ans.* $SrCl_2 \cdot 6 \ H_2O$.

**11.89.** A mass of hydrated sodium phosphate, $Na_3PO_4 \cdot x \ H_2O$, weighing 3.615 g. lost 2.055 g. when heated to form the anhydrous salt. What is the value of $x$ in the above formula? *Ans.* 12.

**11.90.** What would be the weight of the residue if 8.375 g. of $U(SO_4)_2 \cdot 9 \ H_2O$ were heated until the water of hydration had been lost? *Ans.* 6.074 g.

# 12

# Some Quantitative Relationships Involving Energy

Every chemical change and every physical change of state involves an energy change. To make the study of chemical changes more complete, the energy changes accompanying them should be understood. With the advent of atomic energy the interrelationship between matter and energy has been greatly clarified. When electrical energy, or potential energy such as water stored in a dam, is used to do useful work, the end product usually is energy in the form of heat. For this reason energy frequently is expressed in terms of its equivalence in heat units such as the calorie.

## The Relationship between Matter and Energy

**12.1. The Einstein Equation Relating Matter and Energy.** The equivalence between matter and energy was first postulated by Einstein in 1905. The interconversion of matter and energy, as suggested by Einstein, is expressed in the following mathematical equation:

$$E = (2.2 \times 10^{13}) \text{ g.}$$

    grams of matter converted to energy

    constant relating matter and energy

energy in calories

That is, the conversion of one gram of any form of matter to energy would result in the release of $2.2 \times 10^{13}$ calories. This quantity of heat would raise the temperature of 250,000 tons of water from $0°$ C. to $100°$ C. It is approximately the amount of heat obtained by burning 300 tons of coal. Modern developments in atomic energy support the early postulates of Einstein.

## Units Used to Measure Quantity of Heat

**12.2. The Calorie and the British Thermal Unit.** Heat is a form of energy which may be measured quantitatively. The unit of heat energy used in the metric system is the *calorie* (cal.). For all practical purposes the calorie may be defined as the quantity of heat necessary to raise the temperature of one gram of water one degree centigrade. A larger unit, the *kilogram calorie* (kcal.), is equal to 1000 cal. The unit of heat energy used in the English system is the *British thermal unit* (BTU), which is defined as the amount of heat necessary to raise the temperature of one pound of water one degree Fahrenheit.

**Example 12.1.** How many calories would be required to heat 125 g. of water from 23° C. to 100° C.?

**Solution.** By definition:

Calories = (grams of water)(°C. temperature change).

Therefore:

Calories = (125)(100 − 23) = 9625.

**Example 12.2.** How many BTU's would be required to heat one gallon of water from 70° F. to 212° F.?

**Solution.** By definition:

BTU = (lb. of water)(°F. temperature change).

Since one gallon of water = 8.3 lb., then:

BTU = (8.3)(212 − 70) = 1179.

## The Heat Involved in Physical Changes

**12.3. The Specific Heats of Substances.** The *specific heat* of a substance is defined as the number of calories required to raise the temperature of one gram of the substance one degree centigrade.

TABLE 12.1

THE SPECIFIC HEATS OF SOME COMMON SUBSTANCES
IN CALORIES PER GRAM

| Alcohol | 0.581 | Iron | 0.107 |
|---|---|---|---|
| Aluminum | 0.214 | Lead | 0.031 |
| Copper | 0.092 | Sulfur | 0.137 |
| Diamond | 0.120 | Water | 1.000 |

**Example 12.3.** How many calories would be required to change the temperature of 125 g. of iron from 23° C. to 100° C.?

**Solution.** Note that the mass and temperature changes are the same as for the water in Example 12.1. However, the specific heat of iron is only 0.107 as compared to 1.000 for water. Taking specific heat into consideration, we have:

$$\text{Calories} = (\text{grams})(°\text{C. temperature change})(\text{specific heat}).$$

Therefore:

$$\text{Calories} = (125)(100 - 23)(0.107) = 1030.$$

**Example 12.4.** Calculate the specific heat of silver, given that 280 g. of the metal absorbed 136 cal. when changed from 22.13° C. to 30.79° C.

**Solution.** Solving the equation given in Example 12.3 for specific heat, we have:

$$\text{Specific heat} = \frac{\text{calories}}{(\text{grams})(°\text{C. temperature change})}$$

$$= \frac{136}{(280)(30.79 - 22.13)}$$

$$= 0.056 \text{ cal. per g.} = \text{specific heat of silver.}$$

**Example 12.5.** A mass of 350 g. of copper pellets at 100.0° C. was mixed with 200 g. of water at 22.4° C. The resultant temperature of the mixture was 33.2° C. Calculate the specific heat of copper.

**Solution.** When mixing the above:

$$\text{Heat lost by copper} = \text{heat gained by water.}$$

Let $x$ = specific heat of copper. Then:

$$(350)(100.0 - 33.2)(x) = (200)(33.2 - 22.4).$$
$$23,380x = 2160.$$
$$x = 0.092 \text{ cal. per g.} = \text{specific heat of copper.}$$

## 12.4. The Heats of Fusion and Vaporization of Substances.

The temperature of a crystalline solid remains constant at the melting point until the solid is all melted. This shows that heat is required to melt a crystalline solid without changing its temperature. The *heat of fusion* is defined as the number of calories required to change one gram of crystalline solid to the liquid state without a change in temperature. The heat of fusion of ice is 79.7 calories per gram.

Heat must be applied to a liquid at its boiling point in order to convert it to a vapor without a change in temperature. The *heat of vaporization* is defined as the number of calories required to change one gram of a liquid to vapor without a change in temperature. The heat of vaporization of water is 539.6 calories per gram.

**Example 12.6.** How many calories would be required to change 10.0 g. of ice at 0° C. to steam at 100° C.?

**Solution.** Three steps are involved in the solution of the problem:

(1) The heat required to melt the ice.

$$10.0 \ \cancel{g}. \times 80 \ \frac{cal.}{\cancel{g}.} = 800 \text{ calories.}$$

(2) The heat required to raise the temperature to 100° C.

$$10.0 \text{ g.} \times 100° \text{ C. temperature rise} = 1000 \text{ calories.}$$

(3) The heat required to vaporize the water.

$$10.0 \ \cancel{g}. \times 540 \ \frac{cal.}{\cancel{g}.} = 5400 \text{ calories.}$$

The total heat required would, therefore, be:

$$800 \text{ cal.} + 1000 \text{ cal.} + 5400 \text{ cal.} = 7200 \text{ cal.}$$

TABLE 12.2

HEATS OF FUSION AND VAPORIZATION IN CALORIES PER GRAM

| Substance | Formula | Heat of Fusion | Heat of Vaporization |
|---|---|---|---|
| Ammonia | $NH_3$ | 108.1 | 327.1 |
| Benzene | $C_6H_6$ | 30.3 | 94.3 |
| Carbon dioxide | $CO_2$ | 45.3 | 71.4 |
| Carbon tetrachloride | $CCl_4$ | 4.2 | 46.4 |
| Ethyl alcohol | $C_2H_5OH$ | 24.9 | 204.0 |
| Water | $H_2O$ | 79.7 | 539.6 |

## Problems

### Part I

12.1. How many calories are there in one BTU?          *Ans.* 252 cal.

12.2. How many calories would be required to change the temperature of 750 g. of water from 15.0° C. to 90.0° C.?

*Ans.* $5.63 \times 10^4$ cal.

12.3. How many calories would be required to change the temperature of 500 g. of water from 50° F. to 50° C.?          *Ans.* 20,000 cal.

12.4. How many calories would be required to change the temperature of 250 g. of aluminum from 15° C. to 75° C.?          *Ans.* 3210 cal.

12.5. Given 800 g. of water at 22° C., calculate the resultant temperature of the water following absorption of 3600 calories.    *Ans.* 26.5° C.

12.6. How many calories of heat would be liberated if the temperature of 300 g. of iron were changed from 75° C. to 17° C.?

*Ans.* 1.86 × 10³ cal.

12.7. The resultant temperature obtained when 150 g. of water at 28° C. was mixed with 350 g. of copper at 100° C. was 41° C.   Calculate the specific heat of copper.    *Ans.* 0.095 $\frac{cal.}{g.}$.

12.8. How many calories would be required to change 10.0 g. of ice at 0° C. to water at 15° C.?    *Ans.* 950 cal.

12.9. When one gram-atom of helium is formed from hydrogen in the sun, there is a loss of mass of 0.03 g.   What is the energy in calories given off by the sun as a result of this loss of mass?

*Ans.* 6.6 × 10¹¹ cal.

12.10. How many calories are liberated when one mole of steam at 100° C. condenses to water at 100° C.?    *Ans.* 9710 cal.

12.11. How many calories would be required to vaporize one mole of freon, $CCl_2F_2$, given that the heat of vaporization is 35.0 cal. per gram?

*Ans.* 4230 cal.

12.12. How many calories of heat would be required to vaporize one mole of ethyl alcohol without a change in temperature?    *Ans.* 9384 cal.

## Part II

12.13. How many calories would be required to change 25 g. of ice at −10° C. to steam at 110° C., given that the specific heat of ice is 0.51 cal. per g., and that of steam is 0.48 cal. per g.?

*Ans.* 1.82 × 10⁴ cal.

12.14. What temperature would result from mixing 50 g. of water at 20° C. and 250 g. of water at 40° C.?    *Ans.* 36.7° C.

12.15. Ten grams of ice at 0° C. was placed into 100 g. of water at 50° C. What was the temperature after the ice had melted?    *Ans.* 38° C.

12.16. It is estimated that the sun loses 8000 tons of mass per second due to conversion of matter to energy.   What is the caloric output of the sun per second?    *Ans.* 1.6 × 10²³ cal.

12.17. How many calories would be required to change the temperature of one gallon of water one degree centigrade?    *Ans.* 3784 cal.

12.18. How many grams of freon would have to vaporize in a mechanical refrigerator to absorb sufficient heat to freeze 1000 grams of water in the freezing compartment?   Note: see problem 12.11.

*Ans.* 2290 g.

12.19. How many tons of ice at 0° C. could be converted to steam at 100° C. by the heat liberated when one milligram of matter is converted to energy?    *Ans.* 33.6 tons.

12.20. How many BTU units would be required to raise the temperature of one cubic foot of water from a room temperature of 70° F. to a boiling point of 212° F.? *Ans.* 8.86 × 10³ BTU.

12.21. How many BTU units would be required to vaporize one pound of water without a change in temperature? *Ans.* 973 BTU.

12.22. How many BTU units would be required to change 25.0 lb. of ice at 32° F. to steam at 212° F.? *Ans.* 3.24 × 10⁴ BTU.

12.23. What would be the resulting temperature in degrees Fahrenheit if 500 g. of aluminum at 25.0° C. were dropped into 500 ml. of ethyl alcohol, density 0.79 g. per ml., at 70° C.? *Ans.* 132° F.

12.24. How many grams of water at 100° C. could be changed to steam at 100° C. by the amount of heat required to vaporize one kilogram of alcohol with no change in temperature? *Ans.* 378 g.

12.25. One kilogram each of copper and aluminum at 100° C. is placed in an insulated vessel containing one kilogram of water at 40.0° C. What is the resultant temperature of the mixture? *Ans.* 54.0° C.

12.26. Steam at 100° C. was passed through 2000 g. of water at 20.0° C. in an insulated container. After passing the steam through the water it was found that 10.0 g. of steam had condensed, the resulting temperature of the water being 22.7° C. From these data calculate the heat of vaporization of water. *Ans.* 540 cal. per g.

12.27. Seventy-five grams of ice at 0° C. was placed in 250 g. of water at 25.0° C. How much of the ice melted? *Ans.* 78.1 g.

12.28. What is the molar heat of vaporization of water? *Ans.* 9724 cal.

12.29. What is the molar heat of fusion of carbon dioxide? *Ans.* 1994 cal.

12.30. How many calories of heat would be required to convert 5.00 moles of water at 25° C. to steam at 100° C.? *Ans.* 3.65 × 10⁶ cal.

## The Heat Involved in Chemical Changes

**12.5. Heat of Reaction.** Every chemical reaction involves an energy change, usually in the form of heat. Equations indicating such heat exchange are called *thermochemical* equations. When heat is liberated the reaction is *exothermic*, and when heat is absorbed it is *endothermic*. Since the heat exchange is proportional to the amounts of substances reacting, it has become necessary to set up a reference standard for heats of reaction. The *heat of reaction* is defined as the quantity of heat liberated or absorbed when one mole of a substance reacts. Two types of heats of reaction will be discussed: (1) heat of combustion, and (2) heat of formation.

**12.6. Heat of Combustion.** Combustion is the rapid reaction of a substance with oxygen, being accompanied by heat and light. *Heat of combustion* is defined as the quantity of heat liberated when one mole of a substance burns in oxygen. All combustion reactions are exothermic. For example:

$$C \quad + \quad O_2 \quad \rightarrow \quad CO_2 + 94{,}400 \text{ cal.}$$
$$\text{1 mole} \quad \text{1 mole} \quad \text{1 mole}$$
$$\text{12.01 g.} \quad \text{32.00 g.} \quad \text{44.01 g.}$$

The above equation tells us that when one mole of carbon, 12.01 g., reacts with one mole of oxygen, 32.00 g., to form one mole of carbon dioxide, 44.01 g., there will be liberated 94,400 calories of heat. Therefore, by definition, the heat of combustion of carbon is 94,400 cal.

**Example 12.7.** When 1.14 g. of sulfur was burned to $SO_2$, there was liberated 2464 cal. Calculate the heat of combustion of sulfur.

**Solution.** By definition the heat of combustion of sulfur is the heat liberated when one mole of sulfur, 32.066 g., burns to $SO_2$. Therefore:

$$\frac{1.14 \text{ g. S}}{2464 \text{ cal.}} = \frac{32.066 \text{ g. S}}{x \text{ cal.}}$$

or $\qquad\qquad x = 69{,}300$ cal. = heat of combustion of S.

**Example 12.8.** The heat of combustion of heptane, $C_7H_{16}$, is 1150 kcal. How many kcal. would be liberated by the burning of 500 g. of heptane?

**Solution.** One mole, 100.2 g., of $C_7H_{16}$ will liberate 1150 kcal. Therefore:

$$\frac{100.2 \text{ g. } C_7H_{16}}{1150 \text{ kcal.}} = \frac{500 \text{ g. } C_7H_{16}}{x \text{ kcal.}}$$

or $\qquad\qquad x = 5.74 \times 10^3$ kcal.

**12.7. Heat of Formation.** The *heat of formation* is defined as the quantity of heat liberated or absorbed when one mole of a substance is formed from the elements.

**Example 12.9.** When 1.14 g. of sulfur was burned to $SO_2$, there was liberated 2464 cal. Calculate the heat of formation of $SO_2$.

**Solution.** From the equation:

$$S \quad + O_2 \rightarrow \quad SO_2 \quad + \text{ heat}$$
$$\text{1 mole} \qquad\qquad \text{1 mole}$$
$$\text{32.066 g.} \qquad\qquad \text{64.066 g.}$$

we see that one mole of $SO_2$ is formed for each mole of sulfur reacting. Therefore, the heat of combustion of sulfur and the heat of formation of $SO_2$ are numerically the same, 69,300 cal. This relationship exists in all reactions of direct combination of an element with oxygen.

**Example 12.10.** When hydrogen was burned in chlorine, 1000 cal. was liberated and 1.650 g. of HCl formed. Calculate the heat of formation of HCl.

**Solution.** By definition, the heat of formation of HCl is the heat liberated when one mole, 36.47 g., of HCl is formed from the elements. Therefore:

$$\frac{1.650 \text{ g. HCl}}{1000 \text{ cal.}} = \frac{36.47 \text{ g. HCl}}{x \text{ cal.}}$$

or                    $x = 22,100$ cal. = heat of formation of HCl.

**12.8. The Measurement of Heat of Reaction.** The experimental measurement of heat of reaction may be brought about by *calorimetry*. Many types of calorimeters are in use for such measurements. Fig. 12.1 shows the general construction of a bomb type of instrument.

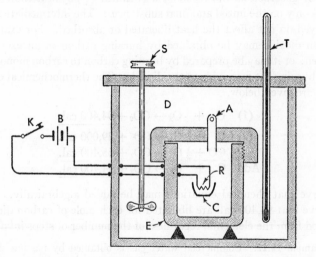

Fig. 12.1. The bomb calorimeter. The weighted sample is placed in the cup C, and the bomb E is filled with oxygen under pressure through the valve A. The outer jacket D is filled with water. S is a stirrer and T a thermometer. When K is closed the wire R becomes red-hot, causing the substance in the cup to burn. The heat is absorbed by the water, metal, and glass of the instrument. By means of the rise in temperature after the ignition, the heat of combustion of the substance in cup C may be calculated.

**Example 12.11.** A sample of carbon weighing 0.463 g. was placed in the cup C in Fig. 12.1. The calorimeter was assembled and 2500 g. of water placed in the outer jacket D. As a result of burning the carbon, the temperature of the water rose from 22.54° C. to 23.82° C. The metal and glass of the calorimeter were equivalent to 350 g. of water in terms of their heat-absorbing ability. Calculate the heat of combustion of carbon.

**Solution.** The heat of combustion of carbon is the amount of heat liberated when 12.01 g. of carbon burns to $CO_2$. First calculate the heat liberated when 0.463 g. of carbon burns. The heat liberated raised the temperature of an equivalent of $2500 + 350 = 2850$ g. of water $23.82 - 22.54 = 1.28$ degrees centigrade. Therefore:

$2850 \times 1.28 = 3648$ cal. liberated by burning 0.463 g. of carbon. Then:

$$\frac{0.463 \text{ g. C.}}{3648 \text{ cal.}} = \frac{12.01 \text{ g. C.}}{x \text{ cal.}}$$

or $\qquad\qquad\qquad x = 94,600$ cal. = heat of combustion of C.

**12.9. The Law of Hess.** The law of Hess states that the heat liberated or absorbed as the result of a chemical or physical change depends only on the initial and final subst nces. The intermediate steps involved do not affect the heat liberated or absorbed. For example, carbon dioxide may be obtained by burning carbon in an excess of oxygen; or it may be prepared by burning carbon to carbon monoxide, then burning the monoxide to the dioxide. The thermochemical equations are given below.

$$(1) \quad C \;+\; O_2 \rightarrow CO_2 + \underline{94,400 \text{ cal.}}$$

$$(2) \left\{ \begin{array}{l} C \;+ \tfrac{1}{2} O_2 \rightarrow \cancel{CO} + 29,000 \text{ cal.} \\ \cancel{CO} + \tfrac{1}{2} O_2 \rightarrow CO_2 + 65,400 \text{ cal.} \\ \hline C \;+\; O_2 \rightarrow CO_2 + \underline{94,400 \text{ cal.}} \end{array} \right.$$
$$\text{Add}$$

Observe that chemical equations may be added algebraically. Also observe that 94,400 cal. are liberated for each mole of carbon dioxide formed from the elements, regardless of the number of steps involved.

**Example 12.12.** Commercial water gas is obtained by passing superheated steam over carbon, in the form of coke.

$$H_2O + C \rightarrow H_2 + CO.$$

Given $\qquad$ (1) $H_2 + \tfrac{1}{2} O_2 \rightarrow H_2O + 58,700$ cal.
$\qquad\qquad\quad$ (2) $C \;+ \tfrac{1}{2} O_2 \rightarrow CO \;+ 29,000$ cal.

Calculate the heat of reaction for the formation of water gas.

**Solution.** Subtract (1) from (2) and simplify by transposing terms. Then:

$$C + \tfrac{1}{2} O_2 \rightarrow CO + \qquad\quad 29,000 \text{ cal.}$$
$$H_2 + \tfrac{1}{2} O_2 \rightarrow H_2O + \qquad\quad 58,700 \text{ cal.}$$
$$\overline{C + \cancel{\tfrac{1}{2}O_2} - H_2 - \cancel{\tfrac{1}{2}O_2} \rightarrow CO \;- H_2O - 29,700 \text{ cal.}}$$

and $\qquad\qquad\qquad C + H_2O \rightarrow CO + H_2 - 29,700$ cal.

The value $-29,700$ cal. indicates an endothermic reaction. That is, 29,700 cal. are absorbed during the course of the reaction.

**Example 12.13.** From the equations:

(1) $H_2$ (gas) $+ \frac{1}{2} O_2$ (gas) $\rightarrow H_2O$ (gas)     $+ 58,700$ cal.
(2) $H_2$ (gas) $+ \frac{1}{2} O_2$ (gas) $\rightarrow H_2O$ (liquid) $+ 68,400$ cal.,

calculate the heat of vaporization of water.

**Solution.** Subtract (1) from (2) and transpose.

$$H_2 \text{ (gas)} + \tfrac{1}{2} O_2 \text{ (gas)} \rightarrow H_2O \text{ (liquid)} + 68,400 \text{ cal.}$$
$$H_2 \text{ (gas)} + \tfrac{1}{2} O_2 \text{ (gas)} \rightarrow H_2O \text{ (gas)}    + 58,700 \text{ cal.}$$

$$\cancel{H_2}(g) + \cancel{\tfrac{1}{2}O_2}(g) - \cancel{H_2}(g) - \cancel{\tfrac{1}{2}O_2}(g) \rightarrow H_2O \text{ (l)} - H_2O \text{ (g)} + 9700 \text{ cal.}$$

$$H_2O \text{ (g)} \rightarrow H_2O \text{ (l)} + 9700 \text{ cal.}$$
$$18 \text{ g.}    \quad 18 \text{ g.}$$

That is, 18 g. of water vapor condenses to form 18 g. of water with the liberation of 9700 cal.   Therefore, 1.00 g. of water would liberate

$$\tfrac{9700}{18} = 540 \text{ cal.} = \text{heat of vaporization of water.}$$

TABLE 12.3

HEATS OF REACTION IN CALORIES PER MOLE

| Substance | Formula | Heat of Formation | Heat of Combustion |
|-----------|---------|-------------------|--------------------|
| Acetylene | $C_2H_2$ | $-53,700$ | 312,000 |
| Ammonia | $NH_3$ | 11,100 | — |
| Benzene | $C_6H_6$ | $-11,600$ | 780,000 |
| Butane | $C_4H_{10}$ | — | 683,400 |
| Carbon | C | — | 94,400 |
| Hydrogen | $H_2$ | — | 68,400 |
| Hydrogen chloride | HCl | 22,000 | — |
| Magnesium oxide | MgO | 145,000 | — |
| Methane | $CH_4$ | 18,100 | 210,800 |
| Nitric oxide | NO | $-21,500$ | — |
| Octane (gasoline) | $C_8H_{18}$ | — | 1,303,000 |
| Sugar | $C_{12}H_{22}O_{11}$ | — | 1,350,000 |
| Sulfur | S | — | 70,900 |
| Sulfur dioxide | $SO_2$ | 70,900 | — |
| Water | $H_2O$ | 68,400 | — |

## Problems

### Part I

**12.31.** When 1.20 g. of benzene, $C_6H_6$, was burned to $CO_2$ and $H_2O$, 12.0 kcal. was liberated.   Calculate the heat of combustion of benzene.

*Ans.* 780 kcal.

**12.32.** When 0.327 g. of carbon combined with sulfur to form $CS_2$, 0.691 kcal. was absorbed. Calculate the heat of formation of $CS_2$.

*Ans.* −25.4 kcal.

**12.33.** How many calories would be liberated by the complete combustion of 250 liters of $CH_4$ at S.C., given that the heat of combustion of $CH_4$ is 211 kcal.?      *Ans.* 2355 kcal.

**12.34.** The heat of formation of water is 68.4 kcal. How many calories would be liberated by burning 12 g. of hydrogen?      *Ans.* 410 kcal.

**12.35.** Magnesium was burned in oxygen until one gram of MgO had formed. The heat liberated was 3.60 kcal. Calculate the heat of formation of MgO.      *Ans.* 145 kcal.

**12.36.** When 0.327 g. of carbon was burned to $CO_2$, 0.257 kcal. was liberated. Calculate the heat of formation of $CO_2$.      *Ans.* 94.4 kcal.

**12.37.** A sample of coal weighing 0.875 g., when burned in a calorimeter, liberated enough heat to raise the temperature of 2500 g. of water from 18.50° C. to 20.60° C. Calculate the BTU value of the coal per pound.      *Ans.* 10,810 BTU.

**12.38.** The burning of 1.00 g. of sulfur to $SO_2$ resulted in the liberation of 2200 calories. Calculate the heat of formation of $SO_2$. *Ans.* 70.6 kcal.

**12.39.** Given the equations:

$$H_2 \text{ (gas)} + \tfrac{1}{2} O_2 \text{ (gas)} \rightarrow H_2O \text{ (liquid)} + 68,400 \text{ cal.}$$
$$H_2 \text{ (gas)} + \tfrac{1}{2} O_2 \text{ (gas)} \rightarrow H_2O \text{ (ice)} \quad + 69,840 \text{ cal.}$$

Calculate the heat of fusion of ice.      *Ans.* 80 cal.

**12.40.** How much heat would be liberated by the combustion of 2.75 moles of carbon?      *Ans.* 260 kcal.

**12.41.** From the following equations calculate the heat of formation of methane:

$$H_2 \text{ (g)} + \tfrac{1}{2} O_2 \text{ (g)} \rightarrow H_2O \text{ (l)} + 68,400 \text{ cal.}$$
$$C \text{ (s)} + O_2 \text{ (g)} \rightarrow CO_2 \text{ (g)} + 94,400 \text{ cal.}$$
$$CH_4 \text{ (g)} + 2 O_2 \text{ (g)} \rightarrow CO_2 \text{ (g)} + 2 H_2O \text{ (l)} + 210,800 \text{ cal.}$$

*Ans.* 20,400 cal.

**12.42.** The heat of combustion of acetylene is 312,000 cal. per mole. How many liters of carbon dioxide (at S.C.) are released for each kilocalorie produced?      *Ans.* 0.144 *l.*

**12.43.** The burning of sufficient magnesium in oxygen to form 2.00 g. of oxide resulted in the liberation of 7200 cal. Calculate the heat of combustion of magnesium.      *Ans.* 145 kcal.

**12.44.** Calculate the heat of formation of nitric oxide, NO, from the following equations:

$$N_2 \text{ (g)} + 2 O_2 \text{ (g)} \rightarrow 2 NO_2 \text{ (g)} - 15,000 \text{ cal.}$$
$$2 NO \text{ (g)} + O_2 \text{ (g)} \rightarrow 2 NO_2 \text{ (g)} + 28,000 \text{ cal.}$$

*Ans.* −21,500 cal.

## Part II

**12.45.** Assuming methane costs 75 cents per 1000 ft.$^3$, calculate the cost per 1,000,000 BTU. *Ans.* 71 cents.

**12.46.** Given the equation:

$$C_2H_4 \text{ (g)} + 3 O_2 \text{ (g)} \rightarrow 2 CO_2 \text{ (g)} + 2 H_2O \text{ (l)} + 313,000 \text{ cal.}$$

Calculate the heat of formation of ethylene, $C_2H_4$. *Ans.* −12,600 cal.

**12.47.** How many liters of water could be changed from 0° C. to 100° C. by the combustion of one mole of carbon? *Ans.* 0.944 *l.*

**12.48.** The heat of combustion of acetylene is 311.2 kcal. Calculate the heat of formation of acetylene. *Ans.* −54 kcal.

**12.49.** Given the equation:

$$N_2 + O_2 \rightarrow 2 NO - 43.2 \text{ kcal.}$$

Calculate the number of calories required to convert 25 liters of $N_2$ to NO at standard conditions. *Ans.* 48.2 kcal.

**12.50.** How much heat would be liberated by 18 g. of carbon when burned to $CO_2$? *Ans.* 141.9 kcal.

**12.51.** How many grams of magnesium oxide would have to be formed from the elements in order to liberate 18.0 kcal.? *Ans.* 5.0 g.

**12.52.** How many calories are liberated when 1.00 g. of $SO_2$ is formed from the elements? *Ans.* 1082 cal.

**12.53.** When 0.500 g. of coal was burned in a calorimeter, sufficient heat was formed to raise the temperature of 1500 g. of water from 23.00° C. to 25.50° C. Calculate the heat value of the coal in (a) calories per gram, and (b) BTU per pound.
*Ans.* (a) 7.5 kcal. per g.; (b) 13,500 BTU per lb.

**12.54.** How much heat would be liberated by the combustion of 2.5 pound-moles of carbon? *Ans.* $1.07 \times 10^5$ kcal.

**12.55.** How much heat would be liberated by the formation of one pound-mole of $SO_2$? *Ans.* $3.15 \times 10^4$ kcal.

**12.56.** Given the thermochemical equations:

$$4 \text{ Fe (s)} + 3 O_2 \text{ (g)} \rightarrow 2 Fe_2O_3 \text{ (s)} + 398 \text{ kcal.}$$
$$4 \text{ Al (s)} + 3 O_2 \text{ (g)} \rightarrow 2 Al_2O_3 \text{ (s)} + 798 \text{ kcal.}$$

Calculate the heat of the reaction:

$$Fe_2O_3 \text{ (s)} + 2 \text{ Al (s)} \rightarrow Al_2O_3 \text{ (s)} + 2 \text{ Fe (s)} + x \text{ kcal.}$$

*Ans.* 200 kcal.

**12.57.** The heat liberated from the combustion of 1.250 g. of coke raised the temperature of 1000 g. of water from 22.5° C. to 30.1° C. What was the per cent of carbon in the coke, assuming the impurities to be noncombustible? *Ans.* 77.4%.

**12.58.** A fuel oil has a heat of combustion of 16,500 BTU per lb.  The boiler of a furnace holds 100 gallons of water.  Assuming 60 per cent efficiency in heat transfer, how many pounds of fuel oil would be required to heat the water in the boiler from 70° F. to 180° F.?

*Ans.* 9.3 lb.

**12.59.** An anthracite coal containing 95 per cent carbon costs $21 per ton. What is the cost of the fuel in terms of dollars per 1,000,000 BTU?

*Ans.* $0.78.

**12.60.** A coal is purchased having a fuel value of 12,630 BTU per lb. Assuming carbon to be the only combustible constituent of the coal, what is the per cent of carbon in the coal?        *Ans.* 89.1%.

# 13

# Determination of the Atomic Weights of the Elements

The use of atomic weights in the quantitative treatment of chemical data is evidence of the need for accurate atomic weights. The atomic weights of the elements are constantly being redetermined as better techniques are developed. The corrections obtained are small but important. It may be of interest to present a few of the experimental methods which have been used to determine the atomic weights of the elements. The methods may be classified as either physical or chemical. The chemical methods for the determination of atomic weights give the more accurate values.

## Physical Methods for the Determination of Atomic Weights

**13.1. From Specific Heats.** The law of Dulong and Petit, proposed by the two scientists about 1818, states that the product of the atomic weight and specific heat of an element is essentially a constant equal to 6.3. That is:

$$\text{Atomic weight} \times \text{specific heat} = 6.3.$$

The method is principally of historical interest. An inspection of Table 13.1 will show that the law is only an approximation.

TABLE 13.1

| Element | Specific Heat | $\dfrac{6.3}{Sp.\ Ht.}$ | Atomic Weight |
|---------|------|------|------|
| Aluminum | 0.214 | 29 | 26.98 |
| Copper | 0.092 | 68 | 63.54 |
| Iron | 0.107 | 59 | 55.85 |
| Lead | 0.031 | 203 | 207.21 |
| Magnesium | 0.246 | 26 | 24.32 |
| Sulfur | 0.176 | 36 | 32.066 |

**Example 13.1.** The experimental value for the specific heat of silver is 0.058 cal. per g. Calculate the approximate atomic weight of silver.

**Solution.** From the law of Dulong and Petit:

$$\text{At. wt. of silver} = \frac{6.3}{0.058} = 109.$$

**Example 13.2.** Calculate the approximate specific heat of gold and compare to the accepted value.

**Solution.**

$$\text{Sp. ht. of gold} = \frac{6.3}{197} = 0.032 \text{ cal. per g.}$$

The experimental value for the specific heat of gold is 0.031 cal. per g.

## Chemical Methods for the Determination of Atomic Weights

**13.2. From Percentage Composition.** By means of chemical analysis it is possible to determine the composition of a compound to five decimal places in terms of grams (0.00000 g.). Atomic weights calculated from such data give correspondingly accurate values.

**Example 13.3.** Chemical analysis of silver nitrate gave the composition, 63.500 per cent silver, 8.245 per cent nitrogen, and 28.255 per cent oxygen. Calculate the atomic weight of silver with an accuracy consistent with the data. The approximate atomic weight of silver is 109, as determined from specific heat (Example 13.1).

**Solution.** Calculate the formula (Sec. 10.2). Then:

$$\text{Silver} \quad = \frac{63.500}{109} = 0.583.$$

$$\text{Nitrogen} = \frac{8.245}{14} = 0.589.$$

$$\text{Oxygen} \quad = \frac{28.255}{16} = 1.766.$$

The simplest integer ratio is 1 : 1 : 3. The formula is therefore $AgNO_3$.

From the formula $AgNO_3$ we see that there are 3 gram-atoms of oxygen associated with 1 gram-atom of silver. Therefore, the atomic weight of silver would be equal numerically to the number of grams of silver combined with $3 \times 16.000 = 48.000$ g. of oxygen. Then:

$$\frac{63.500 \text{ g. Ag}}{28.255 \text{ g. O}_2} = \frac{x \text{ g. Ag}}{48.000 \text{ g. O}_2}$$

or
$$x = 107.88 \text{ g.} = \text{atomic weight of Ag.}$$

**13.3. From Gram-equivalent Weights.** The gram-equivalent weights of the elements may be determined by chemical analysis, and are therefore quite accurate. The atomic weight of an element is a multiple of the gram-equivalent weight, the numerical value of the multiple being termed the *oxidation number*. That is:

$$\text{Oxidation number} = \frac{\text{atomic weight}}{\text{equivalent weight}}.$$

**Example 13.4.** The specific heat of gold is 0.031 cal. per g., and the gram-equivalent weight is 65.67 g. Calculate the atomic weight of gold.

**Solution.**

$$\text{Approximate at. wt. of gold} = \frac{6.3}{0.031} = 203.$$

$$\text{Oxidation number of gold} = \frac{203}{65.67} = 3.$$

That is, the accurate atomic weight of gold is 3 times the gram-equivalent weight, or:

$$\text{Atomic weight of gold} = 65.67 \times 3 = 197.0.$$

**Example 13.5.** The approximate atomic weight of zinc is 65, as determined from its specific heat. It was found that 1.632 g. of zinc replaced 559.7 ml. of hydrogen from a solution of $H_2SO_4$, measured at S.C. Calculate a more accurate atomic weight of zinc.

**Solution.** One gram-equivalent weight of zinc will replace 1.008 g. of hydrogen or 11.2 $l$. However, 11.2 $l$. is not so accurate a value as 1.008 g. We will therefore use 1.008 g. of hydrogen. Since one liter of hydrogen weighs 0.0899 g., then 559.7 ml. will weigh $0.5597 \times 0.0899 = 0.05032$ g. Therefore:

$$\frac{1.632 \text{ g. Zn}}{0.05032 \text{ g. } H_2} = \frac{x \text{ g. Zn}}{1.008 \text{ g. } H_2}$$

or $\qquad\qquad x = 32.69 = \text{gram-equivalent weight of } \mathbf{Zn}.$

Then, $\qquad$ oxidation number of Zn $= \dfrac{65}{32.69} = 2,$

and $\qquad$ atomic weight of zinc $= 32.69 \times 2 = 65.38.$

**Example 13.6.** The following data were recorded in the determination of the atomic weight of tin. The specific heat is 0.0542 cal. per g. It was found that 2.1440 g. of tin combined with oxygen to form 2.7219 g. of oxide. Calculate the atomic weight of tin.

**Solution.**

$$\text{Approximate atomic weight} = \frac{6.3}{0.0542} = 116.$$

The gram-equivalent weight would be the amount of tin that will combine with 8.0000 g. of oxygen. Therefore:

$$\frac{(2.7219 - 2.1440) \text{ g. O}_2}{2.1440 \text{ g. Sn}} = \frac{8.0000 \text{ g. O}_2}{x \text{ g. Sn}}$$

or
$$x = 29.68 \text{ g.} = \text{gram-equivalent weight of Sn.}$$

$$\text{Oxidation number of tin} = \frac{116}{29.68} = 4.$$

Atomic weight of tin $= 29.68 \times 4 = 118.7$.

## Problems

### Part I

13.1. Calculate the approximate specific heat of uranium.

*Ans.* 0.026 cal. per g.

13.2. Given the specific heat of lead as 0.031, calculate the atomic weight of lead and compare to the accepted value. *Ans.* 203.

13.3. The gram-equivalent weight of magnesium was found experimentally to be 12.16 g. The specific heat of magnesium is 0.24 cal. per g. Calculate the accurate atomic weight of magnesium. *Ans.* 24.32.

13.4. An oxide of vanadium was found to contain 2.123 g. of vanadium for each 1.000 g. of oxygen. Calculate the atomic weight of vanadium, given that the approximate atomic weight is 50. *Ans.* 50.95.

13.5. Sodium oxalate, $Na_2C_2O_4$, contains 34.314 per cent sodium and 47.760 per cent oxygen. Calculate the atomic weight of sodium.

*Ans.* 22.991.

13.6. The equivalent weight of zinc is 32.69. Its approximate atomic weight is 65. Calculate a more exact atomic weight. *Ans.* 65.38.

13.7. An oxide of lead contains 13.377 per cent oxygen. Knowing the approximate atomic weight of lead to be 205, calculate a more exact atomic weight for the element. *Ans.* 207.21.

13.8. The approximate atomic weight of aluminum is 25. Calculate a more accurate atomic weight, given that 1.334 g. of aluminum displaced 1.778 liters of hydrogen measured at 23° C. and 770 mm· of Hg. *Ans.* 26.98.

### Part II

13.9. One hundred grams of a metal at 100° C., when added to 300 g. of water at 28.3° C., gave a mixture with a temperature of 31.6° C. Calculate the approximate atomic weight of the metal. *Ans.* 43.

13.10. The specific heat of an element was found to be 0.100 cal. per g. It was found that 0.749 g. of the element formed 0.937 g. of oxide. Calculate the atomic weight of the element. *Ans.* 63.6.

13.11. It was found that 144 cal. was required to change the temperature of 260 g. of aluminum from 20.00° C. to 22.50° C. Calculate the approximate atomic weight for aluminum. *Ans.* 29.

13.12. An oxide of iron was found to contain 30.06 per cent oxygen. When 400 g. of iron at 100° C. was mixed with 220 g. of water at 20° C., the resulting temperature was 33.0° C. Calculate the atomic weight of iron. *Ans.* 55.83.

13.13. Calculate the number of calories required to change the temperature of one atom of a metal one degree centigrade.
*Ans.* $1.06 \times 10^{-23}$ cal.

13.14. When 350 g. of platinum at 100° C. was added to 250 g. of water at 16° C., the temperature of the resulting mixture was 19.5° C. Calculate the atomic weight of platinum. *Ans.* 206.

13.15. The gram-equivalent weight of chlorine was found to be 8.865 as calculated from an oxide of the element. Calculate (a) the atomic weight of chlorine given that the specific heat is 0.19 cal. per g., and (b) the formula of the oxide. *Ans.* (a) 35.46; (b) $ClO_2$.

13.16. Analysis showed that magnesium pyrophosphate, $Mg_2P_2O_7$, contains 0.1086 g. of magnesium to 0.2501 g. of oxygen. Calculate the atomic weight of magnesium as accurately as the data will permit.
*Ans.* 24.32.

13.17. The oxide of a metal contains 21.35 per cent oxygen. The specific heat of the metal is 0.100 cal. per g. What is the metal? *Ans.* Co.

13.18. It was found that 0.709 g. of iron combined with 1.350 g. of chlorine. Determine the atomic weight of iron. *Ans.* 55.9.

13.19. A metal X forms two oxides containing 36.81 per cent oxygen and 46.63 per cent oxygen, respectively. The specific heat of the metal is 0.121 cal. per g. What are the formulas for the oxides?
*Ans.* $MnO_2$ and $MnO_3$.

13.20. A mass of metal at 100° C. and weighing 150 g. was added to 246 g. of water at 25.0° C. The resulting temperature of the mixture was 27.4° C. When 1.395 g. of the metal was added to a sulfuric acid solution there was collected over water 358.9 ml. of gas at 23° C. and 660 mm. of Hg.

a. Determine the atomic weight of the metal. *Ans.* 112.4.
b. What was the metal? *Ans.* Cd.

# 14

# Oxidation-Reduction Equations

Chemical reactions may be divided into two general types. In one type, known as metathesis reactions, there is merely a rearrangement of the reactant ions to form the products. In the second type of reaction some of the atoms in the reactants undergo a change in oxidation state to form the products. These are known as oxidation-reduction reactions. Reactions of metathesis, and oxidation-reduction reactions involving elements in the free state or as simple ions, were presented in Chapter 8. The present chapter deals with the more complex reactions of oxidation and reduction.

**14.1. Introduction.** *Oxidation* is the process in which atoms or ions lose electrons; *reduction* is the process in which electrons are gained by atoms or ions. The *oxidant* (oxidizing agent) is effective in bringing about oxidation. The oxidant therefore is reduced. Conversely the *reductant* (reducing agent) is oxidized. For example, in the reaction, $Ca + Cl_2 \rightarrow CaCl_2$, the calcium atom loses $2e^-$, $Ca \rightarrow Ca^{+2} + 2e^-$, while the chlorine molecule gains the $2e^-$, $Cl_2 + 2e^- \rightarrow 2\,Cl^-$. This is expressed in the following diagram.

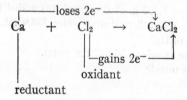

If, in a reaction, any atoms or ions have undergone a change in oxidation state, it is an oxidation-reduction type of reaction. For example:

$$(+4)(-2) \quad (+1)(-1) \quad (+2)(-1) \quad (+1)(-2) \quad (0)$$
$$MnO_2 \;+\; 4\,HCl \;\rightarrow\; MnCl_2 \;+\; 2\,H_2O \;+\; Cl_2.$$

Above each atom, in both the reactants and products, the oxidation

state has been indicated. The following changes in oxidation state
have taken place:

$$(+4) \qquad\qquad (+2)$$
$$\text{Mn} + 2e^- \rightarrow \text{Mn, reduction;}$$

and $\qquad\qquad 2\,\text{Cl}^- \rightarrow \text{Cl}_2 + 2e^-, \text{ oxidation.}$

The following generalities will help in writing oxidation-reduction
reactions.

1. The reactants and products must be known.

2. The oxidation number of an element in the free state is zero.

3. The oxidation number of combined oxygen is $-2$.

4. The oxidation number of combined hydrogen is $+1$, except for
hydrides in which it is $-1$.

5. A decrease in oxidation number indicates a gain of electrons, and
an increase in oxidation number a loss of electrons.

6. The algebraic sum of the oxidation numbers in a formula is equal
to zero. For example:

$$(+1)(-1) \qquad\qquad\qquad (+3)(-2)$$
$$\text{HCl} \qquad\qquad\qquad\qquad \text{Al}_2\text{O}_3$$

$$(+1) + (-1) = 0. \qquad [2 \times (+3)] + [3 \times (-2)] = 0.$$

$$(+1)(+7)(-2) \qquad\qquad\qquad (+1)(+6)(-2)$$
$$\text{KMnO}_4 \qquad\qquad\qquad\qquad \text{K}_2\text{Cr}_2\text{O}_7$$

$$(+1)+(+7)+[4\times(-2)]=0. \qquad [2\times(+1)]+[2\times(+6)]+[7\times(-2)]=0.$$

**Example 14.1.** What is the oxidation number of:
(a) Sulfur in $H_2SO_4$?
(b) Arsenic in $H_3AsO_4$?
(c) Phosphorus in $Ca_3(PO_4)_2$?

**Solution.** In each compound let $x$ be the oxidation number of the unknown element.

$$(+1)(x)(-2)$$
(a)   $\text{H}_2\text{SO}_4$

$$[2 \times (+1)] + (x) + [4 \times (-2)] = 0$$
or    $x = +6 = $ oxidation number of sulfur.

$$(+1)(x)(-2)$$
(b)   $\text{H}_3\text{AsO}_4$

$$[3 \times (+1)] + (x) + [4 \times (-2)] = 0$$
or    $x = +5 = $ oxidation number of arsenic.

$$(+2)(x)(-2)$$
(c) $Ca_3(PO_4)_2$

$$[3 \times (+2)] + (2x) + [8 \times (-2)] = 0$$

or    $x = +5$ = oxidation number of phosphorus.

Two methods will be presented for writing oxidation-reduction equations: (1) method based on change in oxidation state (or electron transfer), and (2) ion-electron method.

**14.2. Writing Equations by Change in Oxidation State.** In assigning an oxidation state to an atom it must be *assumed* that all bonds between unlike atoms are ionic bonds.

**Example 14.2.** Write the equation for the reaction between $HNO_3$ and $H_2S$.

**Solution.** Write down the reactants and products. Above each atom indicate its oxidation number.

$$\begin{array}{ccccc}
& & \text{loses } 2e^- & & \\
(+1)(+5)(-2) & (+1)(-2) & (+1)(-2) & (+2)(-2) & (0) \\
HNO_3 & + \quad H_2S & \to \quad H_2O & + \quad NO & + \quad S. \\
& & \text{gains } 3e^- & &
\end{array}$$

In changing from $S^{-2}$ to $S^0$ there is a loss of $2e^-$, and in changing from $N^{+5}$ to $N^{+2}$ there is a gain of $3e^-$. Evidently, in any oxidation-reduction equation:

Number of $e^-$ lost = number of $e^-$ gained.

To meet this requirement there must be:

$$3\, S^{-2} \to 3\, S^0 + 6e^-,$$
and $$2\, N^{+5} + 6\, e^- \to 2\, N^{+2}. \quad \text{Therefore:}$$
$$2\, HNO_3 + 3\, H_2S \to H_2O + 2\, NO + 3\, S.$$

The last step is indicating the number of molecules of water. Since there are 8 $H^+$ there must be 4 $H_2O$. The complete equation will be:

$$2\, HNO_3 + 3\, H_2S \to 4\, H_2O + 2\, NO + 3\, S.$$

**Example 14.3.** Balance the reaction:

$$KMnO_4 + FeSO_4 + H_2SO_4 \to K_2SO_4 + MnSO_4 + Fe_2(SO_4)_3 + H_2O.$$

**Solution.** Proceed as in Example 14.2. Then:

$$\begin{array}{ccccccc}
& \text{gains } 5e^- & & & & & \downarrow \\
(+1)(+7)(-2) & (+2)(+6)(-2) & (+1)(+6)(-2) & (+1)(+6)(-2) & (+2)(+6)(-2) & (+3)(+6)(-2) & (+1)(-2) \\
KMnO_4 & + \quad FeSO_4 & + \quad H_2SO_4 & \to \quad K_2SO_4 & + \quad MnSO_4 & + \quad Fe_2(SO_4)_3 & + \quad H_2O\,. \\
& & \text{loses } 1e^- & & & &
\end{array}$$

Then                    $5\, Fe^{+2} \to 5\, Fe^{+3} + 5e^-,$

and $\qquad$ $Mn^{+7} + 5e^- \rightarrow Mn^{+2}$.  Therefore:

$$KMnO_4 + 5\ FeSO_4 + x\ H_2SO_4 \rightarrow \tfrac{1}{2}\ K_2SO_4 + MnSO_4 + 2\tfrac{1}{2}\ Fe_2(SO_4)_3$$
$$+ y\ H_2O.$$

Multiply the equation by 2 to eliminate fractions.

Then, $\quad 2\ KMnO_4 + 10\ FeSO_4 + 2x\ H_2SO_4 \rightarrow K_2SO_4 + 2\ MnSO_4$
$$+ 5\ Fe_2(SO_4)_3 + 2y\ H_2O.$$

Next evaluate $x$.  In the products there are 18 $SO_4$ radicals.  To have 18 $SO_4$ radicals in the reactants, $2x = 8$.  As in Example 14.2, $2y$ must be equal to 4.  Therefore:

$$2\ KMnO_4 + 10\ FeSO_4 + 8\ H_2SO_4 \rightarrow K_2SO_4 + 2\ MnSO_4 + 5\ Fe_2(SO_4)_3$$
$$+ 4\ H_2O.$$

**Example 14.4.**  Balance the reaction:

$$K_2Cr_2O_7 + HCl \rightarrow KCl + CrCl_3 + H_2O + Cl_2.$$

**Solution.**  Proceeding as in the previous examples:

$$\underbrace{\qquad\qquad}_{\text{2 atoms gain } 6e^-}$$

$$(+6) \qquad\quad (-1) \qquad (-1) \quad (+3)(-1) \qquad\qquad\qquad (0)$$
$$K_2Cr_2O_7 \;+\; HCl \;\rightarrow\; KCl \;+\; CrCl_3 \;+\; H_2O \;+\; Cl_2.$$

$$\underbrace{\qquad\qquad\qquad}_{\text{loses } 1e^-}$$

**Observe:** (1) The gain or loss of electrons is given in terms of the expressed formula.  The two Cr atoms gain $3e^-$ each, or a total of $6e^-$.  (2) Some of the $Cl^-$ ions from HCl form free $Cl_2$, while the $Cl^-$ ions forming KCl and $CrCl_3$ have not changed their oxidation state.  Then:

$$K_2Cr_2O_7 + 6\ HCl + x\ HCl \rightarrow 2\ KCl + 2\ CrCl_3 + y\ H_2O + 3\ Cl_2.$$

The arrows indicate the origin of the $Cl^-$ and $Cl_2$ in the products.  Evidently $x = 8$, and $y = 7$.  Collecting the HCl molecules gives:

$$K_2Cr_2O_7 + 14\ HCl \rightarrow 2\ KCl + 2\ CrCl_3 + 7\ H_2O + 3\ Cl_2.$$

**Example 14.5.**  Balance the reaction:

$$Na_2TeO_3 + NaI + HCl \rightarrow NaCl + H_2O + Te + I_2.$$

**Solution.**

$$\underbrace{\qquad\qquad}_{\text{gains } 4e^-}$$

$$(+4) \qquad\qquad\qquad\qquad\qquad\qquad (0)$$
$$Na_2TeO_3 + NaI + HCl \rightarrow NaCl + H_2O + Te + I_2.$$

$$\underbrace{\qquad\qquad\qquad}_{\text{loses } 1e^-}$$

$$Na_2TeO_3 + 4\ NaI + x\ HCl \rightarrow 6\ NaCl + y\ H_2O + Te + 2\ I_2.$$
$$x = 6 \text{ and } y = 3.$$

$$Na_2TeO_3 + 4\ NaI + 6\ HCl \rightarrow 6\ NaCl + 3\ H_2O + Te + 2\ I_2.$$

The above method of writing oxidation-reduction reactions is sometimes referred to as the "electron transfer method" or the "molecular method."

**14.3. Writing Equations by the Ion-Electron Method.** In the ion-electron method only the molecules and ions which participate in the chemical change are shown. There are four steps to follow in writing oxidation-reduction equations by the ion-electron method.

Step 1. Pick out the oxidant and the reductant molecule or ion and their products.

Step 2. Write the partial equation for each, balancing in terms of both atoms and electrons.

Step 3. Multiply each partial equation by a number such that there are the same number of electrons in each partial equation.

Step 4. Add the two partial equations and simplify by canceling molecules and ions. The four equations given in the preceding section will now be written using the ion-electron method.

**Example 14.6.** Write the equation for the reaction between $HNO_3$ and $H_2S$.

**Solution.**

Step 1. Oxidant: $NO_3^- \rightarrow NO$.

Reductant: $H_2S \rightarrow S$.

Since $H_2S$ exists predominantly in the molecular state, the molecule $H_2S$ is used as the reductant rather than the sulfide ion, $S^{-2}$.

Step 2. For the oxidant, $NO_3^- \rightarrow NO$, the 2 remaining oxygen atoms require 4 $H^+$ to form $H_2O$. Then, $NO_3^- + 4\ H^+ \rightarrow NO + 2\ H_2O$. To balance in terms of electrons, $3e^-$ are needed on the reactant side. Then:

$$3e^- + NO_3^- + 4\ H^+ \rightarrow NO + 2\ H_2O. \tag{1}$$

For the reductant, $H_2S \rightarrow S$:

$$H_2S \rightarrow S + 2\ H^+.$$

To balance in terms of electrons:

$$H_2S \rightarrow S + 2\ H^+ + 2e^-. \tag{2}$$

Step 3. Multiply equation (1) by 2, and equation (2) by 3. Then:

$$6e^- + 2\ NO_3^- + 8\ H^+ \rightarrow 2\ NO + 2\ H_2O \tag{3}$$

and

$$3\ H_2S \rightarrow 3\ S + 6\ H^+ + 6e^-. \tag{4}$$

Step 4. Add equations (3) and (4) and cancel terms.

$$6e^- + 2\,NO_3^- + \overset{2}{8}\,H^+ + 3\,H_2S \rightarrow 2\,NO + 2\,H_2O + 3\,S + 6\,H^+ + 6e^-$$

or        $2\,NO_3^- + 2\,H^+ + 3\,H_2S \rightarrow 2\,NO + 2\,H_2O + 3\,S.$

Compare the above equation to the one obtained in **Example 14.2.**

**Example 14.7.**  Balance the reaction:

$$KMnO_4 + FeSO_4 + H_2SO_4 \rightarrow K_2SO_4 + MnSO_4 + Fe_2(SO_4)_3 + H_2O.$$

**Solution.**

**Step 1.**  Oxidant:    $MnO_4^- \rightarrow Mn^{+2}.$
            Reductant: $Fe^{+2}\quad \rightarrow Fe^{+3}.$

**Step 2.**           $MnO_4^- + 8\,H^+ + 5e^- \rightarrow Mn^{+2} + 4\,H_2O.$           (5)

Observe that, in terms of electrons:

$$(1-) + (8+) + (5-) \rightarrow (2+)$$
or                    $$(2+) \rightarrow (2+).$$
$$Fe^{+2} \rightarrow Fe^{+3} + 1e^-.$$           (5a)

**Step 3.**  Multiply equation (5a) by 5.  Then:

$$5\,Fe^{+2} \rightarrow 5\,Fe^{+3} + 5e^-.$$           (6)

**Step 4.**  Add equations (5) and (6).  Then:

$$MnO_4^- + 8\,H^+ + 5e^- \rightarrow Mn^{+2} + 4\,H_2O$$
$$5\,Fe^{+2} \rightarrow 5\,Fe^{+3} + 5e^-$$

Add:    $\overline{MnO_4^- + 8\,H^+ + 5\,Fe^{+2} \rightarrow Mn^{+2} + 4\,H_2O + 5\,Fe^{+3}.}$

Again, the equation is correct in terms of electrons.

$$(1-) + (8+) + (10+) \rightarrow (2+) + (15+)$$
or                    $$(17+) \rightarrow (17+).$$

Compare the above equation to the one obtained in **Example 14.3.**

**Example 14.8.**  Balance the reaction:

$$K_2Cr_2O_7 + HCl \rightarrow KCl + CrCl_3 + H_2O + Cl_2.$$

**Solution.**

**Step 1.**  $Cr_2O_7^{-2} \rightarrow Cr^{+3}.$
            $Cl^- \rightarrow Cl_2.$

**Step 2.**    $Cr_2O_7^{-2} + 14\,H^+ + 6e^- \rightarrow 2\,Cr^{+3} + 7\,H_2O.$
               $2\,Cl^- \rightarrow Cl_2 + 2e^-.$

**Step 3.**           $6\,Cl^- \rightarrow 3\,Cl_2 + 6e^-.$

**Step 4.**    $Cr_2O_7^{-2} + 14\,H^+ + 6e^- \rightarrow 2\,Cr^{+3} + 7\,H_2O$
               $6\,Cl^- \rightarrow 3\,Cl_2 + 6e^-$

$$\overline{Cr_2O_7^{-2} + 14\,H^+ + 6\,Cl^- \rightarrow 2\,Cr^{+3} + 7\,H_2O + 3\,Cl_2.}$$

The equation obtained in Example 14.4 is identical to the above. This may be shown by writing the equation from Example 14.4 in ionic form and canceling like terms.  Then:

$$K_2Cr_2O_7 + 14\,HCl \quad \rightarrow \quad 2\,KCl + 2\,CrCl_3 \quad + 7\,H_2O + 3\,Cl_2.$$

$$\overset{\cancel{}}{2\,\cancel{K^+}} + Cr_2O_7^{-2} + 14\,H^+ + \overset{6}{\cancel{14}}\,Cl^- \rightarrow 2\,\cancel{K^+} + \cancel{2\,Cl^-} + 2\,Cr^{+3} + \cancel{6\,Cl^-} + 7\,H_2O + 3\,Cl_2.$$

or $\quad Cr_2O_7^{-2} + 14\,H^+ + 6\ Cl^- \rightarrow 2\ Cr^{+3} + 7\,H_2O + 3\,Cl_2.$

The ions canceled served no function in the oxidation-reduction process.

**Example 14.9.**  Balance the reaction:

$$Na_2TeO_3 + NaI + HCl \rightarrow NaCl + H_2O + Te + I_2.$$

**Solution.**

**Step 1.** $TeO_3^{-2} \rightarrow Te.$
$\qquad\qquad\quad I^- \rightarrow I_2.$

**Step 2.** $\qquad TeO_3^{-2} + 6\,H^+ + 4e^- \rightarrow Te + 3\,H_2O.$
$\qquad\qquad\qquad\qquad 2\,I^- \rightarrow I_2 + 2e^-.$

**Step 3.** $\qquad\qquad\qquad 4\,I^- \rightarrow 2\,I_2 + 4e^-.$

**Step 4.** $TeO_3^{-2} + 6\,H^+ + \cancel{4e^-} + 4\,I^- \rightarrow Te + 3\,H_2O + 2\,I_2 + \cancel{4e^-}$

or $\qquad\qquad TeO_3^{-2} + 6\,H^+ + 4\,I^- \rightarrow Te + 3\,H_2O + 2\,I_2.$

## Problems

### Part I

14.1. Show how the equation in Example 14.9 may be obtained from the equation in Example 14.5.

14.2. Given:

$$KMnO_4 + HCl \rightarrow KCl + MnCl_2 + H_2O + Cl_2.$$

a. Write the equation using change in oxidation state.
b. Write the equation using the ion-electron method.
c. Show that the two are identical equations.

14.3. Balance the following in terms of atoms and electrons:
a. $Sn^{+2} \rightarrow Sn^{+4}.$
b. $I^- \rightarrow I_2.$
c. $H_2O_2 \rightarrow O_2 + H^+.$
d. $H_2O + Mn^{+2} \rightarrow MnO_2 + H^+.$
e. $ClO_3^- + H^+ \rightarrow Cl_2 + H_2O.$
f. $ClO_3^- + H^+ \rightarrow Cl^- + H_2O.$

14.4. Balance the following reactions using change in oxidation state:
a. $PbO_2 + HCl \rightarrow PbCl_2 + Cl_2 + H_2O.$
b. $CuS + HNO_3 \rightarrow Cu(NO_3)_2 + S + H_2O + NO.$
c. $KMnO_4 + Na_2SO_3 + H_2O \rightarrow MnO_2 + Na_2SO_4 + KOH.$

d. $K_2Cr_2O_7 + NO_2 + HNO_3 \rightarrow KNO_3 + Cr(NO_3)_3 + H_2O$.

14.5. Balance the following reactions using the ion-electron method:

a. $Cu + HNO_3 \rightarrow Cu(NO_3)_2 + H_2O + NO$.

b. $Cu + HNO_3 \rightarrow Cu(NO_3)_2 + H_2O + NO_2$.

c. $KMnO_4 + H_2SO_4 + H_2S \rightarrow K_2SO_4 + MnSO_4 + H_2O + S$.

d. $Zn + NaOH + NaNO_3 \rightarrow Na_2ZnO_2 + NH_3 + H_2O$.

## Part II

14.6. Balance the reactions in problem 14.4 using the ion-electron method.

14.7. Balance the reactions in problem 14.5 using change in oxidation state.

14.8. Balance the following in terms of atoms and electrons:

a. $Cr^{+6} \rightarrow Cr^{+3}$.

b. $CrO_4^{-2} + H^+ \rightarrow Cr^{+3} + H_2O$.

c. $BrO_3^- + H^+ \rightarrow Br_2 + H_2O$.

d. $MnO_2 + H^+ \rightarrow Mn^{+2} + H_2O$.

e. $NO_3^- + H^+ \rightarrow NO + H_2O$.

f. $NO_3^- + H^+ \rightarrow NO_2 + H_2O$.

g. $N^{+5} \rightarrow N^{-3}$.

h. $S_2O_3^{-2} \rightarrow S_4O_6^{-2}$.

i. $N^{+5} \rightarrow N^{+3}$.

j. $I_2 + H_2O \rightarrow IO_3^- + H^+$.

14.9. Balance the following reactions (1) by change in oxidation state, (2) by the ion-electron method, and (3) show that in each case the two equations are identical:

a. $As_2S_5 + HNO_3 \rightarrow H_3AsO_4 + H_2SO_4 + H_2O + NO_2$.

b. $CdS + I_2 + HCl \rightarrow CdCl_2 + HII + S$.

c. $CrI_3 + KOH + Cl_2 \rightarrow K_2CrO_4 + KIO_4 + KCl + H_2O$.

d. $HNO_3 + I_2 \rightarrow HIO_3 + NO_2 + H_2O$.

14.10. Convert the following to the molecular form; then write the equation by the change in oxidation number:

a. $Cr_2O_7^{-2} + H^+ + H_2SO_3 \rightarrow Cr^{+3} + H_2SO_4 + H_2O$.

b. $NO_3^- + H^+ + Cl^- \rightarrow NO + H_2O + Cl_2$.

c. $Zn + NO_3^- + H^+ \rightarrow Zn^{+2} + NH_3 + H_2O$.

d. $Cu + NO_3^- + H^+ \rightarrow Cu^{+2} + NO + H_2O$.

14.11. Balance the following reactions by the ion-electron method:

a. $Zn + HNO_3 \rightarrow Zn(NO_3)_2 + NH_4NO_3 + H_2O$.

b. $KMnO_4 + H_2O_2 + H_2SO_4 \rightarrow KHSO_4 + MnSO_4 + H_2O + O_2$.

c. $Ag + HNO_3 \rightarrow AgNO_3 + NO + H_2O$.

d. $Ag + HNO_3 \rightarrow AgNO_3 + NO_2 + H_2O$.

14.12. Balance the following reactions by the ion-electron method:

a. $MnO_4^- + H_2O_2 + H^+ \rightarrow Mn^{+2} + H_2O + O_2$.

b. $S^{-2} + H_2O_2 \rightarrow SO_4^{-2} + H_2O$.

c. $MnO_2 + H^+ \rightarrow Mn^{+2} + H_2O + Cl_2$.

    d. $S_2O_3^{-2} + I_2 \rightarrow S_4O_6^{-2} + I^-$.

14.13. Balance the reactions in problem 14.11 using the change in oxidation number.

14.14. Balance the reactions in problem 14.12 using the change in oxidation number.

14.15. Show how the equation in Example 14.6 may be obtained from the equation in Example 14.2.

14.16. Show how the equation in Example 14.7 may be obtained from the equation in Example 14.3.

14.17. What are the partial equations (half-reactions) for each of the following?

    a. $Al + CuSO_4 \rightarrow Al_2(SO_4)_3 + Cu$.

    b. $I + H_2S \rightarrow HI + S$.

    c. $FeCl_3 + SnCl_2 \rightarrow FeCl_2 + SnCl_4$.

    d. $FeCl_3 + H_2S \rightarrow FeCl_2 + HCl + S$.

14.18. Balance the following reactions:

    a. $Bi(OH)_3 + Na_2SnO_2 \rightarrow Na_2SnO_3 + H_2O + Bi$.

    b. $Br_2 + SO_2 + H_2O \rightarrow H_2SO_4 + HBr$.

    c. $H_2SO_3 + HNO_3 \rightarrow H_2SO_4 + H_2O + NO$.

    d. $KClO_3 + Na_2SnO_2 \rightarrow KCl + Na_2SnO_3$.

14.19. Balance the following reactions:

    a. $KClO_3 + H_2SO_4 + FeSO_4 \rightarrow Fe_2(SO_4)_3 + KCl + H_2O$.

    b. $KClO_3 + HCl + SnCl_2 \rightarrow SnCl_4 + KCl + H_2O$.

    c. $Na_2SO_3 + Br_2 + H_2O \rightarrow Na_2SO_4 + HBr$.

    d. $KMnO_4 + HCl + FeCl_2 \rightarrow FeCl_3 + MnCl_2 + KCl + H_2O$.

14.20. Balance the following reactions:

    a. $Cr_2O_7^{-2} + I^- + H^+ \rightarrow Cr^{+3} + H_2O + I_2$.

    b. $CrO_4^{-2} + S^{-2} + H^+ \rightarrow Cr^{+3} + H_2O + S$.

    c. $IO_3^- + I^- + H^+ \rightarrow H_2O + I_2$.

    d. $MnO_4^- + H_2O_2 + H^+ \rightarrow Mn^{+2} + H_2O + O_2$.

# 15
# Solutions

Many chemical reactions take place in water solution. In order to treat solutions quantitatively it is necessary to set up standards for representing the strengths of solutions. Most of the previous discussions have involved weight relationships between reactants and products, which are appropriately termed *gravimetric methods*. When solutions are involved, the term *volumetric methods* applies.

**15.1. Standard Solutions.** A *standard solution* is one the strength of which is known. That is, the amounts of solute and solvent in a given quantity of solution are known. A number of methods for expressing standard solutions have already been discussed, such as percentage by weight and by volume. Four other methods in common use for expressing the strengths of solutions are: (1) mole fraction, (2) molarity, (3) molality, and (4) normality.

**15.2. Strengths of Solutions Expressed as Mole Fractions.** *Mole fraction*, $N_x$, is defined as the fractional part of the total number of moles in a solution contributed by each component, $x$, of that solution.

**Example 15.1.** A given solution contains 100 g. of salt, NaCl, and 900 g. of water. What are the mole fractions of the components of the solution?

**Solution.** Since the unit of concentration must be the mole, each of the given quantities of the components must be changed to moles. Then:

$$100 \text{ g. NaCl} = 100 \text{ g.} \div 58.45 \frac{\text{g.}}{\text{mole}} = 1.71 \text{ moles of NaCl.}$$

$$900 \text{ g. H}_2\text{O} = 900 \text{ g.} \div 18.02 \frac{\text{g.}}{\text{mole}} = 49.94 \text{ moles of H}_2\text{O.}$$

$$\text{Total} = \overline{51.65 \text{ moles.}}$$

Therefore, by definition:

$$\text{Mole fraction of NaCl} = N_{\text{NaCl}} = \frac{1.71}{51.65} = 0.0331.$$

$$\text{Mole fraction of } H_2O \; = N_{H_2O} = \frac{49.94}{51.65} = 0.9669.$$

$$N_{NaCl} + N_{H_2O} = 1.0000.$$

Observe that the sum of the mole fractions of the components of a given solution equals one.

Mole fraction is an important method of expressing concentrations since it represents the ratio of particles of the components in the solution, a factor upon which many physical and chemical properties of solutions depend.

**Example 15.2.** Given that $N_{KOH} = 0.100$ for a water solution of potassium hydroxide, how many grams of KOH are there in 25.0 g. of the solution?

**Solution.**

Since      $N_{KOH} + N_{H_2O} = 1.000,$

then             $N_{H_2O} = 1.000 - 0.100 = 0.900.$

That is,     $\dfrac{\text{moles KOH}}{\text{moles } H_2O} = \dfrac{0.100}{0.900}$

and       $\dfrac{\text{g. KOH}}{\text{g. } H_2O} = \dfrac{0.100 \times 56.1 = 5.61 \text{ g. KOH}}{0.900 \times 18.0 = 16.2 \text{ g. } H_2O}.$

Let             $x = $ g. of KOH in 25.0 g. of solution.

Then       $25.0 - x = $ g. of $H_2O$ in 25.0 g. of solution,

and      $\dfrac{5.61 \text{ g. KOH}}{16.2 \text{ g. } H_2O} = \dfrac{x \text{ g. KOH}}{(25.0 - x) \text{ g. } H_2O}$

or            $218\,x = 1403$

and          $x = 6.44$ g. KOH in 25.0 g. of solution.

**15.3. Strengths of Solutions Expressed as Molarity.** *Molarity*, M, is defined as the number of moles of solute contained in one liter of solution. A one-molar, 1M, solution of NaCl, therefore, contains 58.454 g. of NaCl dissolved in sufficient water to make one liter of solution.

**Example 15.3.** How many grams of NaOH would be required to prepare five liters of 0.100M solution?

**Solution.**

Since    1.00 $l$. of 1M NaOH      $= 40.005$ g. NaOH,

then    1.00 $l$. of 0.100M NaOH $= 40.005 \times 0.100 = $  4.001 g. NaOH,

and     5.00 $l$. of 0.100M NaOH $= $  4.001 $\times$ 5.00  $= 20.005$ g. NaOH.

**Example 15.4.** Calculate the molarity of a solution containing 8.82 g. of HCl in 100 ml. of solution.

**Solution.** By definition, the molarity is the number of moles of HCl per liter of solution. Therefore:

$$\frac{100 \text{ ml. solution}}{8.82 \text{ g. HCl}} = \frac{1000 \text{ ml. solution}}{x \text{ g. HCl}}$$

or $\quad\quad\quad\quad\quad\quad\quad x = 88.2$ g. HCl per liter of solution.

Since $\quad\quad\quad 1.00$ mole HCl $= 36.465$ g.,

then $\quad\quad 88.2$ g̸. $\div 36.465 \dfrac{g̸.}{\text{mole}} = 2.42$ moles HCl per liter.

That is, the above solution is 2.42M with respect to HCl.

**Example 15.5.** How many grams of $Al_2(SO_4)_3$ are there in 300 ml. of 1.50M solution?

**Solution.**

Since $\quad 1.00$ *l.* of 1M $Al_2(SO_4)_3 \quad\quad = 342.14$ g. $Al_2(SO_4)_3$,

then $\quad 1.00$ *l.* of 1.5M $Al_2(SO_4)_3 \quad = 342.14 \times 1.5 = 513.21$ g. $Al_2(SO_4)_3$,

and $\quad 0.300$ *l.* of 1.5M $Al_2(SO_4)_3 = 513.21 \times 0.300 = 154.0$ g. $Al_2(SO_4)_3$.

**15.4. Strengths of Solutions Expressed as Molality.** *Molality*, m, is defined as the number of moles of solute per 1000 grams of solvent. A one-molal, 1m, solution of NaCl contains 58.454 g. of NaCl dissolved in 1000 g. of water.

**Example 15.6.** How many grams of NaOH would have to be added to 5000 grams of water to prepare a 0.1000m solution?

**Solution.**

Since $\quad 40.005$ g. of NaOH added to 1000 g. of $H_2O = 1.00$m solution, then:

$40.005 \times 0.100 = 4.001$ g. NaOH added to 1000 g. $H_2O = 0.100$m solution, and $5 \times 4.001 = 20.005$ g. NaOH must be added to 5000 g. of water to produce the required solution.

**Example 15.7.** Calculate the molality of a solution containing 8.82 g. of HCl dissolved in 100 g. of water.

**Solution.** The molality is the number of moles of HCl dissolved in 1000 g. of water. Therefore:

$$\frac{100 \text{ g. } H_2O}{8.82 \text{ g. HCl}} = \frac{1000 \text{ g. } H_2O}{x \text{ g. HCl}}$$

or $\quad\quad\quad\quad\quad\quad x = 88.2$ g. HCl per 1000 g. $H_2O$.

Then $\quad\quad\quad 8.82 \div 36.465 = 2.42$ moles HCl per 1000 g. $H_2O$.

That is, the above solution is 2.42m with respect to HCl.

**Example 15.8.** How many grams of aluminum sulfate, $Al_2(SO_4)_3$, are there in 300 ml. of 1.50m solution, the density of which is 1.40 g. per ml.?

**Solution.**

$$1.50m \ Al_2(SO_4)_3 = 513 \text{ g. } Al_2(SO_4)_3 + 1000 \text{ g. } H_2O$$
$$= 1513 \text{ g. of solution,}$$

and　　　　　300 ml. of 1.50m $Al_2(SO_4)_3$ weighs $300 \times 1.40 = 420$ g.

Let　　　　　　　　　$x = $ g. of $Al_2(SO_4)_3$ in 420 g. of solution.

Then　　$\dfrac{513 \text{ g. } Al_2(SO_4)_3}{1513 \text{ g. solution}} = \dfrac{x \text{ g. } Al_2(SO_4)_3}{420 \text{ g. solution}}$

or　　　　　　　　　$x = 142$ g. $Al_2(SO_4)_3$ in 300 ml. of solution.

**15.5. Strengths of Solutions Expressed as Normality.** *Normality*, N, is defined as the number of gram-equivalent weights of a substance per liter of solution. That is:

$$\text{Normality} = \frac{\text{gram-equivalent weights}}{\text{liters of solution}}$$

or　　　　　　　　　$N = \dfrac{E}{V}.$

The concept of normality may be applied to acids, bases, and salts.

**15.6. The Gram-equivalent Weights of Acids and Bases.** The gram-equivalent weight of an acid or a base is equal numerically to the formula weight divided by the sum of the positive (or negative) charges represented by the formula. That is:

$$1.00 \text{ g.-equivalent weight} = \frac{\text{formula weight}}{\text{sum of positive charges}}.$$

**Example 15.9.** How many grams are there in 1.00 g.-equivalent weight of (a) HCl, (b) $H_2SO_4$, (c) KOH, and (d) $Ca(OH)_2$?

**Solution.**

(a) In HCl there is $1+$ and $1-$ charge. Therefore:

$$1.00 \text{ g.-equivalent weight of HCl} = \frac{36.47}{1} = 36.47 \text{ g.}$$

(b) In $H_2SO_4$ there are $2+$ and $2-$ charges. Therefore:

$$1.00 \text{ g.-equivalent weight of } H_2SO_4 = \frac{98.08}{2} = 49.04 \text{ g.}$$

(c) In KOH there is $1+$ and $1-$ charge. Therefore:

$$1.00 \text{ g.-equivalent weight of KOH} = \frac{56.11}{1} = 56.11 \text{ g.}$$

(d) In $Ca(OH)_2$ there are $2+$ and $2-$ charges. Therefore:

$$1.00 \text{ g.-equivalent weight of } Ca(OH)_2 = \frac{74.10}{2} = 37.05 \text{ g.}$$

In a neutralization reaction one gram-equivalent weight of an acid will neutralize one gram-equivalent weight of a base. That is, acids and bases react in equal gram-equivalent quantities as shown in the following equations. This is the principal value of the concept of normality.

$$
\begin{array}{cccc}
NaOH & + & HCl & \rightarrow & NaCl & + H_2O. \\
40.0 \text{ g.} & & 36.5 \text{ g.} & & 58.5 \text{ g.} \\
1.00 \text{ g.-eq. wt.} & & 1.00 \text{ g.-eq. wt.} & & 1.00 \text{ g.-eq. wt.}
\end{array}
$$

$$
\begin{array}{cccc}
2\,NaOH & + & H_2SO_4 & \rightarrow & Na_2SO_4 & + 2\,H_2O. \\
80.0 \text{ g.} & & 98.1 \text{ g.} & & 142.1 \text{ g.} \\
2.00 \text{ g.-eq. wt.} & & 2.00 \text{ g.-eq. wt.} & & 2.00 \text{ g.-eq. wt.}
\end{array}
$$

$$
\begin{array}{cccc}
Al(OH)_3 & + & 3\,HCl & \rightarrow & AlCl_3 & + 3\,H_2O. \\
78.0 \text{ g.} & & 109.4 \text{ g.} & & 133.4 \text{ g.} \\
3.00 \text{ g.-eq. wt.} & & 3.00 \text{ g.-eq. wt.} & & 3.00 \text{ g.-eq. wt.}
\end{array}
$$

**15.7. The Gram-equivalent Weights of Salts.** The gram-equivalent weight of a salt is dependent upon its role as a reactant in a particular equation. In reactions of metathesis, where no change in oxidation state is involved, the gram-equivalent weight of a salt is determined in the same manner as are those of acids and bases.

**Example 15.10.** How many grams are there in one gram-equivalent weight of (a) NaCl, (b) $Na_2SO_4$, and (c) $AlCl_3$, based on the equations of neutralization given in Sec. 15.6?

**Solution.** Proceeding as in Example 15.9:

(a) $1.00 \text{ g.-eq. wt. of } NaCl = \dfrac{58.5}{1} = 58.5 \text{ g.}$

(b) $1.00 \text{ g.-eq. wt. of } Na_2SO_4 = \dfrac{142.1}{2} = 71.1 \text{ g.}$

(c) $1.00 \text{ g.-eq. wt. of } AlCl_3 = \dfrac{133.4}{3} = 44.5 \text{ g.}$

Observe that, in neutralization equations, the equivalents of acid, base, and salt involved in a given reaction are equal numerically.

The concept of normality, as applied to salts, finds its greatest use in oxidation-reduction reactions. One gram-equivalent weight of an oxidant or reductant is equal to the formula weight divided by the sum of the change in oxidation number of the atoms in the formula of the oxidant or reductant.

**Example 15.11.** How many grams are there in 1.00 gram-equivalent weight of both oxidant and reductant in each of the following reactions?

(a) $HNO_3 + H_2S \rightarrow H_2O + NO + S$.

(b) $HNO_3 + Cu \rightarrow Cu(NO_3)_2 + NO_2 + O_2$.

(c) $KMnO_4 + FeSO_4 + H_2SO_4 \rightarrow K_2SO_4 + MnSO_4 + Fe_2(SO_4)_3 + H_2O$.

(d) $K_2Cr_2O_7 + HCl \rightarrow KCl + CrCl_3 + H_2O + Cl_2$.

**Solution.** Only the reactants and products need be known. It is not necessary to write the equation. Also, the answers may be obtained using either the molecular or ionic expressions as given in Chapter 14.

$$\begin{array}{cccc} (+5) & (+2) & (+5) & (+2) \end{array}$$

(a) Oxidant: $HNO_3 \rightarrow NO$  or  $NO_3^- \rightarrow NO$. Therefore:

$$1.00 \text{ g.-eq. wt. of } HNO_3 = \frac{63.02}{3} = 21.01 \text{ g.}$$

$$\begin{array}{cc} (-2) & (0) \end{array}$$

Reductant: $H_2S \rightarrow S$. Therefore:

$$1.00 \text{ g.-eq. wt. of } H_2S = \frac{34.09}{2} = 17.05 \text{ g.}$$

$$\begin{array}{cccc} (+5) & (+4) & (+5) & (+4) \end{array}$$

(b) Oxidant: $HNO_3 \rightarrow NO_2$  or  $NO_3^- \rightarrow NO_2$. Therefore:

$$1.00 \text{ g.-eq. wt. of } HNO_3 = \frac{63.02}{1} = 63.02 \text{ g.}$$

$$\begin{array}{cccc} (0) & (+2) & (0) & (+2) \end{array}$$

Reductant: $Cu \rightarrow Cu(NO_3)_2$  or  $Cu \rightarrow Cu$. Therefore:

$$1.00 \text{ g.-eq. wt. of } Cu = \frac{63.54}{2} = 31.77 \text{ g.}$$

$$\begin{array}{cccc} (+7) & (+2) & (+7) & (+2) \end{array}$$

(c) Oxidant: $KMnO_4 \rightarrow MnSO_4$  or  $MnO_4^- \rightarrow Mn$. Therefore:

$$1.00 \text{ g.-eq. wt. of } KMnO_4 = \frac{158.04}{5} = 31.61 \text{ g.}$$

$$\begin{array}{cccc} (+2) & (+3) & (+2) & (+3) \end{array}$$

Reductant: $FeSO_4 \rightarrow Fe_2(SO_4)_3$  or  $Fe \rightarrow Fe$. Therefore:

$$1.00 \text{ g.-eq. wt. of } FeSO_4 = \frac{151.92}{1} = 151.92 \text{ g.}$$

$$\begin{array}{cccc} 2(+6) & 2(+3) & 2(+6) & 2(+3) \end{array}$$

(d) Oxidant: $K_2Cr_2O_7 \rightarrow CrCl_3$  or  $Cr_2O_7^{-2} \rightarrow Cr$. Therefore:

$$1.00 \text{ g.-eq. wt. of } K_2Cr_2O_7 = \frac{294.21}{6} = 49.04 \text{ g.}$$

$$(-1) \quad (0) \qquad (-1) \quad (0)$$

Reductant: $HCl \rightarrow Cl_2$ or $Cl^- \rightarrow Cl_2$. Therefore:

$$1.00 \text{ g.-eq. wt. of } HCl = \frac{36.47}{1} = 36.47 \text{ g.}$$

As in neutralization reactions, equal gram-equivalent quantities of oxidants and reductants react, as shown in the equation for Example 15.11c.

$$2\,KMnO_4 + 10\,FeSO_4 + 8\,H_2SO_4 \rightarrow K_2SO_4 + 2\,MnSO_4 + 5\,Fe_2(SO_4)_3 + 8\,H_2O.$$

| 316.06 g. | 151.91 g. |
|-----------|-----------|
| 10 g.-eq. | 10 g.-eq. |
| wt.       | wt.       |

## 15.8. Solved Problems Involving Normality.

**Example 15.12.** Sufficient water was added to 100 g. of NaOH to make one liter of solution. What was the normality of the solution?

**Solution.** In the formula $N = \frac{E}{V}$:

$$E = \frac{100 \text{ g.}}{40 \dfrac{\text{g.}}{\text{g.-eq.-wt.}}} = 2.5 \text{ gram-equivalent weights,}$$

and    $V = 1.0$ liter. Therefore:

$$N = \frac{2.5 \text{ g.-eq.-wt.}}{1.0 \text{ } l.} = 2.5 = \text{the normality of the solution.}$$

**Example 15.13.** How much $Ca(OH)_2$ must be dissolved in water to prepare five liters of 0.050N solution?

**Solution.** $N = 0.050$ and $V = 5.0$. Therefore:

$$E = NV = (0.050)(5) = 0.25 \text{ gram-equivalent of } Ca(OH)_2.$$

Since          37.05 g. $Ca(OH)_2$ = one gram-equivalent weight,

then  $37.05 \times 0.25 = 9.263$ g. $Ca(OH)_2$ is needed to prepare the solution.

**Example 15.14.** What is the normality of a solution containing 35.0 g. of KOH dissolved in sufficient water to make 400 ml. of solution?

**Solution.** $E = 35.0 \div 56.10 = 0.624$ and $V = 0.400$. Therefore:

$$N = \frac{0.624}{0.400} = 1.56 = \text{the normality of the solution.}$$

**Example 15.15.** How many gram-equivalent weights of solute are there in 400 ml. of 6.00M $H_2SO_4$?

**Solution.**

1.00 $l$. of 1.00M $H_2SO_4$ =   2.00 g.-eq.-wt.

1.00 $l$. of 6.00M $H_2SO_4$ = 12.00 g.-eq.-wt.   Therefore:

0.400 $l$. of 6.00M $H_2SO_4$ =   0.40 $\times$ 12 = 4.8 g.-eq. wt. of $H_2SO_4$.

**Example 15.16.** How many grams of $KMnO_4$ would be required to prepare 2500 ml. of 0.010N solution, based on the reaction:

$$MnO_4^- + Fe^{+2} \rightarrow Mn^{+2} + Fe^{+3}?$$

$(+7)$

**Solution.** $MnO_4^- \rightarrow Mn^{+2}$.   Therefore:

1.00 g.-eq. wt. of $KMnO_4 = \frac{158}{5} = 31.6$ g.

1.00 $l$. of 1.00N $KMnO_4$   = 31.6 g.

1.00 $l$. of 0.010N $KMnO_4$ = 31.6 $\times$ 0.01 = 0.316 g.

2.50 $l$. of 0.010N $KMnO_4$ = 0.316 $\times$ 2.50 = 0.790 g.

**Example 15.17.** What would be the normality of the solution obtained by diluting 100 ml. of 12.0N HCl to a volume of one liter?

**Solution.** The solution was diluted $\frac{1000}{10} = 10$ times.   The resultant solution therefore will be $\frac{1}{10}$ as strong as the original solution, or:

$$\tfrac{12}{10} = 1.2N.$$

**Example 15.18.** How many milligrams of $Cu^{+2}$ ion are there in 1.00 ml. of 1.00N cupric sulfate solution?

**Solution.** 1.00 $l$. of 1.00N $CuSO_4$ contains 1.00 g.-eq. wt. of $CuSO_4$, and 1.00 g.-eq. wt. of $CuSO_4$ contains 1.00 g.-eq. wt. of $Cu^{+2}$ ion + 1.00 g.-eq. wt. of $SO_4^{-2}$ ion.

$$1.00 \text{ g.-eq. wt. of } Cu^{+2} \text{ ion} = \frac{63.54}{2} = 31.77 \text{ g.}$$

and 31.77 g. of $Cu^{+2}$ = 31,770 mg. That is, 1.00 $l$. of 1.00N $CuSO_4$ = 31,770 mg. of $Cu^{+2}$ ion or 1.00 ml. of 1.00N $CuSO_4$ = $\frac{31,770}{1000}$ = 31.77 mg. of $Cu^{+2}$ ion.

**Example 15.19.** How many milligram-equivalent weights of $Na^+$ ion are there in 1.00 ml. of a solution containing 50.0 g. of NaCl per liter?

**Solution.** One milligram-equivalent weight is $\frac{1}{1000}$ part of one gram-equivalent weight.   That is:

$$1.00 \text{ g.-eq. wt.} = 1000 \text{ mg.-eq. wt.}$$

$$50.0 \text{ g. of NaCl} = \frac{50.0}{58.5} = 0.855 \text{ g.-eq. wt.}$$

and 0.855 g.-eq. wt. of NaCl contains 0.855 g.-eq. wt. of $Na^+$ ion + 0.855 g.-eq. wt. of $Cl^-$ ion.

Also        0.855 g.-eq. wt. of $Na^+$ ion = 855 mg.-eq. wt. of $Na^+$ ion.

Then        1.00 *l*. of solution contains 855 mg.-eq. wt. of $Na^+$ ion,

and   1.00 ml. of solution will contain $\frac{855}{1000} = 0.855$ mg.-eq. wt. of $Na^+$ ion.

**Example 15.20.** An excess of silver nitrate solution was added to 25.0 ml. of an HCl solution of unknown strength. The precipitated AgCl weighed 2.125 g. What was the normality of the HCl solution?

**Solution.** From the equation:

$$AgNO_3 + \quad HCl \quad \rightarrow \quad AgCl \downarrow \quad + HNO_3,$$
$$\text{1.00 g.-eq. wt.} \quad \text{1.00 g.-eq. wt.}$$

we see that equal numbers of gram-equivalent weights of HCl and AgCl are represented in the equation. Therefore, the number of gram-equivalent weights in 2.125 g. of AgCl would also be the number of gram-equivalent weights of HCl in the 25.0 ml. of solution. Then:

$$\frac{2.125}{169.9} = 0.0125 \text{ g.-eq. wt. of AgCl and of HCl.}$$

That is, 25.0 ml. of the HCl solution contains 0.0125 g.-eq. wt. of HCl. Therefore:

$$\text{Normality of HCl} = \frac{0.0125}{0.025} = 0.500.$$

## Problems

### Part I

15.1. A water solution contains 8.00 per cent sugar by weight and has a density of 1.03 g. per ml. How many grams of sugar are there in 400 ml. of the solution?               *Ans.* 33.0 g.

15.2. Concentrated hydrochloric acid has a density of 1.20 g. per ml. and is 35.0 per cent HCl by weight. What is the mole fraction composition of concentrated hydrochloric acid?        *Ans.* $N_{HCl} = 0.210$.

15.3. How many grams of NaCl are there in 250 ml. of a 2.50M solution?
                                                                *Ans.* 36.53 g.

15.4. What volume of 0.75M solution could be prepared from 500 g. of $Na_2SO_4$?                                    *Ans.* 4.70 *l*.

15.5. What is the molarity of a solution containing 250 g. of $CaCl_2$ in 1500 ml. of solution?                          *Ans.* 1.50M.

15.6. One liter of 12M HCl is diluted to 20 liters. What is the molarity of the diluted solution?                        *Ans.* 0.6M.

15.7. A solution contains 17.0 g. of sodium nitrate in 100 ml. of solution, the density of which is 1.10 g. per ml. Calculate:

  a. The per cent by weight of sodium nitrate.        *Ans.* 15.5%.
  b. The molarity of the solution.                    *Ans.* 2.00M.

15.8. How many milligrams each of $Na^+$ ion and $Cl^-$ ion are there in 1.00 ml. of 1.00M NaCl solution?

*Ans.* 23.0 mg. $Na^+$, 35.5 mg. $Cl^-$.

15.9. What is the molarity of a solution obtained by diluting 250 ml. of 6.0M HCl to one liter volume? *Ans.* 1.5M.

15.10. What is the molality of a solution in which 250 g. of $CaCl_2$ is dissolved in 1500 g. of water? *Ans.* 1.50m.

15.11. How many grams of water would have to be added to 1000 g. of sugar, $C_{12}H_{22}O_{11}$, in order to prepare a 1m solution? *Ans.* 2924 g.

15.12. To what volume would 10.0 ml. of 2.0M $Pb(NO_3)_2$ have to be diluted in order that the resulting solution will contain 10.0 mg. of $Pb^{+2}$ ion per milliliter? *Ans.* 414 ml.

15.13. How many grams each of $H_3PO_4$ and $Ca(OH)_2$ would be required to prepare 250 ml. of 0.100N solution? *Ans.* 0.82 g., 0.93 g.

15.14. Calculate in terms of normality and molarity the strength of a solution containing 275 g. of KOH in 800 ml. of solution.

*Ans.* 6.13N, 6.13M.

15.15. How many milliliters of 0.50N solution could be prepared from 50.0 g. of NaOH? *Ans.* 2500 ml.

15.16. What volume of $H_2SO_4$, density 1.84 g. per ml. and containing 98 per cent acid by weight, would be required to prepare one liter of 6N acid? *Ans.* 164 ml.

15.17. Concentrated HCl has a density of 1.20 g. per ml. and is 39 per cent acid by weight. What is its normality? *Ans.* 12.8N.

15.18. What volume of 1.75N KOH solution, diluted to one liter, would give a 1.00N solution of KOH? *Ans.* 571 ml.

15.19. An experiment calls for 300 ml. of 1.00N HCl. The only acid available is 6.0N HCl. How much water and 6.0N HCl must be used?

*Ans.* 250 ml. water, 50 ml. acid.

15.20. What is the strength of each of the following solutions in terms of normality?
   a. 6.00M HCl. *Ans.* 6.00N.
   b. 0.75M $CaCl_2$. *Ans.* 1.50N.
   c. 0.20M $H_2S$. *Ans.* 0.40N.

15.21. What is the gram-equivalent weight of the oxidant and reductant in the reaction:

$$Na_2SO_3 + Br_2 + H_2O \rightarrow Na_2SO_4 + HBr?$$

*Ans.* 79.92 g. $Br_2$, 63.1 g. $Na_2SO_3$.

15.22. What is the gram-equivalent weight of the oxidant and reductant in the reaction: $MnO_4^- + Fe^{+2} \rightarrow Mn^{+2} + Fe^{+3}$? Assume that $KMnO_4$ is the source of the $MnO_4^-$ ion and $FeSO_4$ the source of the $Fe^{+2}$ ion. *Ans.* 31.6 g. $KMnO_4$, 151.9 g. $FeSO_4$.

15.23. How many gram-equivalent weights of $H_2SO_4$ are there in 250 ml. of 0.15M $H_2SO_4$? *Ans.* 0.075.

15.24. How many gram-equivalent weights of $Ba^{+2}$ ion are there in 100 g. of $BaSO_4$? *Ans.* 0.857.

## Part II

15.25. Calculate the mole fraction composition of a solution containing 500 g. of $C_2H_5OH$ and 500 g. of $H_2O$.
*Ans.* $C_2H_5OH = 0.28$, $H_2O = 0.72$.

15.26. Calculate the mole fraction composition of a saturated solution of NaCl at 0° C. At 0° C., 35.7 g. of NaCl will dissolve in 100 g. of water. *Ans.* NaCl = 0.099, $H_2O = 0.901$.

15.27. An excess of silver nitrate solution was added to 10.0 g. of a solution of sodium chloride of unknown strength. The AgCl which precipitated out was found to weigh 1.22 g. What was the per cent by weight of NaCl in the solution? *Ans.* 5.0%.

15.28. How many molecules of solute are there in 100 ml. of a 0.100M solution? *Ans.* $6.0 \times 10^{21}$.

15.29. A solution of NaCl contained 30 g. of NaCl in 1500 ml. of solution. What was the molarity of the solution? *Ans.* 0.34M.

15.30. How many grams of KBr could be obtained by evaporating 50 ml. of a 0.50M solution of the salt? *Ans.* 2.98 g.

15.31. What would be the molarity of a solution in which 50 liters of HCl gas measured at standard conditions is dissolved in 2.0 liters of water? Assume no change in volume. *Ans.* 1.12M.

15.32. Calculate the molarity of a solution prepared by adding 500 ml. of water to 100 ml. of 0.60M solution. *Ans.* 0.10M.

15.33. Which solution would have the greater concentration of NaCl, a 1.00M solution of NaCl or one containing 10 per cent by weight NaCl (density 1.07 g. per ml.)? *Ans.* 10% solution.

15.34. Which of the following solutions would contain the greater number of molecules of solute, 100 ml. of 3M sugar solution or 200 ml. of 2M sugar solution? *Ans.* 2M solution.

15.35. How many grams of HCl are there in 750 ml. of 0.50M HCl?
*Ans.* 13.7 g.

15.36. What is the molarity of a solution containing 75 g. of KOH dissolved in water to make one liter of solution? *Ans.* 1.34M.

15.37. What weight of $BaCl_2$ would be required to prepare 1500 ml. of 1.50M solution? *Ans.* 469 g.

15.38. How many grams each of $Na^+$ ion and of $Cl^-$ ion are there in 500 ml. of 1.5M NaCl solution? *Ans.* 17.3 g. $Na^+$, 26.6 g. $Cl^-$.

15.39. How many milligrams each of $Na^+$ ion and $Cl^-$ ion are there in 5.00 ml. of 0.100M solution of NaCl?
*Ans.* 11.5 mg. $Na^+$, 17.8 mg. $Cl^-$.

15.40. To what volume must 100 ml. of 6.0M HCl be diluted in order that the resulting solution be 1.00M? *Ans.* 600 ml.

15.41. How many grams of $CuSO_4 \cdot 5 H_2O$ would be required to prepare 2500 ml. of 0.100M solution?          *Ans.* 62.4 g.

15.42. How many molecules of sugar are there in 1.00 ml. of a ten per cent sugar solution, density 1.20 g. per ml.?          *Ans.* $2.1 \times 10^{20}$.

15.43. What is the molarity of a solution prepared by dissolving 100 *l.* of HCl (S.C.) in sufficient water to make 800 ml. of solution?

*Ans.* 5.59M.

15.44. How many grams of calcium chloride would be required to prepare 750 ml. of a solution containing 1.00 millimole of calcium chloride per milliliter?          *Ans.* 83.3 g.

15.45. How many grams of a 5.0 per cent solution of calcium chloride would have to be evaporated in order to obtain 25.0 g. of calcium chloride as a residue?          *Ans.* 500 g.

15.46. A solution containing 10.0 mg. of $Cu^{+2}$ ion per milliliter is desired. How many grams of $CuSO_4 \cdot 5 H_2O$ must be dissolved per liter of solution in order to obtain the desired solution?          *Ans.* 39.2 g.

15.47. A 12-liter bottle is to be filled with 6.0M $H_2SO_4$. How much 18M $H_2SO_4$ must be added to the bottle before filling with water?

*Ans.* 4.0 *l.*

15.48. What is the molarity of $Fe^{+2}$ ion in a solution containing 100 g. of $FeCl_2$ per liter of solution?          *Ans.* 0.789M.

15.49. What is the concentration of $Cd^{+2}$ ion in milligrams per milliliter in a 1.00M $CdCl_2$ solution?          *Ans.* 112.4.

15.50. How many grams of KOH would be required to prepare 2.5 *l.* of 6.0M KOH solution?          *Ans.* 842 g.

15.51. At 25° C., 0.200 g. of $CaSO_4$ will dissolve in 100 ml. of solution. What is the molarity of the solution?          *Ans.* 0.0147M.

15.52. How many grams of $NH_4NO_3$ would be required to prepare 500 ml. of 0.25M solution?          *Ans.* 10.0 g.

15.53. Calculate (a) the molarity, and (b) the molality, of a solution of $K_2CO_3$ which contains 22 per cent of the salt by weight and has a density of 1.21 g. per ml.          *Ans.* (a) 1.93M; (b) 2.04m.

15.54. The acid solution in a fully charged lead storage cell contains 33 per cent $H_2SO_4$ by weight and has a density of 1.25 g. per ml. Calculate (a) the mole fraction composition, (b) the molarity, and (c) the molality of the acid solution.

*Ans.* (a) $N_{H_2O} = 0.917$; (b) 4.21M; (c) 5.02m.

15.55. How many molecules of sugar would there be in 1.00 ml. of 1.00M solution?          *Ans.* $6.024 \times 10^{20}$.

15.56. How many grams of $CuSO_4 \cdot 5 H_2O$ would be required to prepare one liter of 2.0M $CuSO_4$ solution?          *Ans.* 499.4 g.

15.57. What is the molarity of a solution containing 25.0 g. of $K_2CrO_4$ dissolved in water to make 300 ml. of solution?          *Ans.* 0.429M.

15.58. Make a table showing the number of grams of each of the following compounds required to make one liter of 1.0M, 1.0N, 2.0N, and 3.0N solutions: NaOH, $Ca(OH)_2$, $Al(OH)_3$, HCl, $H_2SO_4$, and $H_3PO_4$. *Ans.* NaOH 40.0, 40.0, 80.0, 120.0; $Ca(OH)_2$ 74.1, 37.1, 74.1, 111.2; $Al(OH)_3$ 78.0, 26.0, 52.0, 78.0; HCl 36.5, 36.5, 72.9, 109.4; $H_2SO_4$ 98.1, 49.0, 98.1, 147.1; $H_3PO_4$ 98.0, 32.7, 65.3, 98.0.

15.59. Concentrated $NH_4OH$ has a density of 0.90 g. per ml. and is 28 per cent $NH_3$ by weight. What is its normality? *Ans.* 15N.

15.60. Water was added to 25.0 ml. of 98 per cent $H_2SO_4$, density 1.84 g. per ml., to make 100 ml. of solution. Calculate the normality and molarity of the solution. *Ans.* 9.20N, 4.60M.

15.61. How many grams of zinc would be dissolved by the action of one liter of 1.00N HCl? *Ans.* 32.69 g.

15.62. How many liters of $CO_2$, measured at standard conditions, would be liberated by the action of 1500 ml. of 2N $H_2SO_4$ on $CaCO_3$?
*Ans.* 33.6 *l.*

15.63. It was found that 0.3031 g. of Mg required 27.40 ml. of 0.910N HCl to react to form $MgCl_2$. Calculate the atomic weight of magnesium, knowing that it is approximately 25. *Ans.* 24.32.

15.64. How many grams are there in 2.50 gram-equivalent weights of $BaCl_2 \cdot 2 H_2O$? *Ans.* 306 g.

15.65. A five per cent solution of phosphoric acid, $H_3PO_4$, has a density of 1.03 g. per ml. What is the strength of the solution in terms of normality? *Ans.* 1.57N.

15.66. What is the per cent by weight of $NH_3$ in 12.0N $NH_4OH$, the density being 0.90 g. per ml.? *Ans.* 22.7%.

15.67. How many gram-equivalent weights of $Fe^{+3}$ ion are there in 100 g. of $FeCl_3$? *Ans.* 1.85.

15.68. What is the normality of the $Ba^{+2}$ ion in a solution containing 20.0 mg. of $Ba^{+2}$ ion per milliliter? *Ans.* 0.291N.

15.69. How many milligram-equivalent weights of HCl are there in 1.00 ml. of 6.0N HCl? *Ans.* 6.0.

15.70. What is the normality of a solution prepared by dissolving 20.0 g. of $Na_2CO_3$ in sufficient water to make 600 ml. of solution?
*Ans.* 0.629N.

15.71. What is the normality of a solution of $AgNO_3$ containing 10.0 mg. of $Ag^+$ ion per milliliter? *Ans.* 0.0926N.

15.72. How many grams of $KMnO_4$ per liter of solution would be required to prepare 0.01N $KMnO_4$ based upon each of the reactions:
a. $MnO_4^- + Fe^{+2} \rightarrow Mn^{+2} + Fe^{+3}$. *Ans.* 0.316 g.
b. $KMnO_4 + KOH \rightarrow K_2MnO_4 + H_2O$. *Ans.* 1.58 g.

15.73. How many milligrams of $Al^{+3}$ ion are there in 1.00 ml. of 0.25N $AlCl_3 \cdot 6 H_2O$? *Ans.* 2.25 mg.

15.74. How many $Al^{+3}$ ions and how many $Cl^-$ ions are there in 1.00 ml. of 0.001N $AlCl_3 \cdot 6 H_2O$? *Ans.* $2.0 \times 10^{17}$ $Al^{+3}$, $6.0 \times 10^{17}$ $Cl^-$.

15.75. A $K_2Cr_2O_7$ solution was prepared by dissolving 10.0 g. of $K_2Cr_2O_7$ in sufficient water to make one liter of solution. What was the normality of the solution based on the reaction:

$$Cr_2O_7^{-2} + Fe^{+2} \rightarrow Cr^{+3} + Fe^{+3}?$$

*Ans.* 0.204N.

15.76. How many gram-equivalent weights of $HNO_3$ are there in 1500 ml. of 0.80N $HNO_3$?          *Ans.* 1.2.

15.77. How many gram-equivalent weights of $KClO_3$ are there in 2500 ml. of a 0.100N solution?          *Ans.* 0.25.

15.78. How many milligram-equivalent weights of solute are there in 0.25 ml. of 0.100N solution?          *Ans.* 0.025.

15.79. With how many grams of zinc will 250 ml. of 6.00N HCl react?

*Ans.* 49.0 g.

15.80. With how many grams of CuS will 50.0 ml. of 3.0M $HNO_3$ react according to the reaction:

$$CuS + HNO_3 \rightarrow Cu(NO_3)_2 + S + H_2O + NO?$$

*Ans.* 5.38 g.

# 16

# Volumetric Analysis

Methods for expressing the strengths of solutions in terms of the solute and solvent were discussed in Chapter 15. Use will now be made of these methods, particularly normality. *Titration* is the process of analyzing a substance by determining the volume of a standard solution required to react with a known amount of the substance. For each titration some method must be available for determining the end point of the chemical reaction taking place in the solution. Many indicators are known for acid-base titration; the change in color of a reactant may indicate the end point; and electrical methods are used extensively in industry.

**16.1. Arithmetical Calculations.** In Sec. 15.5 normality, N, was defined as the number of gram-equivalent weights of solute per liter of solution. That is, $N = \dfrac{E}{V}$. At the end point of a titration the same number of gram-equivalent weights of reactants have been involved. That is:

$$E_A = E_B,$$

where A and B are the reactants. Also:

$$N_A = \frac{E_A}{V_A} \quad \text{and} \quad N_B = \frac{E_B}{V_B},$$

or $\qquad\qquad E_A = N_A V_A \quad \text{and} \quad E_B = N_B V_B.$

Therefore, at the end point:

$$N_A V_A = N_B V_B.$$

When V is given in liters the product NV represents gram-equivalent weights of reactant. When V is given in milliliters the product NV represents milligram-equivalent weights of reactant.

It is seldom necessary to write the equation for the chemical reaction taking place during titration. For the sake of better understanding the examples which follow and the problems, it is suggested that the equations be written.

**16.2. Titration of Acids and Bases.** Chemical indicators are commonly used to determine the end point in an acid-base titration. The method used for determining the end point in a titration does not affect the calculations.

**Example 16.1.** In a titration experiment 23.05 ml. of 0.100N NaOH was required to neutralize 10.00 ml. of a solution of $H_2SO_4$ of unknown strength. What was the normality of the acid solution?

**Solution.** From the relationship $N_A V_A = N_B V_B$ we have:

$$N_A = \frac{N_B V_B}{V_A} = \frac{(0.100)(23.05)}{(10.00)} = 0.231 = \text{normality of } H_2SO_4.$$

**Example 16.2.** A solution containing 0.275 g. of NaOH required 35.4 ml. of HCl for neutralization. What was the normality of the HCl?

**Solution.** One gram-equivalent weight of NaOH = 40.0 g. Therefore:

$$0.275 \text{ g. NaOH} = \frac{0.275}{40.0} \times 1000 = 6.88 \text{ milliequivalents.}$$

Since $N_A V_A = N_B V_B$ = milliequivalents when V is measured in milliliters, then:

$$35.4 \, x = 6.88$$

or        $x = 0.194 =$ normality of the HCl solution.

**Example 16.3.** What volume of 0.250N acid would be required to react with 0.500 g. of $Ca(OH)_2$?

**Solution.**

$$0.500 \text{ g. } Ca(OH)_2 = \frac{0.500}{37.05} \times 1000 = 13.5 \text{ milliequivalents.}$$

Since        $N_A V_A = N_B V_B,$

then        $0.250x = 13.5$

or        $x = 54.0$ ml. = volume of acid required.

**Example 16.4.** What would be the normality of a solution prepared by diluting 250 ml. of 0.400N $H_2SO_4$ with 1000 ml. of water?

**Solution.** The same number of milliequivalents must be in the diluted solution as in the original solution. That is:

$$N_1 V_1 = N_2 V_2.$$

Therefore,    $(0.400N)(250 \text{ ml.}) = (xN)(1250 \text{ ml.})$

or        $x = 0.080 =$ normality of diluted solution.

**Example 16.5.** A 0.311 g. sample of crude NaOH, when dissolved in water, required 46.1 ml. of 0.122N $H_2SO_4$ to neutralize the NaOH in the sample. Calculate the per cent of NaOH in the sample.

**Solution.** First calculate the number of grams of NaOH in the 0.311 g. sample. Then:

$$(0.122N)(46.1 \text{ ml.}) = 5.62 \text{ milliequivalents of NaOH.}$$

Since 1.00 milliequivalent of NaOH $= 0.0400$ g.,
then 5.62 milliequivalents of NaOH $= 0.0400 \times 5.62 = 0.225$ g.

The per cent of NaOH in the sample is:

$$\frac{0.225 \text{ g. NaOH}}{0.311 \text{ g. sample}} \times 100 = 72.3 \text{ per cent NaOH.}$$

**Example 16.6.** A solution was prepared by dissolving 25.0 g. of $Ba(OH)_2$ in water to make one liter of solution. How many milliliters of 0.200M $H_2SO_4$ would be required to react with 25.0 ml. of the $Ba(OH)_2$ solution?

**Solution.** Express each in terms of normality. Then:

$$0.200M \ H_2SO_4 = 0.400N \ H_2SO_4$$

and    1.00 g.-eq. wt. of $Ba(OH)_2 = \dfrac{171.4}{2} = 85.7$ g.

Therefore,    normality of $Ba(OH)_2 = \dfrac{E}{V} = \dfrac{25.0/85.7}{1.00} = 0.292.$

Since    $N_A V_A = N_B V_B$, then:

$$V_A = \frac{N_B V_B}{N_A} = \frac{(0.292)(25.0)}{(0.400)} = 18.3 \text{ ml. of } 0.200M \ H_2SO_4.$$

**Example 16.7.** A volume of 22.5 ml. of 2.50N NaOH was required to neutralize 10.5 ml. of a solution of $H_2SO_4$ of unknown strength. The density of the $H_2SO_4$ solution was 1.16 g. per ml. Calculate the per cent by weight of $H_2SO_4$ in the solution.

**Solution.** At the end point of the titration the number of gram-equivalent weights of base used equals the number of gram-equivalent weights of acid used. Therefore:

$$\text{g.-eq. wts. of acid used} = (2.50)(0.0225) = 0.0563.$$

Since    1.00 g.-eq. wt. of $H_2SO_4 = \dfrac{98.1}{2} = 49.1$ g.,

then 0.0563 g.-eq. wt. of $H_2SO_4 = (0.0563)(49.1) = 2.76$ g. $=$ amount of $H_2SO_4$ in $10.5 \times 1.16 = 12.2$ g. of the $H_2SO_4$ solution.

Therefore,    $\dfrac{2.76}{12.2} \times 100 = 22.6$ per cent $H_2SO_4$ by weight.

**16.3. Miscellaneous Types of Titration.** Standard solutions other than of acid and base may react chemically. The end point of the titration may be determined providing there is a color change, precipitate, gas, or other visual effect to indicate the end point. In the problems given it must be assumed that the end point can be determined.

**Example 16.8.** How many liters of hydrogen, at standard conditions, would be liberated by the action of 250 ml. of 6.0N $H_2SO_4$ on magnesium?

**Solution.**

1.00 g.-eq. wt. of any acid will liberate 11.2 $l$. of $H_2$ at S.C.
250 ml. of 6.0N $H_2SO_4$ contains $(0.250)(6.0) = 1.50$ g.-eq. wts. of acid.

Therefore, $11.2 \times 1.50 = 16.8$ $l$. of $H_2$ at S.C. is liberated.

**Example 16.9.** An excess of $BaCl_2$ solution was added to 25.0 ml. of a solution of $Na_2SO_4$ of unknown strength. The precipitated $BaSO_4$ weighed 0.864 g. What was the molarity of the $Na_2SO_4$ solution?

**Solution.** From the equation:

$$Na_2SO_4 + BaCl_2 \rightarrow 2\ NaCl + BaSO_4,$$
$$\text{1.00 mole} \qquad\qquad\qquad\qquad \text{1.00 mole}$$

we see that there is a 1 : 1 mole ratio between $Na_2SO_4$ and $BaSO_4$.

$$0.864 \text{ g. BaSO}_4 = \frac{0.864}{233.5} = 0.00370 \text{ mole.}$$

Therefore, 25.0 ml. of the $Na_2SO_4$ solution contains 0.00370 mole. Then:

$$\text{molarity} = \frac{\text{moles}}{\text{liters}} = \frac{0.00370}{0.025} = 0.15\text{M Na}_2\text{SO}_4.$$

**Example 16.10.** What must be the molarity of a solution of NaCl in order that 1.00 ml. will precipitate (or be equivalent to) 20.0 mg. of $Ag^+$ ion?

**Solution.** The $Cl^-$ ion will precipitate the $Ag^+$ ion as insoluble AgCl. That is:

$$Ag^+ + Cl^- \rightarrow AgCl \downarrow.$$
$$\text{1.00 mole} \quad \text{1.00 mole}$$

Then, 20.0 mg. of $Ag^+$ ion $= \dfrac{20.0}{107.9} = 0.185$ millimole of $Ag^+$ ion. Since the ratio of $Ag^+$ to $Cl^-$ is a 1 : 1 mole ratio, then 1.00 ml. of the NaCl solution must contain 0.185 millimole of $Cl^-$ ion, the source of which is 0.185 millimole of NaCl. Then, 1000 ml., or 1.00 $l$., of the NaCl solution will contain $1000 \times 0.185 = 185$ millimoles of NaCl $= 0.185$ mole of NaCl per liter. By definition, the solution of NaCl is 0.185M.

**16.4. Titration of Oxidants and Reductants.** For each titration involving oxidation and reduction some method must have been established for the determination of the end point.  The methods are so varied that no attempt will be made to give them.

**Example 16.11.**  It required 33.6 ml. of a 0.100N $K_2Cr_2O_7$ solution to oxidize the $Fe^{+2}$ to $Fe^{+3}$ in 21.6 ml. of a solution of $FeSO_4$ of unknown strength.

(a) What was the normality of the $FeSO_4$ solution?

(b) What was the concentration of $Fe^{+2}$ in terms of milligrams per milliliter?

**Solution.**

(a) Normality of $FeSO_4 = \dfrac{(0.100)(33.6)}{(21.6)} = 0.156.$

(b) 1.00 $l$. of 1.00N $FeSO_4$ contains 55.85 g. of $Fe^{+2}$ ions $+$ 96.1 g. of $SO_4^{-2}$ ions.  Since we are interested only in the $Fe^{+2}$ ion concentration: 1.00 $l$. of 0.156N $FeSO_4$ contains $(55.85)(0.156) = 8.71$ g. of $Fe^{+2}$ ions.  And: 1.00 ml. of 0.156N $FeSO_4$ contains $\dfrac{8.71}{1000} = 0.00871$ g. of $Fe^{+2}$ ions $= 8.71$

mg. of $Fe^{+2}$ ions.

**Example 16.12.**  A solution was prepared by dissolving 0.865 g. of $FeCl_2$ in water.  What volume of 0.150N $KMnO_4$ solution would react with the solution of $FeCl_2$?

**Solution.**

1.00 g.-eq. wt. of $FeCl_2 = 126.8$ g.   Then:

$$0.865 \text{ g. of } FeCl_2 = \frac{0.865}{126.8} = 0.00682 \text{ g.-eq. wt.}$$

Therefore, the product NV for the $KMnO_4$ must equal 0.00682 g.-eq. wt.

That is,     0.150 V $= 0.00682$

or                     V $= 0.0455$ $l$. $= 45.5$ ml. of 0.150N $KMnO_4$.

**Example 16.13.**  How many grams of iodine will react with 250 ml. of 0.400N $Na_2S_2O_3$ solution?

**Solution.**

250 ml. of 0.400N $Na_2S_2O_3 = (0.250)(0.400) = 0.100$ g.-eq. wt. of $Na_2S_2O_3$.

0.100 g.-eq. wt. of $Na_2S_2O_3$ will react with 0.100 g.-eq. wt. of iodine.  Since 1.00 g.-eq. wt. of iodine $= 127$ g., then:

0.100 g.-eq. wt. of iodine $= (127)(0.100) = 12.7$ g. of iodine.

**Example 16.14.**  How many milliliters of 0.010N $K_2Cr_2O_7$ solution would be equivalent to 1.00 ml. of a solution containing 50.0 mg. of $Sn^{+2}$ ion per millimeter of solution?

**Solution.**  In the reaction $Sn^{+2} \rightarrow Sn^{+4} + 2e$:

$$1.00 \text{ g.-eq. wt. of } Sn^{+2} \text{ ion} = \frac{118.7}{2} = 59.4 \text{ g.} \quad \text{Then:}$$

$$50.0 \text{ mg.} = 0.050 \text{ g.} = \frac{0.050}{59.4} = 0.00084 \text{ g.-eq. wt. of } Sn^{+2} \text{ ion.}$$

This means that the product NV for the $K_2Cr_2O_7$ must be equal to 0.00084 g.-eq. wt. Then:

$$0.010 \text{ V} = 0.00084$$

or
$$V = 0.084 \text{ } l. = 84.0 \text{ ml. of } 0.010N \text{ } K_2Cr_2O_7.$$

## Problems

### Part I

16.1. In a titration, 32.8 ml. of 0.255N $H_2SO_4$ was required to neutralize 42.3 ml. of a solution of NaOH of unknown strength. Calculate (a) the normality of the NaOH solution, and (b) the grams of $Na_2SO_4$ formed. *Ans.* (a) 0.198N; (b) 0.594 g.

16.2. A 2.34 g. sample of impure $H_2SO_4$ required 42.3 ml. of 0.100N NaOH to neutralize the acid in the sample. What was the per cent purity of the acid? *Ans.* 8.86%.

16.3. Commercial lye is principally NaOH. A 0.564 g. sample of lye required 41.6 ml. of 0.251N $H_2SO_4$ to neutralize the NaOH it contained. Calculate the per cent of NaOH in the lye. *Ans.* 74.1%.

16.4. A solution of sodium hydroxide was prepared by dissolving 12.54 g. of NaOH in water to make 250 ml. of solution. There was required 18.23 ml. of the standard NaOH solution to neutralize 12.56 ml. of a solution of sulfuric acid of unknown strength. Calculate (a) the normality, and (b) the molarity of the acid solution.
*Ans.* (a) 1.83N; (b) 0.915M.

16.5. How many milliliters of 6.0N HCl would be required to neutralize 50.0 ml. of 0.100M $Ba(OH)_2$? *Ans.* 1.67 ml.

16.6. How many grams of zinc would react with 1.00 $l.$ of 1.00N HCl?
*Ans.* 32.7 g.

16.7. The addition of excess barium chloride solution to 25.0 ml. of dilute sulfuric acid resulted in the precipitation of 2.675 g. of $BaSO_4$. What was the normality of the acid solution? *Ans.* 0.92N.

16.8. A sample of marble weighing 1.750 g. required 19.5 ml. of 1.50N HCl to react with the $CaCO_3$ in the marble. What per cent of the marble was $CaCO_3$? *Ans.* 83.4%.

16.9. A solution contains 20.0 mg. of $Ag^+$ ion per milliliter. What volume of 0.10N HCl would be required to precipitate the silver in 25.0 ml. of the solution as AgCl? *Ans.* 46.3 ml.

16.10. It required 26.4 ml. of 0.175N $H_2SO_4$ to precipitate the barium ions as $BaSO_4$ from 20.0 ml. of a $BaCl_2$ solution. What was the molarity of the $BaCl_2$ solution? *Ans.* 0.116M.

16.11. In a titration 61.33 ml. of 0.2N $K_2Cr_2O_7$ was required to react with 47.65 ml. of $FeSO_4$ solution. Calculate (a) the normality of the $FeSO_4$ solution, and (b) the number of grams of $K_2Cr_2O_7$ in one liter of the solution.      *Ans.* (a) 0.257N;  (b) 9.81 g.

16.12. Iodine reacts with $Na_2S_2O_3$ according to the equation:

$$I_2 + 2\ Na_2S_2O_3 \rightarrow 2\ NaI + Na_2S_4O_6.$$

A 0.376 g. sample of crude iodine required 17.1 ml. of 0.100N $Na_2S_2O_3$ to react with the iodine in the sample. Calculate the per cent purity of the crude iodine.      *Ans.* 57.7%.

16.13. A solution was prepared by dissolving 1.765 g. of $FeSO_4$ in water. What volume of 0.150N $KMnO_4$ solution would be required to react with the $FeSO_4$ solution?      *Ans.* 77.5 ml.

16.14. How many gram-equivalent weights of $KMnO_4$ will react with 500 ml. of 0.250M $FeSO_4$ solution?      *Ans.* 0.125.

16.15. How many milliliters of a 0.100N solution of any oxidant will react with 250 ml. of a 0.250N solution of any reductant?      *Ans.* 625 ml.

16.16. How many milliliters of 0.100N $KMnO_4$ are equivalent to 1.00 ml. of a solution of $FeSO_4$ containing 40.0 mg. of $Fe^{+2}$ ion per milliliter?      *Ans.* 7.16 ml.


## Part II

16.17. If 22.1 ml. of 0.25N $H_2SO_4$ is required to neutralize 32.1 ml. of a solution of NaOH, calculate the normality of the NaOH solution.      *Ans.* 0.172N.

16.18. A solution containing 6.00 per cent HCl by weight, and density 1.028 g. per ml., was used to determine the strength of a solution of NaOH. It was found that 23.41 ml. of the HCl solution neutralized 28.20 ml. of the NaOH solution. Calculate:

a. The normality of the NaOH solution.      *Ans.* 1.40N.

b. The number of milliequivalents of NaOH used.      *Ans.* 39.6.

c. The number of grams of NaOH used.      *Ans.* 1.58 g.

16.19. How many grams of NaCl would be formed by mixing 50.0 ml. of 1.54N HCl with 50.0 ml. of 1.12N NaOH?      *Ans.* 3.27 g.

16.20. A 10.00 ml. sample of vinegar, density 1.01 g. per ml., was diluted to 100 ml. volume. It was found that 25.0 ml. of the diluted vinegar required 24.15 ml. of 0.0976N NaOH to neutralize it. Calculate the strength of the vinegar in terms of (a) normality, (b) grams of $HC_2H_3O_2$ per liter, and (c) per cent $HC_2H_3O_2$ in the vinegar.      *Ans.* (a) 0.943N;  (b) 56.6 g.;  (c) 5.60%.

16.21. How many milliliters of 12.0N HCl would be required to neutralize 125 ml. of 0.050M $Ba(OH)_2$?      *Ans.* 1.04 ml.

16.22. How many milliliters of 0.500M $H_2SO_4$ will react with 25.00 ml. of 0.100M $Ca(OH)_2$?      *Ans.* 5.00 ml.

**16.23.** It was found that 18.5 ml. of a 1.00N base reacted with 27.2 ml. of a solution of phosphoric acid. Calculate:

    a. The normality of the acid.                    *Ans.* 0.680N.

    b. The molarity of the acid.                    *Ans.* 0.227M.

**16.24.** A sample of vinegar had a density of 1.06 g. per ml. A 3.21 ml. aliquot of the vinegar required 35.4 ml. of 0.100N NaOH to neutralize the acetic acid, $HC_2H_3O_2$, in the vinegar. Calculate the per cent by weight of acetic acid in the vinegar.      *Ans.* 6.23%.

**16.25.** What volume of 6.0N HCl would be required to neutralize 1.250 g. of NaOH?                                *Ans.* 5.22 ml.

**16.26.** A 42.2 ml. sample of KOH solution required 21.1 ml. of a solution of 2.50N $H_2SO_4$ for neutralization.

    a. What was the normality of the KOH?            *Ans.* 1.25N.

    b. How many mg. per ml. of KOH were there in the solution?

                                         *Ans.* 70.1 mg.

**16.27.** With how many grams of $Ca(OH)_2$ will 250 ml. of 6.0N HCl react?

                                         *Ans.* 55.6 g.

**16.28.** How many ml. of 1.00M $H_2SO_4$ would be required to react with 100 ml. of 1.00N KOH?                    *Ans.* 50 ml.

**16.29.** A sample of 25.0 ml. of concentrated $H_2SO_4$ containing 95.0 per cent acid by weight, and having a density of 1.84 g. per ml., is diluted with water to 500 ml. volume. What volume of the acid solution would be required to neutralize 50.0 ml. of 0.50N NaOH solution?

                                         *Ans.* 14.0 ml.

**16.30.** A sample of impure NaOH weighing 0.764 g. required 116 ml. of 0.15N $H_2SO_4$ for neutralization. What was the per cent by weight of NaOH in the sample?                    *Ans.* 91.1%.

**16.31.** A solution of $H_2SO_4$ has a density of 1.60 g. per ml. A 2.50 ml. sample of the acid neutralized 27.8 ml. of 2.00N NaOH. What is the per cent by weight of acid in the solution?      *Ans.* 68%.

**16.32.** How many liters of $CO_2$, at S.C., would be liberated by the action of 1500 ml. of 2.0N $H_2SO_4$ acting on $Na_2CO_3$?      *Ans.* 33.6 *l.*

**16.33.** The addition of a solution of silver nitrate in excess to 25.0 ml. of a solution of HCl resulted in the precipitation of 1.986 g. of AgCl. What is the normality of the HCl solution?      *Ans.* 0.552N.

**16.34.** A volume of 33.6 ml. of a solution of nitric acid of unknown strength was used to react with 0.636 g. of $Na_2CO_3$. What was the normality of the acid solution?                 *Ans.* 0.357N.

**16.35.** A sample of limestone weighing 1.680 g. required 53.8 ml. of 0.50N HCl to react with the $CaCO_3$ in the limestone. What was the per cent by weight of $CaCO_3$ in the limestone?      *Ans.* 80%.

**16.36.** How many milliliters of 0.75N $H_2SO_4$ would be required to react with 2.50 g. of soda ash containing 72.5 per cent of $Na_2CO_3$? Assume that no other constituent reacted with the acid.      *Ans.* 45.6 ml.

16.37. A 1.000 g. sample of limestone is dissolved in 50.00 ml. of 1.00N HCl. The excess acid required 59.33 ml. of 0.60N NaOH for neutralization. Calculate the per cent of $CaCO_3$ in the sample. *Ans.* 72%.

16.38. One gram of a silver alloy was dissolved in $HNO_3$. It required 72.5 ml. of 0.075N HCl to precipitate the silver as AgCl. Calculate:
   a. The number of grams of AgCl precipitated. *Ans.* 0.78 g.
   b. The per cent of silver in the alloy. *Ans.* 58.8%.

16.39. What volume of 0.35N HCl would be required to precipitate as AgCl the silver in 100 ml. of 0.50M $AgNO_3$? *Ans.* 143 ml.

16.40. How many milliliters of 6N HCl would be required to react with 1.45 g. of Mg? *Ans.* 20 ml.

16.41. An experiment calls for 300 ml. of 1.00N HCl. The only acid available is 6.0N HCl. How much water and 6.0N HCl must be used? *Ans.* 250 ml. water, 50 ml. acid.

16.42. How many milliequivalents of zinc will react with 320 ml. of 0.100M $H_2SO_4$? *Ans.* 64 milliequivalents.

16.43. It required 26.2 ml. of a solution of $AgNO_3$ to react with 25.0 ml. of 0.253M NaCl. What was the concentration of the $AgNO_3$ solution in milligrams of $Ag^+$ ion per milliliter? *Ans.* 26 mg.

16.44. There was required 16.5 ml. of 0.325N $H_2SO_4$ to precipitate the $Ba^{+2}$ ion as $BaSO_4$ from 25.0 ml. of a $BaCl_2$ solution. What was the molarity of the $BaCl_2$ solution? *Ans.* 0.107M.

16.45. It is desired to prepare one liter of 0.100N HCl from a solution which is known to be approximately 2N. It required 47.68 ml. of 1.123N NaOH to neutralize 25.00 ml. of the 2N HCl. How many milliliters of the approximately 2N HCl would be required to prepare the desired solution? *Ans.* 46.7 ml.

16.46. How many milliliters of 6.00N HCl would be required to react with FeS in order to prepare 3.00 $l$. (S.C.) of $H_2S$? *Ans.* 44.6 ml.

16.47. What must be the normality of an acid in order that 1.00 ml. of the acid is equivalent to 20.0 mg. of NaOH? *Ans.* 0.500N.

16.48. A solution was prepared containing 50.0 g. of $BaCl_2$ per liter of solution. How many milliliters of 0.65M $Na_2SO_4$ would be required to react with 25.0 ml. of the $BaCl_2$ solution? *Ans.* 9.23 ml.

16.49. How many grams of $KClO_3$ will react with 500 ml. of 12.0N HCl according to the equation:

$$KClO_3 + 6\ HCl \rightarrow 3\ H_2O + KCl + 3\ Cl_2?\quad \textit{Ans.}\ 122.6\ g.$$

16.50. A solution was prepared by dissolving 2.168 g. of $FeSO_4$ in water. What volume of 0.500N $K_2Cr_2O_7$ would react with the $FeSO_4$ solution? *Ans.* 28.6 ml.

16.51. What volume of $H_2S$, at standard conditions, would react with 100 ml. of 0.100N $HNO_3$? *Ans.* 112 ml.

16.52. How many grams of $FeCl_2$ would be oxidized to $FeCl_3$ by 500 ml. of 0.100N $KMnO_4$?        *Ans.* 6.34 g.

16.53. How many gram-equivalent weights of $K_2Cr_2O_7$ will react with 50.0 g. of $FeSO_4$, according to the equation:

$$K_2Cr_2O_7 + 7\,H_2SO_4 + 6\,FeSO_4 \rightarrow K_2SO_4 + Cr_2(SO_4)_3 + 3\,Fe_2(SO_4)_3 + 7\,H_2O?\ \ Ans.\ 0.329.$$

16.54. How many grams of $KMnO_4$ would be required to oxidize 100 g. of $FeCl_2$?        *Ans.* 24.9 g.

16.55. How many gram-equivalent weights of $HNO_3$ will react with 10.00 g. of iodine?        *Ans.* 0.0788.

16.56. A solution was prepared by dissolving 500 ml. of $H_2S$ at S.C. in 3000 ml. of water. How many milliliters of chlorine at S.C. would react with 100 ml. of the $H_2S$ solution?        *Ans.* 16.7 ml.

16.57. How many milliliters of 0.200N $KMnO_4$ solution are equivalent to 1.00 ml. of $FeSO_4$ solution containing 20 mg. of $Fe^{+2}$ ion per milliliter?        *Ans.* 1.79 ml.

16.58. It is desired to prepare a 0.100N solution of $Na_2S_2O_3$. It was found that 25.0 ml. of a given solution of $Na_2S_2O_3$ was equivalent to 0.470 g. of iodine. To what volume would 1000 ml. of the $Na_2S_2O_3$ solution have to be diluted in order to obtain a 0.100N solution?

*Ans.* 1480 ml.

16.59. An iodine solution is prepared by dissolving 0.562 g. of crude iodine in a strong solution of KI in water. The solution of iodine required 6.96 ml. of 0.150N $Na_2S_2O_3$ for complete reaction. What was the per cent of iodine in the crude sample?        *Ans.* 23.6%.

16.60. How many milliliters of a solution containing 25.00 g. of $KMnO_4$ per liter will react with 1.50 g. of $FeSO_4$?        *Ans.* 12.5 ml.

# 17

# Determination of the Molecular Weights of Compounds

Physical methods will be described by means of which molecular weights may be determined for substances in water solution. The methods are limited to nonvolatile, nonionizable solutes which do not react chemically with water. Physical methods for the determination of molecular weights give approximate values. Such approximate values are used in conjunction with the more accurate values obtained by chemical methods to determine the molecular weights of compounds (Chapter 13). An understanding of the experimental methods for the determination of molecular weights gives one a greater appreciation of the meaning and usage of the concept of molecular weight.

**17.1. Introduction.** Solutions of the same molality contain the same ratio of solute to solvent molecules. For example, in a one-molal water solution there is one solute molecule for every 55.5 molecules of water, since:

$$1 \text{ mole of solute} = N \text{ molecules,}$$

and $$1000 \text{ g. } H_2O = \frac{1000}{18.016} = 55.5 \text{ moles} = 55.5N \text{ molecules.}$$

The addition of an impurity to a liquid such as water will affect certain physical properties of the liquid in direct proportion to the number of particles present. The vapor pressure is a physical property of water so affected. The vapor pressure of water in turn determines the freezing point and boiling point of the solution. The discussion which follows will show how the molecular weight of the solute may be determined from the *freezing-point lowering* and the *boiling-point elevation* of water solutions.

**17.2. Determination of the Molecular Weight of the Solute from the Freezing-Point Lowering.** The addition of one mole of solute to

1000 grams of water produces a solution freezing at $-1.86°$ C. This quantity, $1.86°$ C., is called the *molal freezing-point lowering constant* for water. The constant is different for different liquids. The addition of one mole of methyl alcohol, $CH_3OH = 32$ g., or one mole of sugar, $C_{12}H_{22}O_{11} = 342$ g., to 1000 g. of water produces a solution which freezes at $-1.86°$ C. The freezing point of a 0.100m solution would be one-tenth this amount, or $-0.186°$ C. This would be expected since the number of solute molecules in the latter solution is only one-tenth that in a one-molal solution.

The above relationships hold only for very dilute solutions. Solutions actually containing one mole of solute in 1000 grams of water would give experimental values quite different from the calculated values. Solutions of such strength are used only as reference concentrations.

**Example 17.1.** Calculate the molecular weight of urea, given that 4.00 g. dissolved in 1000 g. of water produces a solution freezing at $-0.124°$ C.

**Solution.** Two principles are involved: (1) the lowering of the freezing point is directly proportional to the molal concentration, and (2) one mole of urea dissolved in 1000 g. of water would give a solution freezing at $-1.86°$ C. Then:

$$\frac{4.00 \text{ g. urea}}{0.124° \text{ C.}} = \frac{x \text{ g. urea}}{1.86° \text{ C.}}$$

or                    $x = 60$ g. = molecular weight of urea, $CON_2H_4$.

**Example 17.2.** Calculate the molecular weight of a substance, 1.00 g. of which dissolved in 250 g. of water produces a solution freezing at $-0.124°$ C.

**Solution.** In order to use the molecular freezing-point lowering constant, all calculations must be based upon grams of solute per 1000 g. of water. Therefore:

$$\frac{1.00 \text{ g. solute}}{250 \text{ g. H}_2\text{O}} = \frac{x \text{ g. solute}}{1000 \text{ g. H}_2\text{O}}$$

or                    $x = 4.00$ g. solute per 1000 g. $H_2O$.

The problem is now identical with Example 17.1. The molecular weight of the solute is, therefore, 60.

**Example 17.3.** Calculate the freezing point of a solution containing 10.0 g. of alcohol, $C_2H_5OH$, dissolved in 1000 g. of water.

**Solution.** One mole of ethyl alcohol, 46 g., dissolved in 1000 g. of water would give a solution freezing at $-1.86°$ C. Any other concentration would lower the freezing point proportionately. Therefore:

$$\frac{46 \text{ g. } C_2H_5OH}{1.86° \text{ C.}} = \frac{10.0 \text{ g. } C_2H_5OH}{x° \text{ C.}}$$

or
$$x = 0.40° \text{ C.}$$

That is, the freezing point of the solution would be $-0.40°$ C.

**17.3. Determination of the Molecular Weight of the Solute from the Boiling-Point Elevation.** The vapor pressure of a solution is always less than that of the pure solvent, provided the solute is nonvolatile. The boiling point of a solution is, therefore, always higher than the boiling point of the solvent. One mole of solute dissolved in 1000 grams of water will result in a solution boiling at 100.52° C., at one atmosphere pressure. This increase in boiling point, 0.52° C., is called the *molal boiling-point elevation constant* for water. The same relationships exist between the freezing-point lowering and concentration as exist between the boiling-point elevation and concentration.

**Example 17.4.** Calculate the molecular weight of a substance, 4.80 g. of which dissolved in 240 g. of water gave a solution boiling at 100.065° C. at a pressure of one atmosphere.

**Solution.** First calculate the concentration in grams of solute per 1000 grams of water. Then:

$$\frac{4.80 \text{ g. solute}}{240 \text{ g. } H_2O} = \frac{x \text{ g. solute}}{1000 \text{ g. } H_2O}$$

or
$$x = 20.0 \text{ g. solute per 1000 g. } H_2O.$$

Next calculate the concentration required to produce a boiling-point elevation of 0.52° C. This will be the molecular weight of the solute. That is:

$$\frac{20.0 \text{ g. solute}}{0.065° \text{ C.}} = \frac{x \text{ g. solute}}{0.52° \text{ C.}}$$

or
$$x = 160 \text{ g.} = \text{molecular weight of solute.}$$

**Example 17.5.** A nonvolatile, nonionizable compound has the empirical formula $CH_2O$. A solution consisting of 2.80 g. of the compound in 250 g. of water freezes at $-0.174°$ C. Determine the molecular formula for the compound.

**Solution.** First calculate the concentration in grams of solute per 1000 g. of water. Then:

$$\frac{2.80 \text{ g. solute}}{250 \text{ g. } H_2O} = \frac{x \text{ g. solute}}{1000 \text{ g. } H_2O}$$

or
$$x = 11.2 \text{ g. solute per 1000 g. water.}$$

Next calculate the concentration of solute required to produce a freezing point lowering of 1.86° C.  Then:

$$\frac{11.2 \text{ g. solute}}{0.174° \text{ C.}} = \frac{x \text{ g. solute}}{1.86° \text{ C.}}$$

or                    $x = 120 = $ approximate molecular weight.

The formula weight of $CH_2O$ is 30.  Therefore, the molecular formula would be $C_4H_8O_4$, corresponding to a molecular weight of 120.

## Problems

### Part I

17.1. A solution containing 2 g. of sugar in 100 g. of water freezes at −0.11° C.  What would be the freezing point of a solution containing 4 g. of sugar in 100 g. of water?          *Ans.* −0.22° C.

17.2. Calculate the molecular weight of a substance, 0.41 g. of which dissolved in 1000 g. of water lowered the freezing point 0.016° C.
*Ans.* 48.

17.3. Calculate the molecular weight of a substance, 1.34 g. of which dissolved in 125 g. of water elevated the boiling point 0.071° C.
*Ans.* 78.

17.4. Calculate the freezing point of the solution given in problem 17.3.
*Ans.* −0.26° C.

17.5. Calculate the boiling point of a solution containing 4.0 g. of sugar, $C_{12}H_{22}O_{11}$, in 250 ml. of water at one atmosphere pressure.
*Ans.* 100.024° C.

17.6. Calculate the freezing point of a solution containing 6.0 g. of urea, $CON_2H_4$, dissolved in 500 g. of water.          *Ans.* −0.37° C.

17.7. What would be the ratio of solute to water molecules in a 0.100m solution?          *Ans.* 1 : 555.

17.8. How would the ratio of solute to water molecules compare in 0.5m and 1.0m solutions?          *Ans.* 1 : 2.

### Part II

17.9. Determine the freezing point of a solution prepared by dissolving 2.50 g. of urea, $CON_2H_4$, in 400 g. of water.          *Ans.* −0.194° C.

17.10. What would be the elevation of the boiling point in problem 17.9?
*Ans.* 0.054° C.

17.11. What would be the freezing point of a solution containing 0.0500 mole fraction of sugar in water?          *Ans.* −5.44° C.

17.12. What would be the boiling point of a water solution containing 0.050 mole fraction of a nonvolatile, nonionizable solute in water at 760 mm. of Hg pressure?          *Ans.* 101.52° C.

17.13. Calculate the molecular weight of a substance, 2.12 g. of which dissolved in 180 g. of water freezes at −0.118° C.          *Ans.* 186.

17.14. Calculate the boiling point of the solution given in problem 17.13, at one atmosphere pressure. *Ans.* 100.033° C.

17.15. Find the molecular weight of a compound, 1.21 g. of which dissolved in 60 g. of water gave a solution boiling at 212.38° F. at a pressure of one atmosphere. *Ans.* 50.

17.16. Calculate the freezing point of the solution given in problem 17.15. *Ans.* 30.67° F.

17.17. What weight of urea, $CON_2H_4$, must be dissolved in 500 g. of water to produce the same lowering of the freezing point as 1.50 g. of sugar, $C_{12}H_{22}O_{11}$, dissolved in 250 g. of water? *Ans.* 0.53 g.

17.18. How much glycerine, $C_3H_8O_3$, must be dissolved in 800 g. of water to produce a freezing-point lowering of 0.186° C.? *Ans.* 7.36 g.

17.19. A 1 per cent solution of each of two compounds A and B is prepared. The freezing-point lowering of A is twice that of B. How do their molecular weights compare? *Ans.* B twice that of A.

17.20. Calculate the boiling point of a water solution containing one-tenth mole of a substance dissolved in 400 ml. of water, pressure one atmosphere. *Ans.* 100.13° C.

17.21. Calculate the freezing point of the solution in problem 17.20. *Ans.* −0.465° C.

17.22. Calculate the freezing points of the following solutions:
   a. Two quarts of alcohol, $C_2H_5OH$, density 0.79 g. per ml., mixed with 8 quarts of water. *Ans.* 17.6° F.
   b. Two quarts of glycol, $C_2H_6O_2$, density 1.10 g. per ml., mixed with 8 quarts of water. *Ans.* 17.1° F.

17.23. Calculate the boiling point of a 5 per cent sugar solution, $C_{12}H_{22}O_{11}$. *Ans.* 100.080° C.

17.24. How many grams of methyl alcohol, $CH_3OH$, would have to be dissolved in 5000 g. of water to produce a solution with a freezing-point lowering of 10° C.? *Ans.* 860 g.

17.25. What would be the freezing point of a solution containing 0.40 mole of $CH_3OH$ dissolved in 800 g. of water? *Ans.* −0.93° C.

17.26. What would be the boiling point at 760 mm. of Hg of a solution containing one mole of solute dissolved in 55.5 moles of water? *Ans.* 100.52° C.

17.27. When one mole of a substance was dissolved in 1000 g. of water, the resultant volume was 1030 ml. How many molecules of solute would there be in one ml. of the solution? *Ans.* $5.8 \times 10^{20}$.

17.28. How many molecules of solvent are there per milliliter in the solution in problem 17.27? *Ans.* $3.2 \times 10^{22}$.

17.29. What is the freezing point of a 5.00 per cent by weight sugar solution? *Ans.* −0.286° C.

17.30. Assuming complete ionization, how many particles in the form of ions would there be in a solution consisting of 1.00 formula weight of NaCl and 1000 g. of water? *Ans.* $1.2048 \times 10^{24}$.

**17.31.** What would be the freezing point of the solution in problem 17.30?

*Ans.* −3.72° C.

**17.32.** Assuming complete ionization, how many particles in the form of ions would there be in a solution consisting of 1.00 formula weight of $CaCl_2$ and 1000 g. of water?       *Ans.* $1.8072 \times 10^{24}$.

**17.33.** What would be the boiling-point elevation of the solution in problem 17.32?       *Ans.* 1.56° C.

**17.34.** A nonelectrolyte has the empirical formula $CH_2O$. A solution was prepared consisting of 8.00 g. of the nonelectrolyte dissolved in 250 g. of water. The freezing point of the solution was found to be −0.331° C. What is the molecular formula of the compound?

*Ans.* $C_6H_{12}O_6$.

**17.35.** What per cent solution of glucose, $C_6H_{12}O_6$, would have the same freezing point as a 1.00 per cent solution of urea, $CO(NH_2)_2$?

*Ans.* 3.00%.

# 18

# Chemical Equilibria

Many chemical processes are reversible. That is, the products of a reaction may themselves interact, thus setting up a reversible process. Under constant conditions, such as temperature and concentration, such interaction of products will result in an equilibrium being established. Such an equilibrium is a dynamic one. That is, the equilibrants are constantly interacting even though at any instant there exists a given mass ratio among the substances involved. A knowledge of the concentrations of the reacting substances at equilibrium is essential in industries which depend upon a chemical change to obtain a marketable product. Chemical equilibria may involve substances in the solid, liquid, or gaseous states. All plant and animal tissues depend upon specific chemical equilibria to function properly.

## Molecular Equilibria

**18.1. The Equilibrium Constant.** Chemical equilibria involve two opposing processes occurring simultaneously and at the same rate. By *rate of reaction* is meant the amount of reacting material converted to products in a given period of time. Amounts are usually given in moles, and time in seconds.

A chemical equilibrium may be represented by the general equation:

$$A + B \underset{S_2}{\overset{S_1}{\rightleftharpoons}} C + D.$$

In the above reaction $S_1$ represents the rate of the forward reaction, and $S_2$ the rate of the reverse reaction.

At equilibrium $S_1 = S_2$. The equilibrium constant for the above reaction would be:

$$K = \frac{(C)(D)}{(A)(B)},$$

where K is called the *equilibrium constant*. The notation ( ) represents concentration in *moles per liter*.

A more general equilibrium equation would be:

$$aA + bB \underset{S_2}{\overset{S_1}{\rightleftharpoons}} cC + dD,$$

for which

$$K = \frac{(C)^c(D)^d}{(A)^a(B)^b}.$$

The value of K for any given reaction is essentially a constant at a given temperature. Note that the value of K is independent of the concentrations of the reacting substances. Any change in the concentrations of the reacting substances by the addition or removal of reacting substances will so shift the equilibrium as to maintain K constant for that temperature. It is evident that the addition of C or D will shift the equilibrium to the left, and the removal of C or D will shift the equilibrium to the right, in either case the value of K remaining constant. Evidently when K is large, C and D predominate; when K is small, A and B predominate.

**Example 18.1.** A closed reaction chamber containing $PCl_5$ was heated to 230° C. at one atmosphere pressure until equilibrium had been established. Analysis showed the following concentrations in the reaction chamber: $(PCl_5) = 0.45$ mole per liter, $(PCl_3) = (Cl_2) = 0.096$ mole per liter. Calculate K for the reaction $PCl_5 \rightleftharpoons PCl_3 + Cl_2$.

**Solution.** The equilibrium constant K for the reaction is given by the expression:

$$K = \frac{(PCl_3)(Cl_2)}{(PCl_5)}.$$

Substituting the given concentrations in the above, we have:

$$K = \frac{(0.096)(0.096)}{(0.45)} = 0.0205 \text{ at } 230° \text{ C.}$$

**Example 18.2.** Quantities of $PCl_3$ and $Cl_2$ were placed in a reaction chamber and heated to 230° C. at one atmosphere pressure. At equilibrium $(PCl_5) = 0.235$ mole per liter, and $(PCl_3) = 0.174$ mole per liter. Calculate $(Cl_2)$.

**Solution.** For the given reaction at 230° C., K = 0.0205. Solving the equilibrium constant expression for $(Cl_2)$, and substituting concentration values, we have:

$$(Cl_2) = \frac{K \times (PCl_5)}{(PCl_3)} = \frac{(0.0205)(0.235)}{(0.174)} = 0.028 \text{ mole per liter.}$$

**Example 18.3.** One liter of HI was heated at 500° C. and constant pressure until equilibrium had been established according to the equation $2 HI \rightleftharpoons H_2 + I_2$. Analysis showed the following concentrations in the reaction chamber: $(H_2) = 0.42$ mole per liter, $(I_2) = 0.42$ mole per liter, and $(HI) = 3.52$ mole per liter. Calculate the value of K for the above equation at 500° C.

**Solution.** For the given equation:

$$K = \frac{(H_2)(I_2)}{(HI)^2} = \frac{(0.42)(0.42)}{(3.52)^2} = 0.014 \text{ at } 500° \text{ C.}$$

**Example 18.4.** One mole of HI is introduced into the system in equilibrium in Example 18.3. Calculate the concentrations of $H_2$, $I_2$, and HI after the system has again reached equilibrium at 500° C.

**Solution.** The addition of one mole of HI would tend to increase the denominator in the expression for K, thereby decreasing the value of K. In order to retain a constant value for K, the system reacts by further dissociation of HI.

Let $x =$ moles of HI dissociating to maintain K a constant. Then, for each mole of HI dissociating, there will be formed 0.50 mole each of $H_2$ and $I_2$. Therefore:

$0.50x =$ moles each of $H_2$ and $I_2$ formed to maintain K constant.

At the new equilibrium:

$$(H_2) = (I_2) = 0.42 + 0.50x$$

and $$(HI) = 3.52 + 1.00 - x.$$

Substituting the above values in the equilibrium equation gives:

$$0.014 = \frac{(0.42 + 0.50x)(0.42 + 0.50x)}{(3.52 + 1.00 - x)^2}.$$

Simplifying and collecting like terms gives:

$$0.24x^2 + 0.55x - 0.11 = 0.$$

Solving the quadratic equation for $x$ gives:

$$x = \frac{-0.55 \pm \sqrt{(0.55)^2 - (4)(0.24)(-0.11)}}{(2)(0.24)}$$
$$= 0.17 \text{ or } -2.3.$$

A negative value has no significance. Therefore, 0.17 mole of HI would dissociate to maintain K constant. Then, under the new equilibrium conditions:

$(H_2) = 0.42 + 0.50x \quad = 0.42 + 0.09 \quad\quad = 0.51$ mole per liter,
$(I_2) = 0.42 + 0.50x \quad = 0.42 + 0.09 \quad\quad = 0.51$ mole per liter,
$(HI) = 3.52 + 1.00 - x = 3.52 + 1.00 - 0.17 = 4.35$ moles per liter.

The validity of the above values may be checked by substituting in the original equation. Then:

$$\frac{(0.51)(0.51)}{(4.35)^2} = 0.014 = K.$$

That is, the value of K has been maintained constant by the system in equilibrium.

**Example 18.5.** Iron filings and water were placed in a 5.0 liter tank and sealed. The tank was heated to 1000° C. Upon analysis the tank was found to contain 1.10 g. of hydrogen and 42.50 g. of water vapor. The following reaction occurred in the tank:

$$3 \text{ Fe} + 4 \text{ H}_2\text{O} \rightleftharpoons \text{Fe}_3\text{O}_4 + 4 \text{ H}_2.$$

Calculate the equilibrium constant for the reaction.

**Solution.** First, set up the formula for the equilibrium constant.

$$K = \frac{(\text{Fe}_3\text{O}_4)(\text{H}_2)^4}{(\text{Fe})^3(\text{H}_2\text{O})^4}.$$

Since concentration $= \dfrac{\text{moles}}{\text{volume}}$, the concentration of a pure solid in a chemical equilibrium has a constant value. Since $\text{Fe}_3\text{O}_4$ and Fe are solids, their concentrations will be represented by the constants k and $k^1$. Then:

$$K = \frac{k(\text{H}_2)^4}{k^1(\text{H}_2\text{O})^4} \quad \text{or} \quad K \times \frac{k^1}{k} = K^1 = \frac{(\text{H}_2)^4}{(\text{H}_2\text{O})^4}.$$

Also $\quad (\text{H}_2) = \dfrac{1.10/1.01}{5.0}$ moles per liter $= 0.22$ mole per $l$.

and $\quad (\text{H}_2\text{O}) = \dfrac{42.50/18.02}{5.0}$ moles per liter $= 0.47$ mole per $l$.

Then $\quad K^1 = \dfrac{(0.22)^4}{(0.47)^4}$

$\qquad\quad = 0.048.$

## Problems

### Part I

18.1. Given the equation $A \rightleftharpoons B + C$, calculate K if, at equilibrium, $A = 4.6$ moles per liter, and $B = C = 2.3$ moles per liter. *Ans.* 1.15.

18.2. Two moles of B were introduced into the system in equilibrium in problem 18.1. Calculate (A), (B), (C) after equilibrium has again been attained. *Ans.* 3.6, 3.3, 1.3.

18.3. Two moles of A were removed from the system in equilibrium in problem 18.1. Calculate (A), (B), (C) at the new equilibrium.

*Ans.* 3.0, 1.9, 1.9.

18.4. Analysis showed the following concentrations at 440° C. for the equilibrium $2 HI \rightleftharpoons H_2 + I_2$. Compare the two values of K at 440° C.

|         | $(H_2)$ | $(I_2)$ | $(HI)$ |
|---------|---------|---------|--------|
| Trial 1 | 0.0317  | 0.0806  | 0.347  |
| Trial 2 | 0.0097  | 0.333   | 0.390  |

*Ans.* 0.0213, 0.0212.

18.5. The following concentrations were obtained at 5000° C. for the reaction in problem 18.4: $(H_2) = 0.22$, $(I_2) = 0.22$, and $(HI) = 1.38$. Compare the value of K with those found in problem 18.4.

*Ans.* 0.0255.

18.6. K is equal to 69 for the reaction $N_2 + 3 H_2 \rightleftharpoons 2 NH_3$ at 500° C. Analysis of a 7-liter container showed that, at 500° C., there were present 3.71 moles of hydrogen and 4.55 moles of ammonia. How many moles of nitrogen were there in the container?

*Ans.* 0.288 mole.

18.7. The equilibrium constant for the reaction $N_2 + O_2 \rightarrow 2 NO$ is $1.2 \times 10^{-4}$ at 2000° C. What would be the concentrations of each of the three equilibrants, after attaining equilibrium, if a charge of 100 g. each of nitrogen and oxygen were placed in a 25 $l.$ sealed flask and heated to 2000° C.?

*Ans.* $N_2 = 0.142$; $O_2 = 0.124$; $NO = 0.00146$.

18.8. Solid carbon and 1.00 g. of hydrogen were placed in a 5-liter tank, sealed, and heated to 1000° C. At equilibrium the tank was found to contain 0.22 g. of $CH_4$. Calculate the equilibrium constant for the reaction C (solid) $+ 2 H_2 \rightleftharpoons CH_4$ at 1000° C. *Ans.* 0.31.

## Part II

18.9. $PCl_5$ is 40 per cent dissociated at a given temperature according to the equation $PCl_5 \rightleftharpoons PCl_3 + Cl_2$. What is the percentage increase in the number of particles in the container due to the dissociation of the $PCl_5$? *Ans.* 40%.

18.10. At 1500° C. water vapor is 5 per cent dissociated according to the equation $2 H_2O \rightleftharpoons 2 H_2 + O_2$. Calculate K for water vapor at 1500° C. Note: assume a concentration of one mole of water per liter before dissociation. *Ans.* 0.000069.

18.11. If there had been one mole of water vapor in the reaction chamber in problem 18.10, calculate the number of molecules of $H_2O$, $H_2$, and $O_2$ present at equilibrium at 1500° C.

*Ans.* 0.95N, 0.05N, 0.025N.

18.12. Nitrogen and hydrogen were added to a 5-liter flask under pressure, sealed, and heated. The equilibrium mixture contained 19.0 g. of ammonia, 0.160 g. of hydrogen, and 3.40 g. of nitrogen. Calculate the equilibrium constant for the reaction. *Ans.* $8.1 \times 10^3$.

18.13. A 2-liter flask contained an equilibrium mixture consisting of 0.050

mole of $SO_3$, 0.100 mole of $SO_2$, and 0.200 mole of $O_2$ at 300° C. Calculate the equilibrium constant for the reaction $2\ SO_2 + O_2 \rightleftharpoons 2\ SO_3$.

*Ans.* 2.5.

18.14. The equilibrium constant for the reaction $N_2 + O_2 \rightleftharpoons 2\ NO$ is $2.6 \times 10^{-4}$ at 4000° C. What would be the concentration in moles of nitrogen and oxygen at equilibrium if 0.250 mole of NO were placed in a 1-liter closed container and heated to 4000° C.?

*Ans.* 0.124 mole each of $N_2$ and $O_2$.

18.15. The equilibrium constant for the reaction $N_2O_4 \rightleftharpoons 2\ NO_2$ is 0.18 at 25° C. What would be the concentration of $N_2O_4$ and $NO_2$ in a 500 ml. flask in which had been placed 0.025 mole of $N_2O_4$ at 25° C.?

*Ans.* $N_2O_4 = 0.020$; $NO_2 = 0.060$.

18.16. At 1500° K. the gaseous mixture represented by the equation $C\ (solid) + CO_2 \rightleftharpoons 2\ CO$ contains 2.0 moles of $CO_2$ and 8.0 moles of CO per liter. Calculate the equilibrium constant for the reaction at 1500° K. *Ans.* 32.

18.17. What is the equilibrium constant for the reaction $PCl_3 + Cl_2 \rightleftharpoons PCl_5$ at 230° C., given that K = 0.0205 for the reaction $PCl_5 \rightleftharpoons PCl_3 + Cl_2$?

*Ans.* 48.8.

18.18. One mole of $PCl_5$ was placed in a 5-liter flask, sealed, and heated to 230° C. Calculate $(PCl_5)$, $(PCl_3)$, and $(Cl_2)$ at equilibrium.

*Ans.* $(PCl_5) = 0.145$; $(PCl_3) = (Cl_2) = 0.055$.

## Ionic Equilibria in Solution

**18.2. The Ionization Constants of Acids and Bases.** Certain covalent compounds such as $HC_2H_3O_2$ and $NH_4OH$ undergo partial ionization when in water solution. An equilibrium is thus established between ionized and nonionized molecules. The equilibrium constant principle may, therefore, be applied to such ionization equations. For example, the ionization equations for acetic acid, $HC_2H_3O_2$, and ammonium hydroxide, $NH_4OH$, and the equilibrium expressions would be:

$$HC_2H_3O_2 \rightleftharpoons H^+ + C_2H_3O_2{}^-,$$

and $$K_a = \frac{(H^+)(C_2H_3O_2{}^-)}{(HC_2H_3O_2)} = 1.84 \times 10^{-5} \text{ at } 25° \text{ C.};$$

$$NH_4OH \rightleftharpoons NH_4{}^+ + OH^-,$$

and $$K_b = \frac{(NH_4{}^+)(OH^-)}{(NH_4OH)} = 1.8 \times 10^{-5} \text{ at } 25° \text{ C.}$$

$K_a$ is called the *acid constant*, and $K_b$ the *basic constant*.

TABLE 18.1
IONIC EQUILIBRIUM CONSTANTS AT 25° C.

| Substance | Equilibrium Equation | Constant |
|---|---|---|
| Acetic acid | $HC_2H_3O_2 \rightleftharpoons H^+ + C_2H_3O_2^-$ | $1.8 \times 10^{-5}$ |
| Carbonic acid | $H_2CO_3 \rightleftharpoons H^+ + HCO_3^-$ | $4.5 \times 10^{-7}$ |
|  | $HCO_3^- \rightleftharpoons H^+ + CO_3^{-2}$ | $6.0 \times 10^{-11}$ |
| Hydrocyanic acid | $HCN \rightleftharpoons H^+ + CN^-$ | $7.0 \times 10^{-10}$ |
| Hydrosulfuric acid | $H_2S \rightleftharpoons H^+ + HS^-$ | $1.1 \times 10^{-7}$ |
|  | $HS^- \rightleftharpoons H^+ + S^{-2}$ | $1.0 \times 10^{-15}$ |
| Nitrous acid | $HNO_2 \rightleftharpoons H^+ + NO_2^-$ | $4.5 \times 10^{-4}$ |
| Phosphoric acid | $H_3PO_4 \rightleftharpoons H^+ + H_2PO_4^-$ | $7.5 \times 10^{-3}$ |
|  | $H_2PO_4^- \rightleftharpoons H^+ + HPO_4^{-2}$ | $2.0 \times 10^{-7}$ |
|  | $HPO_4^{-2} \rightleftharpoons H^+ + PO_4^{-3}$ | $1.0 \times 10^{-12}$ |
| Phosphorous acid | $H_3PO_3 \rightleftharpoons H^+ + H_2PO_3^-$ | $1.7 \times 10^{-2}$ |
| Sulfurous acid | $H_2SO_3 \rightleftharpoons H^+ + HSO_3^-$ | $1.2 \times 10^{-2}$ |
|  | $HSO_3^- \rightleftharpoons H^+ + SO_3^{-2}$ | $1.0 \times 10^{-7}$ |
| Water | $H_2O \rightleftharpoons H^+ + OH^-$ | $1.0 \times 10^{-14}$ |
| Ammonium hydroxide | $NH_4OH \rightleftharpoons NH_4^+ + OH^-$ | $1.8 \times 10^{-5}$ |

**Example 18.6.** Analysis of a solution of acetic acid, $HC_2H_3O_2$, at 25° C. showed the following concentrations:

$$(H^+) = (C_2H_3O_2^-) = 0.00150 \text{ mole per liter,}$$

and $\qquad (HC_2H_3O_2) = 0.122$ mole per liter.

Calculate $K_a$ for acetic acid at 25° C.

**Solution.**

$$K_a = \frac{(H^+)(C_2H_3O_2^-)}{(HC_2H_3O_2)} = \frac{(0.00150)(0.00150)}{(0.122)} = 1.84 \times 10^{-5} \text{ at 25° C.}$$

**Example 18.7.** At 25° C. acetic acid, $HC_2H_3O_2$, is 1.34 per cent ionized in 0.100M solution. Calculate $K_a$.

**Solution.** In one liter of 1.00M $HC_2H_3O_2$ there would be one mole. Therefore, in 0.100M $HC_2H_3O_2$ which is 1.34 per cent ionized:

$$(H^+) = (C_2H_3O_2^-) = 0.100 \times 0.0134 = 0.00134 \text{ mole per liter,}$$

and $\qquad (HC_2H_3O_2) = 0.10000 - 0.00134 = 0.09866$ mole per liter.

Then $K_a = \dfrac{(0.00134)(0.00134)}{(0.09866)} = 1.82 \times 10^{-5}$ at 25° C.

**Example 18.8.** Calculate the hydrogen ion concentration in moles per liter, $(H^+)$, in 1.000M acetic acid.

**Solution.** $K_a$ for acetic acid is equal to $1.84 \times 10^{-5}$ at 25° C.

Let $(H^+) = (C_2H_3O_2^-) = x$ mole per liter.

Then $(HC_2H_3O_2) = 1.000 - x$ mole per liter.

Substituting the above concentrations in the equilibrium expression for acetic acid, we have:

$$1.84 \times 10^{-5} = \frac{(x)(x)}{(1.000 - x)}$$

or $x^2 + 0.0000184x - 0.0000184 = 0.$

Solving for $x$ gives:

$$x = 4.29 \times 10^{-2} \text{ mole of } H^+ \text{ per liter.}$$

**18.3. The $p$H and $p$OH Values of Water Solutions.** The ionic dissociation of water may be represented by the equilibrium:

$$H_2O \rightleftharpoons H^+ + OH^-.$$

Applying the equilibrium constant principle gives:

$$K_1 = \frac{(H^+)(OH^-)}{(H_2O)}.$$

$K_1$ is known as the *ionization constant* for water.

It has been shown experimentally that, at room temperature, 10,000,000 liters of water contain one mole of $H^+$, 1.008 g., and one mole of $OH^-$, 17.008 g.

Therefore:

$$(H^+) = (OH^-) = \frac{1}{10,000,000} = 10^{-7} \text{ mole per liter in water.}$$

A quantity called the *ion product*, $K_w$, for water is given as:

$$K_w = (H^+)(OH^-) = 10^{-7} \times 10^{-7} = 10^{-14} \text{ at } 25° \text{ C.}$$

Since $K_w$ is constant at any given temperature, in any water solution the product of the concentrations of the $H^+$ and $OH^-$ ions must be $10^{-14}$ at 25° C. when concentration is expressed as moles per liter. The addition of an acid to water will increase the hydrogen ion concentration; the addition of a base will increase the hydroxyl ion concentration. The increase in either case will be accompanied by a corresponding decrease in the other ion such that $K_w$ is maintained constant. It is evident that in an acid solution the $H^+$ ion concentration is greater than $10^{-7}$ mole per liter, and in a solution of a base the $H^+$ ion concentration is less than $10^{-7}$ mole per liter.

Concentrations of $H^+$ and $OH^-$ ions as expressed above are somewhat cumbersome to handle. Because of this, a system has been devised in which the acidity or alkalinity of solutions may be expressed as *p*H or *p*OH values. Table 18.2 shows the relationship among the quantities *p*H, *p*OH, (H⁺), and (OH⁻). In Table 18.2 observe that *p*H + *p*OH = 14 at 25° C.

*p*H is defined as the logarithm of the reciprocal of the hydrogen ion concentration. That is:

$$pH = \log \frac{1}{(H^+)}.$$

TABLE 18.2

HYDROGEN ION AND HYDROXYL ION CONCENTRATIONS
AT 25° C.

| (H⁺) | *p*H | (OH⁻) | *p*OH |
|---|---|---|---|
| $10^0$ | 0 | $10^{-14}$ | 14 |
| $10^{-1}$ | 1 | $10^{-13}$ | 13 |
| $10^{-2}$ | 2 | $10^{-12}$ | 12 |
| $10^{-3}$ | 3 | $10^{-11}$ | 11 |
| $10^{-7}$ | 7 | $10^{-7}$ | 7 |
| $10^{-12}$ | 12 | $10^{-2}$ | 2 |
| $10^{-13}$ | 13 | $10^{-1}$ | 1 |
| $10^{-14}$ | 14 | $10^0$ | 0 |

**Example 18.9.** Calculate the *p*H and *p*OH of a water solution containing $1.0 \times 10^{-6}$ mole of H⁺ ion per liter at 25° C.

**Solution.** Substituting the concentration of the hydrogen ion in the above formula gives:

$$pH = \log \frac{1}{1.0 \times 10^{-6}} = \log \frac{1}{0.000001} = \log 1,000,000 = 6.$$

Since *p*H + *p*OH = 14 at 25° C., then:

$$pOH = 14 - 6 = 8.$$

*p*H may be defined as the logarithm of the number of liters of solution containing one mole of H⁺ ion.

**Example 18.10.** Calculate the *p*H of a water solution containing $1.0 \times 10^{-6}$ mole of H⁺ ion per liter at 25° C.

**Solution.** This problem is identical with Example 18.9.

Given that $1.0 \times 10^{-6} = 0.000001$ mole of H⁺ ion is contained in 1.0 liter of water, then 1.0 mole of H⁺ ion would be contained in $\frac{1}{0.000001} = 1,000,000$ liters of water. Therefore:

$$p\text{H} = \log 1{,}000{,}000 = 6.$$

Observe that the above solution is essentially the same as that given for Example 18.9.

**Example 18.11.** A 0.050M solution of hydrocyanic acid, HCN, has a $p\text{H}$ of 5.4 at 25° C. Calculate $K_a$ for HCN at 25° C.

**Solution.**

$$\text{HCN} \rightleftharpoons \text{H}^+ + \text{CN}^-. \quad \text{Therefore:}$$

$$K_a = \frac{(\text{H}^+)(\text{CN}^-)}{(\text{HCN})}$$

and

$$p\text{H} = \log \frac{1}{(\text{H}^+)}$$

or

$$5.4 = \log \frac{1}{(\text{H}^+)}$$

and

$$(\text{H}^+) = 0.0000251 = 2.51 \times 10^{-5} = (\text{CN}^-).$$

Since the degree of ionization is so small the approximation will be made that $(\text{HCN}) = 0.050 = 5.0 \times 10^{-2}$. Then:

$$K_a = \frac{(2.51 \times 10^{-5})(2.51 \times 10^{-5})}{5.0 \times 10^{-2}} = 1.3 \times 10^{-8} \text{ at } 25° \text{ C.}$$

**Example 18.12.** Calculate the $p\text{H}$ of 0.10M $\text{H}_3\text{PO}_4$ at 25° C.

**Solution.** From Table 18.1, $K_a = 7.5 \times 10^{-3}$ for the primary ionization

$$\text{H}_3\text{PO}_4 \rightleftharpoons \text{H}^+ + \text{H}_2\text{PO}_4^-.$$

That is,

$$7.5 \times 10^{-3} = \frac{(\text{H}^+)(\text{H}_2\text{PO}_4^-)}{(\text{H}_3\text{PO}_4)}.$$

Let

$$x = (\text{H}^+) = (\text{H}_2\text{PO}_4^-),$$

and

$$(0.10 - x) = (\text{H}_3\text{PO}_4).$$

Since the degree of ionization is relatively large, a considerable error would be introduced in assuming that $(\text{H}_3\text{PO}_4) = 0.10$. An approximation is made in assuming that the $\text{H}^+$ originates principally from the primary ionization of $\text{H}_3\text{PO}_4$. This is justified on the basis of the relatively small values for $K_a$ for the secondary and tertiary ionizations. Then:

$$7.5 \times 10^{-3} = \frac{x^2}{0.10 - x}$$

or

$$x^2 + 0.0075x - 0.00075 = 0$$

and

$$x = 2.4 \times 10^{-2}.$$

**Example 18.13.** Calculate the per cent of ionization of 0.050M acetic acid.

**Solution.**

Let $(H^+) = (C_2H_3O_2^-) = x$ mole per liter.

Then $(HC_2H_3O_2) = 0.05 - x$. Since $x$ is very small, $(HC_2H_3O_2)$ may be assumed to be equal to 0.05.

$$K_a = \frac{(H^+)(C_2H_3O_2^-)}{(HC_2H_3O_2)}$$

and $\quad 1.8 \times 10^{-5} = \dfrac{x^2}{0.05}$

or $\qquad x = 9.5 \times 10^{-4}$ mole per liter of $H^+$ and $C_2H_3O_2^-$,

and per cent ionization $= \dfrac{9.5 \times 10^{-4} \text{ mole per liter}}{0.050 \text{ mole per liter}} \times 100 = 1.9$ per cent

## Problems

### Part I

18.19. An acid dissociates according to the equation $HA \rightleftharpoons H^+ + A^-$. A one-molar solution of the acid is 1 per cent ionized. What is the value of $K_a$? *Ans.* 0.0001.

18.20. An acid dissociates according to the equation $H_2A \rightleftharpoons H^+ + HA^-$. A 0.100M solution of the acid is 1 per cent ionized. What is the value of $K_a$? *Ans.* $1.0 \times 10^{-5}$.

18.21. The ionization of a one-molar solution of HCN is 0.010 per cent at 18° C. Calculate $K_a$. *Ans.* $1.0 \times 10^{-8}$.

18.22. Calculate the value of $K_a$ for a 0.0010M solution of acetic acid which is 12.6 per cent ionized at 25° C. *Ans.* $1.8 \times 10^{-5}$.

18.23. Solve Example 18.11 using $(HCN) = 0.050 - (2.51 \times 10^{-5})$. *Ans.* $1.3 \times 10^{-8}$.

18.24. Solve Example 18.12 assuming the approximation valid that $(H_3PO_4) = 0.10$. *Ans.* $2.7 \times 10^{-2}$.

18.25. What is the per cent ionization in 0.10M $HNO_2$ at 25° C.? *Ans.* 6.7%.

18.26. What is the hydrogen ion concentration in 0.10M NaOH, assuming 100 per cent ionization? *Ans.* $1.0 \times 10^{-13}$.

18.27. The concentration of hydrogen ion in a solution is 0.001 mole per liter. Calculate: (a) the grams of hydrogen ion per liter, (b) the liters of solution containing one mole of hydrogen ion, and (c) the $p$H and $p$OH values. *Ans.* (a) 0.001008 g.; (b) 1000 l.; (c) 3, 11.

18.28. Calculate the $p$H value of 0.100M HCl, assuming complete ionization. *Ans.* 1.

18.29. Calculate the $p$OH value of 0.100M NaOH, assuming complete ionization. *Ans.* 1.

18.30. Calculate the $p$H and $p$OH of 0.30M HCl which is 88 per cent ionized. *Ans.* 0.6, 13.4.

18.31. Following three successive additions of HCl to water, the respective hydrogen ion concentrations were $10^{-6}$, $10^{-4.8}$, and $10^{-1.65}$. Calculate: (a) the concentration of the hydroxyl ion, (b) the $p$H, and (c) the $p$OH of each of the solutions.          *Ans.* (a) $10^{-8}$, $10^{-9.2}$, $10^{-12.35}$;

(b) 6, 4.8, 1.65;

(c) 8, 9.2, 12.35.

18.32. Following three successive additions of NaOH to water, the respective hydroxyl ion concentrations were $10^{-4}$, $10^{-2.15}$, and $10^{-0.364}$. Calculate (a) the concentration of the hydrogen ion, (b) the $p$H, and (c) the $p$OH of each of the solutions.

*Ans.* (a) $10^{-10}$, $10^{-13.85}$, $10^{-13.636}$;

(b) 10, 13.85, 13.636;

(c) 4, 2.15, 0.364.

## Part II

18.33. Calculate $K_a$ for hydrofluoric acid, HF, given that it is 9.0 per cent ionized in 0.10M solution.          *Ans.* $8.9 \times 10^{-4}$.

18.34. Calculate the percentage of ionization of 0.050M $H_2S$, the secondary ionization being negligible.          *Ans.* 0.15%.

18.35. What is the molarity of an HCN solution having a $CN^-$ ion concentration of $2.0 \times 10^{-5}$ mole per liter?          *Ans.* 0.57M.

18.36. A 0.50M $H_3PO_4$ solution is 12 per cent ionized according to the equation, $H_3PO_4 \rightleftharpoons H^+ + H_2PO_4^-$, at 25° C. Calculate $K_a$ for the above reaction.          *Ans.* $8.2 \times 10^{-3}$.

18.37. In a 0.10M solution of $H_2S$ at 25° C. the primary ionization is 0.080 per cent. Calculate the concentration of $H^+$ due to the primary ionization.          *Ans.* $8.0 \times 10^{-5}$.

18.38. At 25° C. ammonium hydroxide is 1.33 per cent ionized in 0.20M solution. Calculate $K_b$ for ammonium hydroxide at 25° C.

*Ans.* $3.5 \times 10^{-5}$.

18.39. Calculate the hydrogen ion concentration in moles per liter of a 0.010M solution of acetic acid at 25° C.          *Ans.* $4.2 \times 10^{-4}$.

18.40. Calculate the value of $K_a$ for a 0.010M solution of acetic acid, 4.2 per cent ionized, at 25° C.          *Ans.* $1.8 \times 10^{-5}$.

18.41. A 0.10M solution of ammonium hydroxide is 1.3 per cent ionized at 25° C. What is the value of $K_b$?          *Ans.* $1.8 \times 10^{-5}$.

18.42. A one-molar solution of $HNO_2$ is about 2 per cent ionized at room temperature. Calculate $K_a$ for $HNO_2$.          *Ans.* $4.0 \times 10^{-4}$.

18.43. Calculate $(OH^-)$ of 0.10M $NH_4OH$.

*Ans.* $1.3 \times 10^{-3}$ mole per liter.

18.44. What is the per cent ionization of 0.0010M $HNO_2$ solution at 25° C.?

*Ans.* 48%.

18.45. What is the $p$H of the solution in problem 18.44?          *Ans.* 3.32.

18.46. A 0.010M solution of acetic acid has a $p$H of 3.4. What is the per cent ionization?          *Ans.* 3.98%.

18.47. What is the per cent ionization in a solution which contains 100 g of acetic acid dissolved in water to make 1000 ml. of solution?

*Ans.* 0.33%.

18.48. What is the per cent ionization of 6.0M acetic acid at 25° C.?

*Ans.* 0.173%.

18.49. What is the $pH$ of the solution in problem 18.48? *Ans.* 1.98.

18.50. A solution contains 25.0 g. of ammonium hydroxide in 500 ml. of solution. What is the $pH$ of the solution at 25° C.? *Ans.* 2 29.

18 51 In 0.010M solution $HNO_2$ has a $pH$ of 2.7 at 25° C. Calculate $K_a$ for $HNO_2$ at 25° C. *Ans.* $4.0 \times 10^{-4}$.

18.52. Calculate the hydrogen ion concentration in 1.00M hydrocyanic acid solution. *Ans.* $2.6 \times 10^{-5}$.

18.53. Calculate the per cent ionization of the HCN solution in problem 18.52. *Ans.* $2.6 \times 10^{-3}$.

18.54. Calculate the concentration of $H^+$ and $OH^-$ in 1.00M $NH_4OH$ solution at 25° C. *Ans.* $(H^+) = 2.4 \times 10^{-12}$. $(OH^-) = 4.2 \times 10^{-3}$.

18 55. Calculate the $pH$ and the $pOH$ of the solution in problem 18.54.

*Ans.* $pH = 11.6$; $pOH = 2.4$

18.56. The $OH^-$ concentration in 0.10M $NH_4OH$ solution is $1.34 \times 10^{-3}$ mole per liter at 25° C. Calculate $K_b$ for $NH_4OH$ at 25° C.

*Ans.* $1.8 \times 10^{-5}$.

18.57. What concentration of ammonium hydroxide is one per cent ionized at 25° C.? *Ans.* 0.17M.

18.58. What concentration of acetic acid is one per cent ionized at 25° C ?

*Ans.* 0.17M

18.59. Calculate the concentration of hydrogen ion in moles per liter of a water solution having a $pH$ of 4.5. *Ans.* $3.2 \times 10^{-5}$.

18.60. A solution has a hydrogen ion concentration of $2.5 \times 10^{-4}$ mole per liter. Calculate the $pH$ of the solution. *Ans.* 3.6

18.61. Calculate the $pH$, $(OH^-)$, and $(H^+)$ of 0.001M HCl, assuming complete ionization. *Ans.* 3, $10^{-11}$, $10^{-3}$.

18.62. Calculate the $pH$, $(OH^-)$, and $(H^+)$ of 0.001M KOH, assuming complete ionization. *Ans.* 11, $10^{-3}$, $10^{-11}$.

18.63. Calculate the hydroxyl ion concentration in moles per liter of a solution (a) the $pH$ of which is 4.0, and (b) the $pOH$ of which is 4.0.

*Ans.* (a) $10^{-10}$, (b) $10^{-4}$

18.64. What is the concentration of ammonia in grams per liter in 0.10M $NH_4OH$ solution at 25° C.? *Ans.* 1.68 g

18.65. What is the $pH$ value of a 0.00010N solution of acid, assuming 100 per cent ionization? *Ans.* 4.0.

18.66. What is the $pH$ value of a 0.00010N solution of base, assuming 100 per cent ionization? *Ans.* 10.0.

18.67. What is the $HS^-$ ion concentration of 0.0010N $H_2S$ solution?

*Ans.* $1.1 \times 10^{-5}$

## The Solubility Product

**18.4. The Solubility Product Principle.** The *solubility product principle* applies to saturated solutions of very slightly soluble electrolytes. Such electrolytes may be assumed to be 100 per cent ionized in solution, the ions being in equilibrium with the undissolved solid according to the equation:

$$\underset{\text{solid}}{BaSO_4} \rightleftharpoons \underset{\text{ions in solution}}{\underbrace{Ba^{+2} + SO_4^{-2}}}.$$

The equilibrium constant expression for the above equation is:

$$K = \frac{(Ba^{+2})(SO_4^{-2})}{(BaSO_4)}.$$

Since the concentration of an undissolved solid such as $BaSO_4$ is a constant, the above expression becomes:

$$K(BaSO_4) = K_{S.P.} = (Ba^{+2})(SO_4^{-2}),$$

where $K_{S.P.}$ is called the *solubility product constant*. The solubility product is therefore the product of the concentrations of the ions originating from a salt. Evidently, if the product of the concentrations of the ions is less than $K_{S.P.}$, the solution is unsaturated. If two solutions are mixed, one of which contains $Ba^{+2}$ ions and the other $SO_4^{-2}$ ions, precipitation of $BaSO_4$ will occur only if $(Ba^{+2})(SO_4^{-2}) > K_{S.P.}$ for $BaSO_4$.

$$K_{S.P.} = (Ba^{+2})(SO_4^{-2}) = 1.1 \times 10^{-10} \text{ at } 25° \text{ C.}$$

$K_{S.P.}$ varies with temperature, most values being given at 25° C.

TABLE 18.3

SOLUBILITY PRODUCTS AT 25° C.

| Substance | Formula | $K_{S.P.}$ |
|---|---|---|
| Aluminum hydroxide | $Al(OH)_3$ | $3.7 \times 10^{-15}$ |
| Calcium carbonate | $CaCO_3$ | $8.7 \times 10^{-9}$ |
| Copper sulfide (18° C.) | $CuS$ | $8.5 \times 10^{-45}$ |
| Silver bromide | $AgBr$ | $7.7 \times 10^{-13}$ |
| Silver chloride | $AgCl$ | $1.6 \times 10^{-10}$ |
| Silver iodide | $AgI$ | $1.5 \times 10^{-16}$ |
| Silver sulfide (18° C.) | $Ag_2S$ | $1.6 \times 10^{-49}$ |
| Zinc sulfide (18° C.) | $ZnS$ | $1.2 \times 10^{-23}$ |

**Example 18.14.** A solution of AgCl in equilibrium with the solid contained $1.3 \times 10^{-5}$ mole of $Ag^+$ ion per liter and $1.3 \times 10^{-5}$ mole of $Cl^-$ ion per liter. Calculate $K_{S.P.}$ for AgCl.

**Solution.**

$$K_{S.P.} = (Ag^+)(Cl^-) = (1.3 \times 10^{-5})(1.3 \times 10^{-5}) = 1.7 \times 10^{-10}.$$

**Example 18.15.** The solubility of $BaSO_4$ in water at 18° C. is 0.00233 g. per liter. Calculate $K_{S.P.}$ for $BaSO_4$.

**Solution.** The concentrations of the $Ba^{+2}$ and $SO_4^{-2}$ ions must be found. Since 1 mole of barium sulfate yields 1 mole each of the two ions, then:

$$(Ba^{+2}) = (SO_4^{-2}) = (BaSO_4) = \frac{0.00233\ \text{g. BaSO}_4}{233\ \dfrac{\text{g. BaSO}_4}{\text{mole}}} = 0.00001\ \text{mole.}$$

Therefore:

$K_{S.P.} = (0.00001)(0.00001) = 1.0 \times 10^{-10}$ = solubility product constant for $BaSO_4$ at 18° C.

**Example 18.16.** The solubility of $Mg(OH)_2$ in water at 25° C. is 0.00912 g. per liter. Calculate $K_{S.P.}$ for $Mg(OH)_2$, assuming complete ionization.

**Solution.** $Mg(OH)_2$ ionizes according to the equation:

$$Mg(OH)_2 \rightleftharpoons \underset{\text{1 mole}}{Mg^{+2}} + \underbrace{OH^- + OH^-}_{\text{2 moles}}.$$

Therefore:

$$K_{S.P.} = (Mg^{+2})(OH^-)(OH^-) = (Mg^{+2})(OH^-)^2$$

and concentration of $Mg(OH)_2 = \dfrac{0.00912\ \text{g.}}{58.3\ \dfrac{\text{g.}}{\text{mole}}} = 0.000156$ mole per liter.

Since one mole of $Mg(OH)_2$ yields one mole of $Mg^{+2}$ ion and two moles of $OH^-$ ion, then:

$$(Mg^{+2}) = 0.000156\ \text{mole per liter,}$$

and $(OH^-) = 2 \times 0.000156 = 0.000312$ mole per liter.

Substituting the above values in the expression for $K_{S.P.}$ gives:

$K_{S.P.} = (0.000156)(0.000312)^2 = 1.52 \times 10^{-11}$ for $Mg(OH)_2$ at 25° C.

**Example 18.17.** One liter of solution was prepared containing 0.00408 mole of $Pb(NO_3)_2$. To this solution was added 0.0105 mole of $NH_4Cl$. Given that $K_{S.P.}$ for $PbCl_2$ is equal to $2.4 \times 10^{-4}$, determine whether or not $PbCl_2$ will precipitate from the solution.

**Solution.** If the ionic product as given by the expression:

$$K_{S.P.} = (Pb^{+2})(Cl^-)^2$$

is greater than $2.4 \times 10^{-4}$, precipitation of $PbCl_2$ will occur.

Since one mole of $Pb(NO_3)_2$ yields one mole of $Pb^{+2}$ ion and one mole of $NH_4Cl$ yields one mole of $Cl^-$ ion, then:

$$(Pb^{+2}) = 0.00408 \text{ mole per liter,}$$

and $$(Cl^-) = 0.0105 \text{ mole per liter.}$$

Therefore, $(Pb^{+2})(Cl^-)^2 = (0.00408)(0.0105)^2 = 4.5 \times 10^{-7}$.

Since $4.5 \times 10^{-7}$ is less than $2.4 \times 10^{-4}$, the value of $K_{S.P.}$ for $PbCl_2$, precipitation of $PbCl_2$ will not occur.

**Example 18.18.** Given that $K_{S.P.}$ for $Al(OH)_3$ is equal to $3.7 \times 10^{-15}$, calculate the solubility of $Al(OH)_3$ in grams per liter.

**Solution.** From the equation:

$$Al(OH)_3 \rightleftharpoons Al^{+3} + 3 OH^-$$
$$1 \text{ mole} \quad 1 \text{ mole} \quad 3 \text{ moles}$$

we have that:

$$K_{S.P.} = (Al^{+3})(OH^-)^3 = 3.7 \times 10^{-15}.$$

Let $x$ = moles of $Al(OH)_3$ dissolved per liter.

Then $x$ = moles of $Al^{+3}$ ion per liter,

and $3x$ = moles of $OH^-$ ion per liter.

That is, $(x)(3x)^3 = 3.7 \times 10^{-15}$

or $x = 1.1 \times 10^{-4}$ moles of $Al(OH)_3$ per liter.

Since one mole of $Al(OH)_3$ is equal to 78 g., then:

$$1.1 \times 10^{-4} \text{ mole of } Al(OH)_3 = (1.1 \times 10^{-4})(78) = 8.6 \times 10^{-3} \text{ g.}$$

That is, the solubility of $Al(OH)_3$ is $8.6 \times 10^{-3}$ gram per liter.

**Example 18.19.** What must be the concentration of $Ag^+$ ion in a solution containing $2.0 \times 10^{-6}$ mole of $Cl^-$ ion per liter to just start precipitation of $AgCl$, given that $K_{S.P.}$ for $AgCl$ is equal to $1.7 \times 10^{-10}$?

**Solution.** In a saturated solution of $AgCl$:

$$(Ag^+)(Cl^-) = 1.7 \times 10^{-10}$$

or $$(Ag^+) = \frac{1.7 \times 10^{-10}}{(Cl^-)}$$

and $$(Ag^+) = \frac{1.7 \times 10^{-10}}{2.0 \times 10^{-6}} = 8.5 \times 10^{-5} \text{ mole per liter.}$$

The solubility product involves the use of very small quantities. However, such quantities are quite significant and find wide application in qualitative and quantitative analysis.

# Problems

## Part I

18.68. How many grams are there in $4.0 \times 10^{-7}$ mole of $Ag^+$?

$Ans.$ $4.3 \times 10^{-5}$ g.

18.69. How many moles are there in $6.4 \times 10^{-6}$ g. of $S^{-2}$?

$Ans.$ $2.0 \times 10^{-7}$ mole.

18.70. At 25° C. the solubility of AgCl is $1.8 \times 10^{-3}$ gram per liter. Calculate $K_{S.P.}$ for AgCl, assuming complete ionization.

$Ans.$ $1.6 \times 10^{-10}$.

18.71. A saturated solution of $Ag_2CrO_4$ was prepared by shaking the pure compound with water. How much of the salt would dissolve in 500 ml. of water, given that $K_{S.P.}$ for $Ag_2CrO_4$ is $9.0 \times 10^{-12}$?

$Ans.$ 0.022 g.

18.72. $K_{S.P.}$ for ZnS is $1.2 \times 10^{-23}$. Calculate the $S^{-2}$ ion concentration necessary to just start precipitation of ZnS from a 0.005M solution of $ZnSO_4$.                      $Ans.$ $2.4 \times 10^{-21}$.

18.73. $K_{S.P.}$ for $CaSO_4$ is equal to $6.1 \times 10^{-5}$. How many grams of $CaCl_2$ must be added to 500 ml. of 0.01M $H_2SO_4$ to just start precipitation of $CaSO_4$?                      $Ans.$ 0.34 g.

## Part II

18.74. The solubility of ZnS at 25° C. is $3.5 \times 10^{-12}$ mole per liter. Calculate $K_{S.P.}$ for ZnS.                      $Ans.$ $1.2 \times 10^{-23}$.

18.75. $K_{S.P.}$ for $CaC_2O_4$ is equal to $2.6 \times 10^{-9}$. Will $CaC_2O_4$ precipitate from 100 ml. of a solution containing 100 mg. of $Ca^{+2}$ ion, to which has been added 0.02 mole of $(NH_4)_2C_2O_4$?                      $Ans.$ Yes.

18.76. A solution in equilibrium with solid $Ag_2S$ was found to contain $1.8 \times 10^{-16}$ mole of $S^{-2}$ ion per liter and $1.5 \times 10^{-18}$ mole of $Ag^+$ ion per liter. Calculate $K_{S.P.}$ for $Ag_2S$.         $Ans.$ $4.1 \times 10^{-52}$.

18.77. A solution in equilibrium with solid $Bi_2S_3$ contained $9.6 \times 10^{-20}$ mole of $Bi^{+3}$ ion per liter and $2.5 \times 10^{-12}$ mole of $S^{-2}$ ion per liter. Calculate $K_{S.P.}$ for $Bi_2S_3$.                      $Ans.$ $1.4 \times 10^{-73}$.

18.78. How many milligrams of $C_2O_4^{-2}$ ion must be present in 100 ml. of solution containing 0.050 mg. of $Ba^{+2}$ ion in order to just start precipitation of $BaC_2O_4$, given that $K_{S.P.}$ for $BaC_2O_4$ is $1.5 \times 10^{-7}$?

$Ans.$ 363 mg.

18.79. $K_{S.P.}$ for AgCl is equal to $1.7 \times 10^{-10}$. How many grams of AgCl will dissolve in one liter of 0.001M KCl, assuming the KCl to be completely ionized?                      $Ans.$ $2.4 \times 10^{-5}$ g.

18.80. $K_{S.P.}$ for lithium carbonate, $Li_2CO_3$, is $1.7 \times 10^{-3}$ at 25° C. How many grams of lithium carbonate will dissolve in 2500 ml. of water at 25° C.?                      $Ans.$ 13.9 g.

18.81. Will precipitation of calcium carbonate occur if 0.100 ml. of 0.100N $CaCl_2$ is added to 1.00 $l.$ of 0.001M $Na_2CO_3$?         $Ans.$ Yes.

18.82. What is the concentration of sulfide ion, in moles per liter, above which precipitation of $Ag_2S$ will take place in 0.000100M $AgNO_3$ solution?                                     *Ans.* $1.6 \times 10^{-41}$.

18.83. The concentration of $Ag^+$ ion in a saturated solution of silver chromate, $Ag_2CrO_4$, at 25° C. is $1.6 \times 10^{-4}$ mole per liter. Calculate $K_{S.P.}$ for $Ag_2CrO_4$ at 25° C.                      *Ans.* $1.3 \times 10^{-12}$.

18.84. The concentration of $Mg^{+2}$ ion in a solution is 0.010M. Above what concentration of $OH^-$ ion in the given solution will $Mg(OH)_2$ precipitate, given that $K_{S.P.}$ for $Mg(OH)_2$ is equal to $1.2 \times 10^{-11}$ at 18° C.?                                      *Ans.* $3.4 \times 10^{-5}$.

# 19

# Electrochemistry

The passage of an electric current through a solution brings about chemical changes which obey the laws and principles of chemical changes occurring in test tube reactions. First, electric terms are defined; then follows a discussion of the changes brought about in solution due to the passage of an electric current, and, conversely, the production of an electric current by chemical change as in the lead storage battery and dry cell. As in previous discussions the quantitative aspects are stressed.

## Units Associated with the Measurement of Electricity

**19.1. Introduction.** In many chemical reactions the energy is liberated in the form of electricity rather than heat. Such is the case in a dry cell or storage battery. Also, electric energy may be used to bring about chemical changes.

*Electrochemistry* involves the study of electric energy, either in its effect in bringing about a chemical change, or as a product of a chemical change.

**19.2. Practical Units of Electricity.** Certain arbitrary units have been established for the measurement of electric energy. Only the practical units of electricity will be discussed. One *faraday* of electricity is defined as the amount of electric energy required to liberate one gram-equivalent weight of an element from solution. A smaller unit of quantity, the *coulomb*, is defined as the quantity of electricity required to deposit 0.001118 g. of silver from a solution containing $Ag^+$ ions. Since:

1.00 gram-equivalent weight of silver = 107.88 g., then:

$$1.00 \text{ faraday} = \frac{107.88 \text{ g.}}{0.001118 \frac{\text{g.}}{\text{coulomb}}} = 96,490 \text{ coulombs.}$$

An *ampere* is a rate of flow of one coulomb per second. An *ohm* is the resistance of a column of mercury one square millimeter in cross section and 106.300 centimeters in length at 0° C. A *volt* is the potential necessary to drive a current of one ampere through a resistance of one ohm. Ohm's law expresses the relationship among the ampere, volt, and ohm:

$$\text{amperes (I)} = \frac{\text{volts (V)}}{\text{ohms (R)}}.$$

## Laws Relating to Conduction in Solution

**19.3. Faraday's Laws of Electrolysis.** *Electrolysis* is the process resulting from the passage of an electric current through a solution of an electrolyte.

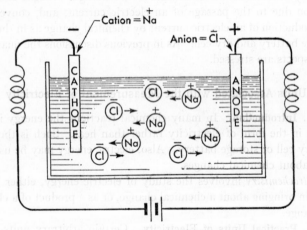

Fig. 19.1. Electric conduction in solutions of electrolytes.

Faraday stated two laws relating to electrolysis. The first law states that the amount of electrochemical change at an electrode is directly proportional to the quantity of electricity flowing through the solution. The number of grams of an element liberated by one coulomb is called the *electrochemical equivalent* of the element; the number of grams liberated by one faraday is called the *gram-equivalent weight* of the element. Below is the mathematical statement of the first law:

m = eQ.

quantity of electricity in coulombs
electrochemical equivalent in grams
weight in grams of substance liberated

When Q is expressed in faradays, then e becomes the gram-equivalent weight.

**Example 19.1.** A current of 0.050 ampere was allowed to pass through a solution of silver nitrate for 30 minutes. How much silver was deposited?

**Solution.** One coulomb will deposit 0.001118 g. of silver. A coulomb is one ampere per second. Since the current of 0.050 ampere flowed for $30 \times 60 = 1800$ seconds:

$$1800 \times 0.050 = 90 \text{ coulombs} = \text{electric energy used.}$$

And    $0.001118 \dfrac{\text{g.}}{\text{coulombs}} \times 90 \text{ coulombs} = 0.10$ g. of silver deposited.

Faraday's second law states that, for a given quantity of electricity, the weights of the elements liberated from solution are directly proportional to their electrochemical equivalents or their gram-equivalent weights. That is:

$$\frac{m_1}{m_2} = \frac{e_1}{e_2},$$

where m is the mass of an element deposited and e its electrochemical equivalent or gram-equivalent weight.

**Example 19.2.** Two electrolytic cells were placed in series. One contained a solution of $AgNO_3$ and the other a solution of $CuSO_4$. Electricity was passed through the cells until 1.273 g. of Ag had been deposited. How much copper was deposited at the same time?

**Solution.** The amounts of the two elements deposited would be in direct proportion to their gram-equivalent weights. Therefore:

$$\frac{1.273 \text{ g. Ag}}{x \text{ g. Cu}} = \frac{107.88 \text{ g. Ag}}{31.77 \text{ g. Cu}}$$

or                      $x = 0.3749$ g. of Cu deposited.

**Example 19.3.** How many grams each of $Ag^+$ and $Cu^{+2}$ ions would be deposited by 0.040 faraday?

**Solution.** Since one faraday deposits one gram-equivalent weight of an element, then 0.040 faraday would deposit 0.040 gram-equivalent weight of an element. Therefore:

$$107.88 \times 0.040 = 4.3 \text{ g. of Ag deposited}$$

and            $31.77 \times 0.040 = 1.3$ g. of Cu deposited.

**Example 19.4.** Calculate the atomic weight of calcium, given that 0.0324 faraday liberated 0.651 g. of the element. The approximate atomic weight of calcium is 40.

**Solution.** The weight of an element deposited by one faraday is the gram-equivalent weight of the element. Therefore:

$$\frac{0.0324 \text{ faraday}}{0.651 \text{ g. Ca}} = \frac{1.00 \text{ faraday}}{x \text{ g. Ca}}$$

or                    $x = 20.1$ g. = gram-equivalent weight of Ca.

Oxidation number of Ca $= \dfrac{40}{20.1} = 2$.  Therefore:

atomic weight of Ca $= 20.1 \times 2 = 40.2$.

**Example 19.5.**  It was found that 0.172 g. of chromium was deposited by 0.0761 ampere in 3 hours and 30 minutes.  Calculate (a) the electrochemical equivalent of chromium, and (b) the gram-equivalent weight of chromium.

**Solution.**  (a) Coulombs used $= 12,600$ sec. $\times 0.0761$ amp. $= 959$.

By definition, one coulomb deposits one electrochemical equivalent of an element.  Therefore:

0.172 g. $\div$ 959 coulombs $= 0.000179$ g. per coulomb

= electrochemical equivalent of chromium.

(b)  By definition, one gram-equivalent weight or 96,490 electrochemical equivalents of chromium would be deposited from solution by one faraday. Therefore:

$0.000179 \dfrac{\text{g.}}{\text{coulomb}} \times 96,490 \text{ coulomb} = 1.73$ g.

= gram-equivalent weight of chromium.

**19.4. The Significance of the Avogadro Number in Electrolysis.** In Sec. 6.4 it was shown that one gram-atom of an element contains N atoms, where N is the Avogadro number equal to $6.024 \times 10^{23}$.  In Sec. 9.3 it was shown that one gram-equivalent weight of an element involves N electrons of that element when it enters into chemical combination with another element.  Therefore, in the process of electrolysis N electrons pass through the solution for each faraday used. That is, one faraday contains $6.024 \times 10^{23}$ electrons.

**Example 19.6.**  What is the charge in coulombs on the $N^{-3}$ ion?
**Solution.**

$6.024 \times 10^{23}$ electrons $= 96,490$ coulombs.  Therefore:

1.00 electron $= 1.60 \times 10^{-19}$ coulombs,

and                3.00 electrons $= 4.80 \times 10^{-19}$ coulombs

= charge in coulombs on the $N^{-3}$ ion.

**Example 19.7.**  How many atoms of calcium will be deposited from a solution of $CaCl_2$ by a current of 25 milliamperes flowing for 60 seconds?
**Solution.**  Coulombs $= 0.025 \times 60 = 1.50$.  Since:

1.00 coulomb $= 6.024 \times 10^{23} \div 96,490 = 6.24 \times 10^{18}$ electrons,

then   1.50 coulombs $= (1.50)(6.24 \times 10^{18}) = 9.36 \times 10^{18}$ electrons.

Two electrons are required for each $Ca^{+2}$ ion deposited. Therefore:

$$\frac{9.36 \times 10^{18}}{2} = 4.68 \times 10^{18} \text{ atoms of calcium deposited.}$$

## Problems

### Part I

**19.1.** An electric motor uses 7.80 amperes of current. How many coulombs of electricity would be used by the motor per hour?

*Ans.* $2.81 \times 10^4$.

**19.2.** What is the resistance of the filament in a light bulb which uses 1.00 ampere at 32 volts? *Ans.* 32.

**19.3.** How much time would be required to use 100,000 coulombs of electricity in an electric iron drawing 10.0 amperes?

*Ans.* 10,000 sec.

**19.4.** How much would a copper plate increase in weight if silver-plated by a current of 650 milliamperes for 24 hours? *Ans.* 62.8 g.

**19.5.** It was found that 0.287 g. of nickel was deposited by a current of 175 milliamperes in 90 minutes. Calculate (a) the electrochemical equivalent of nickel, and (b) the gram-equivalent weight of nickel.

*Ans.* (a) 0.000304 g.; (b) 29.33 g.

**19.6.** How much hydrogen at standard conditions would be deposited by a current of one ampere flowing for one minute? *Ans.* 6.96 ml.

**19.7.** A given quantity of electricity was passed through each of two cells containing $Cu^{+2}$ ions and $Ag^+$ ions, respectively. It was found that 0.637 g. of copper had been deposited in the one cell. How much silver was deposited in the other cell? *Ans.* 2.16 g.

**19.8.** How much mercurous and mercuric mercury would be deposited by 0.100 ampere in 30 minutes? *Ans.* 0.374 g., 0.187 g.

**19.9.** How many electrons are there in one coulomb? *Ans.* $6.2 \times 10^{18}$.

**19.10.** How many molecules of chlorine would be deposited from a solution containing $Cl^-$ ions in one minute by a current of 300 milliamperes?

*Ans.* $5.6 \times 10^{19}$.

### Part II

**19.11.** How many grams each of $Ag^+$ ion, $Cu^{+2}$ ion, and $Fe^{+3}$ ion would be deposited by 50,000 coulombs?

*Ans.* 56.0 g. Ag, 16.5 g. Cu, 9.65 g. Fe.

**19.12.** A current of 500 milliamperes flowing for exactly one hour deposited 0.6095 g. of zinc. Determine the gram-equivalent weight of zinc.

*Ans.* 32.67.

**19.13.** The current in a silver-plating bath was only 80 per cent efficient in depositing silver. How many grams of silver could be deposited in 30 minutes by a current of 0.250 ampere? *Ans.* 0.403 g.

**19.14.** How much current would flow through a heating coil of 60 ohms resistance at 110 volts? *Ans.* 1.8 amp.

19.15. A 100-watt electric bulb draws about 0.90 ampere at 110 volts. What is the resistance of the filament in the bulb? *Ans.* 123 ohms.

19.16. Calculate the quantities of chlorine, calcium, and aluminum that would be deposited by 1500 coulombs.

Ans. 0.553 g., 0.312 g., 0.140 g.

19.17. Calculate the quantities of ferrous and ferric ions that would be deposited by 1.000 faraday. *Ans.* 27.9 g., 18.6 g.

19.18. Chlorine is prepared commercially by the electrolysis of a brine solution. A current of 2500 amperes was passed through a brine solution for 24 hours. Calculate (a) the volume of hydrogen liberated at S.C., (b) the volume of chlorine liberated at S.C., and (c) the amount of NaOH formed at the cathode.

*Ans.* (a) $2.5 \times 10^4$ l.; (b) $2.5 \times 10^4$ l.; (c) 89.6 kg.

19.19. If a given quantity of electricity deposits 1.952 g. of platinic ion, how much auric ion would be deposited by the same amount of electricity? *Ans.* 2.629 g.

19.20. What current strength would be required to deposit 1.50 g. of silver per hour? *Ans.* 0.373 amp.

19.21. A metal A forms the oxide AO. A given quantity of electricity deposited 0.862 g. of silver and 0.321 g. of the metal A. Calculate the atomic weight of the element A. *Ans.* 80.4.

19.22. What weight of water would be decomposed by a current of 100 amperes in 12 hours? *Ans.* 403 g.

19.23. A current of 1.46 amperes was found to liberate 203 ml. of chlorine at S.C. in 20 minutes. What is the gram-equivalent weight of chlorine? *Ans.* 35.5 g.

19.24. How long must a current of one ampere flow through acidulated water in order to liberate one gram of hydrogen? *Ans.* 26.8 hr.

19.25. How many ampere-hours would be required to deposit one gram-equivalent weight of an element? *Ans.* 26.8.

19.26. What weight of sodium would be deposited in one hour with a potential of 100 volts and a resistance of 50 ohms? *Ans.* 1.72 g.

19.27. How much each of $Cu^+$ and $Cu^{+2}$ would be deposited as copper by a current of 0.25 ampere flowing for 60 minutes?

*Ans.* 0.593 g., 0.297 g.

19.28. What volumes each of hydrogen and oxygen would be obtained at 27° C. and 740 mm. of Hg by passing a current of 25 amperes through acidulated water for 24 hours? *Ans.* 284 l., 142 l.

19.29. How many electrons are lost by one gram of $Cl^-$ ions as the result of electrolysis? *Ans.* $1.70 \times 10^{22}$.

19.30. How many electrons are gained by one gram of $Cu^{+2}$ ion as the result of electrolysis? *Ans.* $1.90 \times 10^{22}$.

19.31. What is the charge in coulombs on a $S^{-2}$ ion? *Ans.* $3.2 \times 10^{-19}$.

19.32. How much antimony would be deposited from a solution of $SbCl_3$ by a current of 100 milliamperes in 10.0 minutes? *Ans.* 0.025 g.

19.33. How many minutes would a current of 50 milliamperes have to flow in order to deposit 1.00 gram-equivalent weight of oxygen?

*Ans.* 32,160 min.

19.34. A bar measuring 10.0 cm. by 2.00 cm. by 5.0 cm. was silver plated by a current of 75 milliamperes for three hours. What was the thickness of the silver deposit on the bar, given that the density of silver is 10.5 g. per cm.$^3$? *Ans.* 0.0054 mm.

19.35. How many atoms of copper, as $Cu^{+2}$ ions, would be deposited by a current of 1.00 milliampere in 1.00 second? *Ans.* $3.12 \times 10^{15}$.

19.36. How many grams of $Fe^{+2}$ iron could be oxidized to $Fe^{+3}$ iron by a current of 0.100 ampere in 1.00 hour? *Ans.* 0.208 g.

19.37. A current of 5.00 amperes was allowed to flow through acidified water for 250 minutes. What weight of water was decomposed?

*Ans.* 7.00 g.

19.38. How many electrons will pass through a copper wire if a current of 0.00100 milliampere is allowed to flow for 0.00100 second?

*Ans.* $6.24 \times 10^9$.

19.39. What volume each of oxygen and chlorine, at standard conditions, will be deposited by the passage of 0.0010 faraday of electricity?

*Ans.* 5.60 ml. $O_2$, 11.2 ml. $Cl_2$.

19.40. How many minutes would be required to deposit the copper in 500 ml. of 0.25N $CuSO_4$ by a current of 75 milliamperes?

*Ans.* 2680 min.

# 20

# Nuclear Chemistry

In chemical reactions the electronic structure of the atom is involved, the nucleus remaining unchanged. Within recent years the scope of chemistry has been expanded to include changes within the nucleus of the atom, and the energy associated with such changes. Nuclear chemistry is the study of such changes. The discussion in this chapter will be limited to changes within the nuclei of atoms which have been taking place spontaneously during past ages, and changes within the atom brought about by the inventive genius of man.

In nuclear chemistry we deal with specific isotopes of elements. Isotopes are the atoms of a given element which differ from each other in the number of neutrons in the nucleus, their electronic structure being the same. Two or more isotopes are known for every element.

## Natural Radioactivity

**20.1. Introduction.** Radioactivity involves the nuclei of atoms. The nuclei of certain isotopes are unstable, undergoing disintegration over which man has no control, whereas with stable isotopes no such process occurs. When nuclei undergo disintegration, two types of particles may be lost: (1) *alpha* ($\alpha$) particles of atomic mass 4 and a $+2$ charge, and (2) *beta* ($\beta$) particles of negligible mass and a charge of $-1$. That is, when the nucleus of an atom loses an $\alpha$-particle, its weight decreases by 4 atomic mass units, and the nuclear charge (atomic number) decreases by 2. When the nucleus of an atom loses a $\beta$-particle, there is no change in weight, and the nuclear charge increases by one. For example:

$$_{92}U^{238} \rightarrow {}_{90}Th^{234} + {}_2He^4.$$
Uranium      Thorium      $\alpha$-particle

$$_{90}Th^{234} \rightarrow {}_{91}Pa^{234} + {}_{-1}e^0$$
Thorium     Protactinium     $\beta$-particle

TABLE 20.1

PARTICLES ASSOCIATED WITH RADIOACTIVITY

| Particle | | Description |
|---|---|---|
| Hydrogen | $(_1H^1)$ | Hydrogen atom with mass number of 1. |
| Deuteron | $(_1H^2)$ | Hydrogen atom with mass number of 2. |
| Proton | $(_1H^1)$ | Hydrogen ion, $H^+$, with mass 1.00758. |
| Electron | $(_{-1}e^0)$ | Charge $-1$ and mass 0.0005486. |
| Positron | $(_1e^0)$ | Charge $+1$ and mass 0.0005486. |
| Neutron | $(_0n^1)$ | Charge 0 and mass 1.00897. |
| Alpha | $(_2He^4)$ | Helium ion, $He^{+2}$, with mass number 4 |
| Beta | $(_{-1}e^0)$ | An electron. |

*Gamma* ($\gamma$) radiation is associated with natural radioactivity. Gamma rays are similar to $X$-rays and possess no mass.

**20.2. Rate of Radioactive Disintegration.** The products of disintegration of a naturally occurring radioactive substance appear always to be the same. Two important facts have been established concerning radioactive disintegration: (1) the number of nuclei disintegrating per unit of time for a given substance is directly proportional to the mass undergoing disintegration, and (2) each radioactive substance has a characteristic rate of disintegration.

The *half-life period* of a radioactive substance is the time required for one-half of a given mass of the substance to undergo disintegration. Half-life periods vary enormously with different substances, one product of uranium disintegration having a half-life period of $1.5 \times 10^{-4}$ seconds and another a half-life period of 270,000 years.

**Example 20.1.** The half-life period of radon, $_{86}Rn^{222}$, is approximately 4 days. A tube containing 1.00 microgram (0.000001 g.) of radon was stored in a hospital clinic for 12 days. How much radon remained in the tube?

**Solution.** Every 4 days one-half the remaining radon would disintegrate. Then, according to the following scheme:

days: 0 — 4 — 8 — 12
radon left: 1.00 — 0.50 — 0.25 — 0.125 micrograms left.

## The Transmutation of Elements

**20.3. Introduction.** The development of artificial radioactivity has made possible the conversion of one element into another by means of nuclear changes within the atom. The bombardment of nuclei with certain high energy particles such as protons ($_1H^1$), deuterons ($_1H^2$), alpha particles ($_2H^4$), beta particles ($e^-$), and neutrons ($_0n^1$) may result in the capture of the particle by a nucleus, followed by elimination of a particle from the nucleus different from that captured. The result is the formation of unstable radioactive isotopes of the element, or transmutation into a new element.

**20.4. Nuclear Reactions.** Transmutation of elements and the artificial preparation of unstable radioactive isotopes involve nuclear changes within the atom. For example, when aluminum is bombarded with alpha particles, the products are radioactive phosphorus and neutrons.

$$_{13}Al^{27} + _2He^4 \longrightarrow _{15}P^{30} + _0n^1.$$

When lithium is bombarded with deuterons the product is helium.

$$_3Li^6 + _1H^2 \longrightarrow 2\,_2He^4.$$

The bombardment of lithium 7 with deuterons produces a different type of reaction.

$$_3Li^7 + _1H^2 \longrightarrow _4Be^6 + _0n^1.$$

Any process in which a nucleus reacts with another nucleus, or with the elementary particles previously mentioned, to produce new nuclei is called a *nuclear reaction*.

Following are a number of nuclear reactions known to scientists which involve many of the particles given in Table 20.1.

$$_4Be^9 + _2He^4 \longrightarrow _6C^{12} + _0n^1.$$
$$_{27}Co^{55} \longrightarrow _{26}Fe^{55} + _1e^0.$$
$$_{26}Fe^{54} + _1H^2 \longrightarrow _{27}Co^{55} + _0n^1.$$
$$_{88}Ra^{226} \longrightarrow _{86}Rn^{222} + _2He^4.$$
$$_6C^{14} \longrightarrow _7N^{14} + _{-1}e^0.$$

Observe that, in a nuclear reaction, the sum of the superscripts and of the subscripts of reactants and products are related as follows:

$$(14 + 1) = (11 + 4)$$
$$_7N^{14} + _1H^1 \longrightarrow _6C^{11} + _2He^4.$$
$$(7 + 1) = (6 + 2)$$

**20.5. Energy of Nuclear Reactions.** The number of protons and neutrons in the atoms of the elements is known. The mass of a proton is equal to 1.00758 atomic mass units, and the mass of a neutron to 1.00897 atomic mass units. Since a helium nucleus consists of two protons and two neutrons, its mass should be:

$(2 \times 1.00758) + (2 \times 1.00897) = 4.0331$ atomic mass units.

Actually, the helium nucleus has been found to have a mass of 4.003 atomic mass units. The difference:

$$4.033 - 4.003 = 0.030 \text{ atomic mass units}$$

represents the mass converted to energy in the process of formation of a helium nucleus. This process is probably occurring on the sun at the present time. The difference in nuclear weight is called the *mass defect* of the atom.

The amount of energy liberated may be calculated by means of the Einstein equation (Sec. 12.1). Then, for helium:

$$E = (2.2 \times 10^{13})(0.030) = 6.6 \times 10^{11} \text{ calories.}$$

That is, in the process of formation of 4.003 grams of helium from protons and neutrons, $6.6 \times 10^{11}$ calories are liberated.

## Problems

### Part I

20.1. How much of a one gram mass of a radioactive substance would remain after 30 days if its half-life period is 5 days?    *Ans.* 0.0156 g.

20.2. Explain the nuclear changes necessary to bring about the following transmutations: (a) $_{13}Al^{27} \rightarrow {}_{15}P^{30}$, (b) $_3Li^7 \rightarrow {}_4Be^6$, and (c) $_{92}U^{238} \rightarrow {}_{90}Th^{234}$.

20.3. A radioactive isotope $_{11}A^{24}$ loses a $\beta$-particle, yielding a stable isotope B. What is the element B?    *Ans.* Mg.

20.4. When $_{83}Bi^{209}$ is bombarded with $\alpha$-particles, the bismuth nucleus captures one particle with the accompanying expulsion of two neutrons. What is the new element which is formed?    *Ans.* At.

20.5. Calculate the mass defect for sodium.    *Ans.* 0.194.

20.6. Calculate the energy in calories released when one gram-atom of sodium is formed from neutrons and protons.    *Ans.* $4.3 \times 10^{12}$ cal.

20.7. Complete the following nuclear reactions:

a. $_7N^{14} + {}_2He^4 \rightarrow {}_8O^{17} + $——.    *Ans.* $_1H^1$.

b. $_1H^3 \rightarrow {}_2He^3 + $——.    *Ans.* $_{-1}e^0$.

c. $_{11}Na^{23} + {}_2He^4 \rightarrow {}_{12}Mg^{26} + $——.    *Ans.* $_1H^1$.

d. $2\ _1H^2 \rightarrow {}_2He^3 + $——.    *Ans.* $_0n^1$.

### Part II

20.8. The half-life period of $_{15}P^{30}$ is about 3 minutes. How much of a 16-microgram sample would remain after 15 minutes?

*Ans.* 0.50 microgram.

20.9. The half-life period of radioactive carbon, $C^{14}$, is about 4700 years.

How many years would be required to reduce 32 micrograms of the isotope to one microgram? *Ans.* 23,500 years.

20.10. When $U^{238}$ is bombarded with neutrons, each nucleus captures one neutron. What isotope of uranium is formed? *Ans.* $U^{239}$.

20.11. When $N^{14}$ is bombarded with neutrons, the nitrogen nucleus captures a neutron with the formation of radioactive carbon, $C^{14}$. What particle is expelled from the nitrogen nucleus in order to bring about this transmutation? *Ans.* A proton.

20.12. Calculate the energy in calories released when one atom of beryllium is formed from neutrons and protons. *Ans.* $2.3 \times 10^{-12}$ cal.

20.13. Diffusion methods are employed in the separation of $U^{235}$ and $U^{238}$ (Sec. 7.11). The fluorides, $UF_6$, of the two isotopes exist in the gaseous state above 56° C. at 760 mm. of Hg. What are the relative rates of diffusion of the two fluorides? *Ans.* 1.0043 : 1.0000.

20.14. What is the percentage of radium in a pitchblende which yielded 25 mg. of $RaCl_2$ from 15 tons of ore? *Ans.* $(1.4 \times 10^{-7})\%$.

20.15. The market price of radium is about $50,000 per gram. What would be the cost of 50 micrograms of $RaCl_2$ based on radium content?
*Ans.* $1.90.

20.16. Calculate the mass defect for $C^{12}$. *Ans.* 0.088.

20.17. Calculate the energy in calories released when 1.00 gram-atom of $C^{12}$ is formed from neutrons and protons? *Ans.* $1.94 \times 10^{12}$ cal.

20.18. What is the mass number of the particle formed when an atom of naturally radioactive $U^{238}$ emits an alpha particle? *Ans.* 90.

20.19. Complete the following nuclear reactions:

    a. $_{15}P^{30} \rightarrow {}_{14}Si^{30} +$ ——.                *Ans.* $_{1}e^{0}$.

    b. $_{14}Si^{27} \rightarrow {}_{13}Al^{27} +$ ——.              *Ans.* $_{1}e^{0}$.

    c. $_{20}Ca^{43} + {}_{2}He^{4} \rightarrow {}_{21}Sc^{46} +$ ——.     *Ans.* $_{1}H^{1}$.

    d. $_{48}Cd^{113} +$ —— $\rightarrow {}_{48}Cd^{114}$.           *Ans.* $_{0}n^{1}$.

20.20. Chlorine has two principal stable isotopes of atomic mass 34.9787 and 36.9775. The atomic weight of chlorine is 35.457. What is the per cent natural abundance of the above isotopes of chlorine, assuming other isotopes to be negligible in amount? *Ans.* 76%, 24%.

# APPENDIXES

# APPENDIXES

# I. Graphical Presentation of Data

In Fig. 1, $XX'$ and $YY'$ are two straight lines meeting at right angles at $O$. $YY'$ is called the *ordinate* and $XX'$ the *abscissa*, the two being called the *co-ordinate axes*. The point $O$ is called the *origin*. The $X$- and $Y$-axes divide the plane in which they are drawn into the four quadrants I, II, III, and IV.

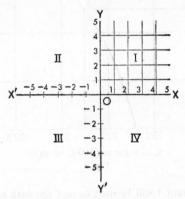

Fig. 1. Co-ordinate axes.

Any point in the plane in Fig. 1 is located by its perpendicular distance to the $X$- and $Y$-axes. Distances measured to the right of the $Y$-axis and above the $X$-axis are considered positive; distances measured to the left of the $Y$-axis and below the $X$-axis are negative. For example, the point $a$, lying in quadrant I, is located by the values $X = 3$ and $Y = 2$.

Since $X$ and $Y$ values for any point lying in quadrant I are positive, this quadrant is most commonly used for making graphs.

Fig. 1 represents a two-dimensional graph using two variables. A three-dimensional graph involving three variables may be used in which the third axis, represented by $ZZ'$, is drawn perpendicular to the paper at point $O$ in Fig. 1.

**Example 1.** The following data give the number of grams of sugar that will dissolve in 100 grams of water at the given temperature.

Temperature, °C.:    0 — 20 — 40 — 60 — 80 — 100
Grams of sugar:    179 — 204 — 238 — 287 — 362 — 487

Plot the above data and determine the solubility of sugar at 50° C.

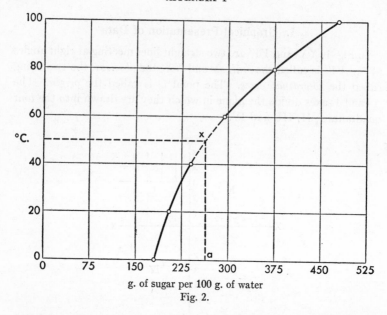

g. of sugar per 100 g. of water
Fig. 2.

**Solution.** Quadrant I will be used to plot the data as shown in Fig. 2.
Let each division on the X-axis represent 75 g. of sugar and each division
on the Y-axis 20° C. The points are plotted and connected by means of a
smooth curve as shown in the figure. A well-plotted graph will utilize
approximately equal portions of the X- and Y-axes.

To find the solubility of sugar at 50° C., draw a line from the 50° C.
point on the Y-axis parallel to the X-axis until it intersects the curve at x.
Drop a line from this point parallel to the Y-axis until it intersects the
X-axis at a. The point a corresponds to 260 g. of sugar. That is, 260 g.
of sugar will dissolve in 100 g. of water at 50° C.

### Problems

1. The following data give the solubility of ammonia in grams per 1000
   grams of water at 760 mm. of Hg. Plot the data and determine the
   solubility of ammonia at 25° C. and at 100° C.

   Temperature, °C.: 10— 20— 30— 40— 50— 60— 70— 80
   Grams of NH₃:     720— 525— 395— 300— 235— 190— 155— 130

2. Plot the data in Appendix II, giving the vapor pressure of water at
   temperatures of from 0° C. to 100° C. At what temperature would
   water boil on the top of Pikes Peak, Colorado, with the barometer
   reading 450 mm. of Hg?

3. Plot the data in Table 7.1.

4. Plot the data in Table 7.2.

5. Calculate $\sqrt{d}$ for each gas in the following table, then plot $\sqrt{d}$ as ordinate values and D as abscissa values (Sec. 7.11).

| Gas | $d\left(\dfrac{g.}{l.}\right)$ | $\sqrt{d}$ | $D\left(\dfrac{ml.}{hr.}\right)$ |
|---|---|---|---|
| $H_2$ | 0.0899 | | 400 |
| $O_2$ | 1.429 | | 100 |
| $Cl_2$ | 3.214 | | 67 |
| Xe | 5.851 | | 50 |

6. Using the data in problem 5, plot d as ordinate values and D as abscissa values.

## II. The Vapor Pressure of Water in mm. of Hg at Temperatures of from 0° C. to 100° C.

| Temp. °C. | Pressure | Temp. °C. | Pressure | Temp. °C. | Pressure |
|-----------|----------|-----------|----------|-----------|----------|
| 0 | 4.6 | 15 | 12.8 | 30 | 31.8 |
| 1 | 4.9 | 16 | 13.6 | 31 | 33.7 |
| 2 | 5.3 | 17 | 14.5 | 32 | 35.7 |
| 3 | 5.7 | 18 | 15.5 | 33 | 37.7 |
| 4 | 6.1 | 19 | 16.5 | 34 | 39.9 |
| 5 | 6.5 | 20 | 17.5 | 35 | 42.2 |
| 6 | 7.0 | 21 | 18.7 | 36 | 44.6 |
| 7 | 7.5 | 22 | 19.8 | 37 | 47.1 |
| 8 | 8.0 | 23 | 21.1 | 38 | 49.7 |
| 9 | 8.6 | 24 | 22.4 | 39 | 52.4 |
| 10 | 9.2 | 25 | 23.8 | 40 | 55.3 |
| 11 | 9.9 | 26 | 25.2 | 50 | 92.5 |
| 12 | 10.5 | 27 | 26.7 | 60 | 149.4 |
| 13 | 11.2 | 28 | 28.3 | 80 | 355.1 |
| 14 | 12.0 | 29 | 30.0 | 100 | 760.0 |

## III. Logarithms

In the expression $a^x = y$, $x$ is the logarithm of $y$ to the base $a$, where $a$ must be a positive number other than one. A *logarithm* is therefore an exponent and, as such, follows the rules applying to exponents (Secs. 1.3 to 1.8). The discussion which follows will be limited to the use of the base 10.

A logarithm is divided into two parts, the integer part called the *characteristic*, and the decimal fraction called the *mantissa*. Remember: the mantissa of a logarithm is always positive, whereas the characteristic may be either positive or negative. The following table shows some important principles relating to logarithms.

$$\log 635 \quad = \log (6.35 \times 10^2) \quad = 2.80277$$
$$\log \phantom{0}63.5 \quad = \log (6.35 \times 10^1) \quad = 1.80277$$
$$\log \phantom{00}6.35 \quad = \log (6.35 \times 10^0) \quad = 0.80277$$
$$\log \phantom{00}0.635 \quad = \log (6.35 \times 10^{-1}) = \bar{1}.80277$$
$$\log \phantom{00}0.0635 = \log (6.35 \times 10^{-2}) = \bar{2}.80277$$

The table shows: (1) that the location of the decimal point determines the value of the characteristic, but does not affect the mantissa; (2) that to find the characteristic, the number must be expressed as the product of two other numbers, one of which is an integer power of 10, and the other a number containing but one digit to the left of the decimal point (Sec. 1.4); then the power of 10 is the value of the characteristic.

From the above we see that the characteristic of the logarithm may be determined by inspection. The mantissa values must be obtained from tables, called *logarithm tables* (Appendix IV).

**Example 1.**  Multiply 235 by 86.

**Solution.**  First find the characteristic of each number.

$$235 = 2.35 \times 10^2. \text{ Characteristic} = 2.$$
$$86 = 8.6 \phantom{0}\times 10^1. \text{ Characteristic} = 1.$$

Next find the mantissa value for each. These values will be found in the table in Appendix IV. Add the logarithms. Then:

$$\log 235 = 2.37107$$
$$\log \phantom{0}86 = \underline{1.93450}$$
$$\text{add} \quad 4.30557$$

Now find the number in the logarithm table in Appendix IV corresponding to the mantissa value 30557. The number is 2021. That is:

$$\text{antilogarithm } 4.30557 = 2.021 \times 10^4 = 20{,}210.$$

**Example 2.** Divide 4.86 by 0.096.

**Solution.** The logarithm of 0.096 must be subtracted from the logarithm of 4.86. Therefore:

$$\log 4.86 = \log (4.86 \times 10^0) = 0.68664$$
$$\log 0.096 = \log (9.6 \times 10^{-2}) = \overline{2}.98227$$

When the characteristic is negative it is advisable to add and subtract 10 to and from the characteristic. Remember, the mantissa is always positive. Then:

$$\log 4.86 = 10.68664 - 10$$
$$\log 0.096 = \underline{\phantom{0}8.98227 - 10}$$
$$\text{subtract} \quad 1.70437$$
$$\text{antilogarithm } 1.70437 = 5.063 \times 10^1 = 50.63.$$

**Example 3.** Simplify the expression $\dfrac{273 \times 0.00783}{486}$.

**Solution.** Subtract the logarithm of 486 from the sum of the logarithms of 273 and 0.00783. Then:

$$\log 273 = 2.43616$$
$$\log 0.00783 = \underline{7.89376 - 10}$$
$$\text{add} \quad 10.32992 - 10$$
$$\log 486 = \underline{2.68664}$$
$$\text{subtract} \quad 7.64328 - 10 = \overline{3}.64328$$
$$\text{antilogarithm } \overline{3}.64328 = 4.398 \times 10^{-3} = 0.004398.$$

**Example 4.** Evaluate $27.5^3$.

**Solution.** Since $27.5^3 = 27.5 \times 27.5 \times 27.5$, then:
$$\log 27.5^3 = 3 \times \log 27.5 = 3(1.43933) = 4.31799.$$
$$\text{antilogarithm } 4.31799 = 2.080 \times 10^4 = 20,800.$$

The mantissa table in Appendix IV gives values for numbers containing four places only. By means of interpolation it is possible to calculate the mantissa of a number containing five places. For example, find the mantissa of 32644 from the table in Appendix IV. The mantissa of 32640 = 51375, and of 32650 = 51388. Evidently the mantissa of 32644 lies between the above values. Considering that there are ten proportional parts between 32640 and 32650, then 32644 is four proportional parts greater than 32640. The difference between the above mantissa values is 51388 − 51375 = 13. In the column marked proportional parts, for a difference of 13 in the mantissa values, four proportional parts require a correction of 5 to be added to the lower value 51375. That is:

$$\log 32644 = 4.51375 + 0.00005 = 4.51380.$$

Similarly, it is possible to determine the antilogarithm of a number to five places.

## Problems

1. Perform the indicated operations using logarithms.
   a. $782 \times 74$.      *Ans.* 57870.
   b. $7340 \div 29$.      *Ans.* 253.
   c. $0.0756 \times 0.34$.      *Ans.* 0.0257.
   d. $0.314 \div 2.14$.      *Ans.* 0.1467.

2. Simplify the expression:
   $326 \times \frac{273}{296} \times \frac{723}{760}$.      *Ans.* 286.

3. Evaluate:
   $32614 \times 78546$.      *Ans.* $2.5617 \times 10^9$.

4. Evaluate:
   a. $\sqrt{7645}$.      *Ans.* 87.44.
   b. $\sqrt[3]{8743}$.      *Ans.* 20.60.
   c. $\sqrt{0.000765}$.      *Ans.* $2.766 \times 10^{-2}$.
   d. $\sqrt[3]{0.00174}$.      *Ans.* 0.1203.

5. Evaluate:
   a. $76.3^2$.      *Ans.* 5822.
   b. $15.2^3$.      *Ans.* 3512.
   c. $0.176^2$.      *Ans.* 0.03098.
   d. $0.034^3$.      *Ans.* $3.93 \times 10^{-5}$.

### 0—50

| N | L 0 | 1 | 2 | 3 | 4 | 5 | 6 | 7 | 8 | 9 |
|---|---|---|---|---|---|---|---|---|---|---|
| 0 | − ∞ | 00 000 | 30 103 | 47 712 | 60 206 | 69 897 | 77 815 | 84 510 | 90 309 | 95 424 |
| 1 | 00 000 | 04 139 | 07 918 | 11 394 | 14 613 | 17 609 | 20 412 | 23 045 | 25 527 | 27 875 |
| 2 | 30 103 | 32 222 | 34 242 | 36 173 | 38 021 | 39 794 | 41 497 | 43 136 | 44 716 | 46 240 |
| 3 | 47 712 | 49 136 | 50 515 | 51 851 | 53 148 | 54 407 | 55 630 | 56 820 | 57 978 | 59 106 |
| 4 | 60 206 | 61 278 | 62 325 | 63 347 | 64 345 | 65 321 | 66 276 | 67 210 | 68 124 | 69 020 |
| 5 | 69 897 | 70 757 | 71 600 | 72 428 | 73 239 | 74 036 | 74 819 | 75 587 | 76 343 | 77 085 |
| 6 | 77 815 | 78 533 | 79 239 | 79 934 | 80 618 | 81 291 | 81 954 | 82 607 | 83 251 | 83 885 |
| 7 | 84 510 | 85 126 | 85 733 | 86 332 | 86 923 | 87 506 | 88 081 | 88 649 | 89 209 | 89 763 |
| 8 | 90 309 | 90 849 | 91 381 | 91 908 | 92 428 | 92 942 | 93 450 | 93 952 | 94 448 | 94 939 |
| 9 | 95 424 | 95 904 | 96 379 | 96 848 | 97 313 | 97 772 | 98 227 | 98 677 | 99 123 | 99 564 |
| 10 | 00 000 | 00 432 | 00 860 | 01 284 | 01 703 | 02 119 | 02 531 | 02 938 | 03 342 | 03 743 |
| 11 | 04 139 | 04 532 | 04 922 | 05 308 | 05 690 | 06 070 | 06 446 | 06 819 | 07 188 | 07 555 |
| 12 | 07 918 | 08 279 | 08 636 | 08 991 | 09 342 | 09 691 | 10 037 | 10 380 | 10 721 | 11 059 |
| 13 | 11 394 | 11 727 | 12 057 | 12 385 | 12 710 | 13 033 | 13 354 | 13 672 | 13 988 | 14 301 |
| 14 | 14 613 | 14 922 | 15 229 | 15 534 | 15 836 | 16 137 | 16 435 | 16 732 | 17 026 | 17 319 |
| 15 | 17 609 | 17 898 | 18 184 | 18 469 | 18 752 | 19 033 | 19 312 | 19 590 | 19 866 | 20 140 |
| 16 | 20 412 | 20 683 | 20 952 | 21 219 | 21 484 | 21 748 | 22 011 | 22 272 | 22 531 | 22 789 |
| 17 | 23 045 | 23 300 | 23 553 | 23 805 | 24 055 | 24 304 | 24 551 | 24 797 | 25 042 | 25 285 |
| 18 | 25 527 | 25 768 | 26 007 | 26 245 | 26 482 | 26 717 | 26 951 | 27 184 | 27 416 | 27 646 |
| 19 | 27 875 | 28 103 | 28 330 | 28 556 | 28 780 | 29 003 | 29 226 | 29 447 | 29 667 | 29 885 |
| 20 | 30 103 | 30 320 | 30 535 | 30 750 | 30 963 | 31 175 | 31 387 | 31 597 | 31 806 | 32 015 |
| 21 | 32 222 | 32 428 | 32 634 | 32 838 | 33 041 | 33 244 | 33 445 | 33 646 | 33 846 | 34 044 |
| 22 | 34 242 | 34 439 | 34 635 | 34 830 | 35 025 | 35 218 | 35 411 | 35 603 | 35 793 | 35 984 |
| 23 | 36 173 | 36 361 | 36 549 | 36 736 | 36 922 | 37 107 | 37 291 | 37 475 | 37 658 | 37 840 |
| 24 | 38 021 | 38 202 | 38 382 | 38 561 | 38 739 | 38 917 | 39 094 | 39 270 | 39 445 | 39 620 |
| 25 | 39 794 | 39 967 | 40 140 | 40 312 | 40 483 | 40 654 | 40 824 | 40 993 | 41 162 | 41 330 |
| 26 | 41 497 | 41 664 | 41 830 | 41 996 | 42 160 | 42 325 | 42 488 | 42 651 | 42 813 | 42 975 |
| 27 | 43 136 | 43 297 | 43 457 | 43 616 | 43 775 | 43 933 | 44 091 | 44 248 | 44 404 | 44 560 |
| 28 | 44 716 | 44 871 | 45 025 | 45 179 | 45 332 | 45 484 | 45 637 | 45 788 | 45 939 | 46 090 |
| 29 | 46 240 | 46 389 | 46 538 | 46 687 | 46 835 | 46 982 | 47 129 | 47 276 | 47 422 | 47 567 |
| 30 | 47 712 | 47 857 | 48 001 | 48 144 | 48 287 | 48 430 | 48 572 | 48 714 | 48 855 | 48 996 |
| 31 | 49 136 | 49 276 | 49 415 | 49 554 | 49 693 | 49 831 | 49 969 | 50 106 | 50 243 | 50 379 |
| 32 | 50 515 | 50 651 | 50 786 | 50 920 | 51 055 | 51 188 | 51 322 | 51 455 | 51 587 | 51 720 |
| 33 | 51 851 | 51 983 | 52 114 | 52 244 | 52 375 | 52 504 | 52 634 | 52 763 | 52 892 | 53 020 |
| 34 | 53 148 | 53 275 | 53 403 | 53 529 | 53 656 | 53 782 | 53 908 | 54 033 | 54 158 | 54 283 |
| 35 | 54 407 | 54 531 | 54 654 | 54 777 | 54 900 | 55 023 | 55 145 | 55 267 | 55 388 | 55 509 |
| 36 | 55 630 | 55 751 | 55 871 | 55 991 | 56 110 | 56 229 | 56 348 | 56 467 | 56 585 | 56 703 |
| 37 | 56 820 | 56 937 | 57 054 | 57 171 | 57 287 | 57 403 | 57 519 | 57 634 | 57 749 | 57 864 |
| 38 | 57 978 | 58 092 | 58 206 | 58 320 | 58 433 | 58 546 | 58 659 | 58 771 | 58 883 | 58 995 |
| 39 | 59 106 | 59 218 | 59 329 | 59 439 | 59 550 | 59 660 | 59 770 | 59 879 | 59 988 | 60 097 |
| 40 | 60 206 | 60 314 | 60 423 | 60 531 | 60 638 | 60 746 | 60 853 | 60 959 | 61 066 | 61 172 |
| 41 | 61 278 | 61 384 | 61 490 | 61 595 | 61 700 | 61 805 | 61 909 | 62 014 | 62 118 | 62 221 |
| 42 | 62 325 | 62 428 | 62 531 | 62 634 | 62 737 | 62 839 | 62 941 | 63 043 | 63 144 | 63 246 |
| 43 | 63 347 | 63 448 | 63 548 | 63 649 | 63 749 | 63 849 | 63 949 | 64 048 | 64 147 | 64 246 |
| 44 | 64 345 | 64 444 | 64 542 | 64 640 | 64 738 | 64 836 | 64 933 | 65 031 | 65 128 | 65 225 |
| 45 | 65 321 | 65 418 | 65 514 | 65 610 | 65 706 | 65 801 | 65 896 | 65 992 | 66 087 | 66 181 |
| 46 | 66 276 | 66 370 | 66 464 | 66 558 | 66 652 | 66 745 | 66 839 | 66 932 | 67 025 | 67 117 |
| 47 | 67 210 | 67 302 | 67 394 | 67 486 | 67 578 | 67 669 | 67 761 | 67 852 | 67 943 | 68 034 |
| 48 | 68 124 | 68 215 | 68 305 | 68 395 | 68 485 | 68 574 | 68 664 | 68 753 | 68 842 | 68 931 |
| 49 | 69 020 | 69 108 | 69 197 | 69 285 | 69 373 | 69 461 | 69 548 | 69 636 | 69 723 | 69 810 |
| 50 | 69 897 | 69 984 | 70 070 | 70 157 | 70 243 | 70 329 | 70 415 | 70 501 | 70 586 | 70 672 |
| N | L 0 | 1 | 2 | 3 | 4 | 5 | 6 | 7 | 8 | 9 |

50—100

| N | L 0 | 1 | 2 | 3 | 4 | 5 | 6 | 7 | 8 | 9 |
|---|---|---|---|---|---|---|---|---|---|---|
| 50 | 69 897 | 69 984 | 70 070 | 70 157 | 70 243 | 70 329 | 70 415 | 70 501 | 70 586 | 70 672 |
| 51 | 70 757 | 70 842 | 70 927 | 71 012 | 71 096 | 71 181 | 71 265 | 71 349 | 71 433 | 71 517 |
| 52 | 71 600 | 71 684 | 71 767 | 71 850 | 71 933 | 72 016 | 72 099 | 72 181 | 72 263 | 72 346 |
| 53 | 72 428 | 72 509 | 72 591 | 72 673 | 72 754 | 72 835 | 72 916 | 72 997 | 73 078 | 73 159 |
| 54 | 73 239 | 73 320 | 73 400 | 73 480 | 73 560 | 73 640 | 73 719 | 73 799 | 73 878 | 73 957 |
| 55 | 74 036 | 74 115 | 74 194 | 74 273 | 74 351 | 74 429 | 74 507 | 74 586 | 74 663 | 74 741 |
| 56 | 74 819 | 74 896 | 74 974 | 75 051 | 75 128 | 75 205 | 75 282 | 75 358 | 75 435 | 75 511 |
| 57 | 75 587 | 75 664 | 75 740 | 75 815 | 75 891 | 75 967 | 76 042 | 76 118 | 76 193 | 76 268 |
| 58 | 76 346 | 76 418 | 76 492 | 76 567 | 76 641 | 76 716 | 76 790 | 76 864 | 76 938 | 77 012 |
| 59 | 77 085 | 77 159 | 77 232 | 77 305 | 77 379 | 77 452 | 77 525 | 77 597 | 77 670 | 77 743 |
| 60 | 77 815 | 77 887 | 77 960 | 78 032 | 78 104 | 78 176 | 78 247 | 78 319 | 78 390 | 78 462 |
| 61 | 78 533 | 78 604 | 78 675 | 78 746 | 78 817 | 78 888 | 78 958 | 79 029 | 79 099 | 79 169 |
| 62 | 79 239 | 79 309 | 79 379 | 79 449 | 79 518 | 79 588 | 79 657 | 79 727 | 79 796 | 79 865 |
| 63 | 79 934 | 80 003 | 80 072 | 80 140 | 80 209 | 80 277 | 80 346 | 80 414 | 80 482 | 80 550 |
| 64 | 80 618 | 80 686 | 80 754 | 80 821 | 80 889 | 80 956 | 81 023 | 81 090 | 81 158 | 81 224 |
| 65 | 81 291 | 81 358 | 81 425 | 81 491 | 81 558 | 81 624 | 81 690 | 81 757 | 81 823 | 81 889 |
| 66 | 81 954 | 82 020 | 82 086 | 82 151 | 82 217 | 82 282 | 82 347 | 82 413 | 82 478 | 82 543 |
| 67 | 82 607 | 82 672 | 82 737 | 82 802 | 82 866 | 82 930 | 82 995 | 83 059 | 83 123 | 83 187 |
| 68 | 83 251 | 83 315 | 83 378 | 83 442 | 83 506 | 83 569 | 83 632 | 83 696 | 83 759 | 83 822 |
| 69 | 83 885 | 83 948 | 84 011 | 84 073 | 84 136 | 84 198 | 84 261 | 84 323 | 84 386 | 84 448 |
| 70 | 84 510 | 84 572 | 84 634 | 84 696 | 84 757 | 84 819 | 84 880 | 84 942 | 85 003 | 85 065 |
| 71 | 85 126 | 85 187 | 85 248 | 85 309 | 85 370 | 85 431 | 85 491 | 85 552 | 85 612 | 85 673 |
| 72 | 85 733 | 85 794 | 85 854 | 85 914 | 85 974 | 86 034 | 86 094 | 86 153 | 86 213 | 86 273 |
| 73 | 86 332 | 86 392 | 86 451 | 86 510 | 86 570 | 86 629 | 86 688 | 86 747 | 86 806 | 86 864 |
| 74 | 86 923 | 86 982 | 87 040 | 87 099 | 87 157 | 87 216 | 87 274 | 87 332 | 87 390 | 87 448 |
| 75 | 87 506 | 87 564 | 87 622 | 87 679 | 87 737 | 87 795 | 87 852 | 87 910 | 87 967 | 88 024 |
| 76 | 88 081 | 88 138 | 88 195 | 88 252 | 88 309 | 88 366 | 88 423 | 88 480 | 88 536 | 88 593 |
| 77 | 88 649 | 88 705 | 88 762 | 88 818 | 88 874 | 88 930 | 88 986 | 89 042 | 89 098 | 89 154 |
| 78 | 89 209 | 89 265 | 89 321 | 89 376 | 89 432 | 89 487 | 89 542 | 89 597 | 89 653 | 89 708 |
| 79 | 89 763 | 89 818 | 89 873 | 89 927 | 89 982 | 90 037 | 90 091 | 90 146 | 90 200 | 90 255 |
| 80 | 90 309 | 90 363 | 90 417 | 90 472 | 90 526 | 90 580 | 90 634 | 90 687 | 90 741 | 90 795 |
| 81 | 90 849 | 90 902 | 90 956 | 91 009 | 91 062 | 91 116 | 91 169 | 91 222 | 91 275 | 91 328 |
| 82 | 91 381 | 91 434 | 91 487 | 91 540 | 91 593 | 91 645 | 91 698 | 91 751 | 91 803 | 91 855 |
| 83 | 91 908 | 91 960 | 92 012 | 92 065 | 92 117 | 92 169 | 92 221 | 92 273 | 92 324 | 92 376 |
| 84 | 92 428 | 92 480 | 92 531 | 92 583 | 92 634 | 92 686 | 92 737 | 92 788 | 92 840 | 92 891 |
| 85 | 92 942 | 92 993 | 93 044 | 93 095 | 93 146 | 93 197 | 93 247 | 93 298 | 93 349 | 93 399 |
| 86 | 93 450 | 93 500 | 93 551 | 93 601 | 93 651 | 93 702 | 93 752 | 93 802 | 93 852 | 93 902 |
| 87 | 93 952 | 94 002 | 94 052 | 94 101 | 94 151 | 94 201 | 94 250 | 94 300 | 94 349 | 94 399 |
| 88 | 94 448 | 94 498 | 94 547 | 94 596 | 94 645 | 94 694 | 94 743 | 94 792 | 94 841 | 94 890 |
| 89 | 94 939 | 94 988 | 95 036 | 95 085 | 95 134 | 95 182 | 95 231 | 95 279 | 95 328 | 95 376 |
| 90 | 95 424 | 95 472 | 95 521 | 95 569 | 95 617 | 95 665 | 95 713 | 95 761 | 95 809 | 95 856 |
| 91 | 95 904 | 95 952 | 95 999 | 96 047 | 96 095 | 96 142 | 96 190 | 96 237 | 96 284 | 96 332 |
| 92 | 96 379 | 96 426 | 96 473 | 96 520 | 96 567 | 96 614 | 96 661 | 96 708 | 96 755 | 96 802 |
| 93 | 96 848 | 96 895 | 96 942 | 96 988 | 97 035 | 97 081 | 97 128 | 97 174 | 97 220 | 97 267 |
| 94 | 97 313 | 97 359 | 97 405 | 97 451 | 97 497 | 97 543 | 97 589 | 97 635 | 97 681 | 97 727 |
| 95 | 97 772 | 97 818 | 97 864 | 97 909 | 97 955 | 98 000 | 98 046 | 98 091 | 98 137 | 98 182 |
| 96 | 98 227 | 98 272 | 98 318 | 98 363 | 98 408 | 98 453 | 98 498 | 98 543 | 98 588 | 98 632 |
| 97 | 98 677 | 98 722 | 98 767 | 98 811 | 98 856 | 98 900 | 98 945 | 98 989 | 99 034 | 99 078 |
| 98 | 99 123 | 99 167 | 99 211 | 99 255 | 99 300 | 99 344 | 99 388 | 99 432 | 99 476 | 99 520 |
| 99 | 99 564 | 99 607 | 99 651 | 99 695 | 99 739 | 99 782 | 99 826 | 99 870 | 99 913 | 99 957 |
| 100 | 00 000 | 00 043 | 00 087 | 00 130 | 00 173 | 00 217 | 00 260 | 00 303 | 00 346 | 00 389 |
| N | L 0 | 1 | 2 | 3 | 4 | 5 | 6 | 7 | 8 | 9 |

100—150

| N | L 0 | 1 | 2 | 3 | 4 | 5 | 6 | 7 | 8 | 9 |
|---|---|---|---|---|---|---|---|---|---|---|
| 100 | 00 000 | 043 | 087 | 130 | 173 | 217 | 260 | 303 | 346 | 389 |
| 101 | 432 | 475 | 518 | 561 | 604 | 647 | 689 | 732 | 775 | 817 |
| 102 | 860 | 903 | 945 | 988 | *030 | *072 | *115 | *157 | *199 | *242 |
| 103 | 01 284 | 326 | 368 | 410 | 452 | 494 | 536 | 578 | 620 | 662 |
| 104 | 703 | 745 | 787 | 828 | 870 | 912 | 953 | 995 | *036 | *078 |
| 105 | 02 119 | 160 | 202 | 243 | 284 | 325 | 366 | 407 | 449 | 490 |
| 106 | 531 | 572 | 612 | 653 | 694 | 735 | 776 | 816 | 857 | 898 |
| 107 | 938 | 979 | *019 | *060 | *100 | *141 | *181 | *222 | *262 | *302 |
| 108 | 03 342 | 383 | 423 | 463 | 503 | 543 | 583 | 623 | 663 | 703 |
| 109 | 743 | 782 | 822 | 862 | 902 | 941 | 981 | *021 | *060 | *100 |
| 110 | 04 139 | 179 | 218 | 258 | 297 | 336 | 376 | 415 | 454 | 493 |
| 111 | 532 | 571 | 610 | 650 | 689 | 727 | 766 | 805 | 844 | 883 |
| 112 | 922 | 961 | 999 | *038 | *077 | *115 | *154 | *192 | *231 | *269 |
| 113 | 05 308 | 346 | 385 | 423 | 461 | 500 | 538 | 576 | 614 | 652 |
| 114 | 690 | 729 | 767 | 805 | 843 | 881 | 918 | 956 | 994 | *032 |
| 115 | 06 070 | 108 | 145 | 183 | 221 | 258 | 296 | 333 | 371 | 408 |
| 116 | 446 | 483 | 521 | 558 | 595 | 633 | 670 | 707 | 744 | 781 |
| 117 | 819 | 856 | 893 | 930 | 967 | *004 | *041 | *078 | *115 | *151 |
| 118 | 07 188 | 225 | 262 | 298 | 335 | 372 | 408 | 445 | 482 | 518 |
| 119 | 555 | 591 | 628 | 664 | 700 | 737 | 773 | 809 | 846 | 882 |
| 120 | 918 | 954 | 990 | *027 | *063 | *099 | *135 | *171 | *207 | *243 |
| 121 | 08 279 | 314 | 350 | 386 | 422 | 458 | 493 | 529 | 565 | 600 |
| 122 | 636 | 672 | 707 | 743 | 778 | 814 | 849 | 884 | 920 | 955 |
| 123 | 991 | *026 | *061 | *096 | *132 | *167 | *202 | *237 | *272 | *307 |
| 124 | 09 342 | 377 | 412 | 447 | 482 | 517 | 552 | 587 | 621 | 656 |
| 125 | 691 | 726 | 760 | 795 | 830 | 864 | 899 | 934 | 968 | *003 |
| 126 | 10 037 | 072 | 106 | 140 | 175 | 209 | 243 | 278 | 312 | 346 |
| 127 | 380 | 415 | 449 | 483 | 517 | 551 | 585 | 619 | 653 | 687 |
| 128 | 721 | 755 | 789 | 823 | 857 | 890 | 924 | 958 | 992 | *025 |
| 129 | 11 059 | 093 | 126 | 160 | 193 | 227 | 261 | 294 | 327 | 361 |
| 130 | 394 | 428 | 461 | 494 | 528 | 561 | 594 | 628 | 661 | 694 |
| 131 | 727 | 760 | 793 | 826 | 860 | 893 | 926 | 959 | 992 | *024 |
| 132 | 12 057 | 090 | 123 | 156 | 189 | 222 | 254 | 287 | 320 | 352 |
| 133 | 385 | 418 | 450 | 483 | 516 | 548 | 581 | 613 | 646 | 678 |
| 134 | 710 | 743 | 775 | 808 | 840 | 872 | 905 | 937 | 969 | *001 |
| 135 | 13 033 | 066 | 098 | 130 | 162 | 194 | 226 | 258 | 290 | 322 |
| 136 | 354 | 386 | 418 | 450 | 481 | 513 | 545 | 577 | 609 | 640 |
| 137 | 672 | 704 | 735 | 767 | 799 | 830 | 862 | 893 | 925 | 956 |
| 138 | 988 | *019 | *051 | *082 | *114 | *145 | *176 | *208 | *239 | *270 |
| 139 | 14 301 | 333 | 364 | 395 | 426 | 457 | 489 | 520 | 551 | 582 |
| 140 | 613 | 644 | 675 | 706 | 737 | 768 | 799 | 829 | 860 | 891 |
| 141 | 922 | 953 | 983 | *014 | *045 | *076 | *106 | *137 | *168 | *198 |
| 142 | 15 229 | 259 | 290 | 320 | 351 | 381 | 412 | 442 | 473 | 503 |
| 143 | 534 | 564 | 594 | 625 | 655 | 685 | 715 | 746 | 776 | 806 |
| 144 | 836 | 866 | 897 | 927 | 957 | 987 | *017 | *047 | *077 | *107 |
| 145 | 16 137 | 167 | 197 | 227 | 256 | 286 | 316 | 346 | 376 | 406 |
| 146 | 435 | 465 | 495 | 524 | 554 | 584 | 613 | 643 | 673 | 702 |
| 147 | 732 | 761 | 791 | 820 | 850 | 879 | 909 | 938 | 967 | 997 |
| 148 | 17 026 | 056 | 085 | 114 | 143 | 173 | 202 | 231 | 260 | 289 |
| 149 | 319 | 348 | 377 | 406 | 435 | 464 | 493 | 522 | 551 | 580 |
| 150 | 17 609 | 638 | 667 | 696 | 725 | 754 | 782 | 811 | 840 | 869 |
| N | L 0 | 1 | 2 | 3 | 4 | 5 | 6 | 7 | 8 | 9 |

### P P

| | 44 | 43 | 42 |
|---|---|---|---|
| 1 | 4.4 | 4.3 | 4.2 |
| 2 | 8.8 | 8.6 | 8.4 |
| 3 | 13.2 | 12.9 | 12.6 |
| 4 | 17.6 | 17.2 | 16.8 |
| 5 | 22.0 | 21.5 | 21.0 |
| 6 | 26.4 | 25.8 | 25.2 |
| 7 | 30.8 | 30.1 | 29.4 |
| 8 | 35.2 | 34.4 | 33.6 |
| 9 | 39.6 | 38.7 | 37.8 |

| | 41 | 40 | 39 |
|---|---|---|---|
| 1 | 4.1 | 4.0 | 3.9 |
| 2 | 8.2 | 8.0 | 7.8 |
| 3 | 12.3 | 12.0 | 11.7 |
| 4 | 16.4 | 16.0 | 15.6 |
| 5 | 20.5 | 20.0 | 19.5 |
| 6 | 24.6 | 24.0 | 23.4 |
| 7 | 28.7 | 28.0 | 27.3 |
| 8 | 32.8 | 32.0 | 31.2 |
| 9 | 36.9 | 36.0 | 35.1 |

| | 38 | 37 | 36 |
|---|---|---|---|
| 1 | 3.8 | 3.7 | 3.6 |
| 2 | 7.6 | 7.4 | 7.2 |
| 3 | 11.4 | 11.1 | 10.8 |
| 4 | 15.2 | 14.8 | 14.4 |
| 5 | 19.0 | 18.5 | 18.0 |
| 6 | 22.8 | 22.2 | 21.6 |
| 7 | 26.6 | 25.9 | 25.2 |
| 8 | 30.4 | 29.6 | 28.8 |
| 9 | 34.2 | 33.3 | 32.4 |

| | 35 | 34 | 33 |
|---|---|---|---|
| 1 | 3.5 | 3.4 | 3.3 |
| 2 | 7.0 | 6.8 | 6.6 |
| 3 | 10.5 | 10.2 | 9.9 |
| 4 | 14.0 | 13.6 | 13.2 |
| 5 | 17.5 | 17.0 | 16.5 |
| 6 | 21.0 | 20.4 | 19.8 |
| 7 | 24.5 | 23.8 | 23.1 |
| 8 | 28.0 | 27.2 | 26.4 |
| 9 | 31.5 | 30.6 | 29.7 |

| | 32 | 31 | 30 |
|---|---|---|---|
| 1 | 3.2 | 3.1 | 3.0 |
| 2 | 6.4 | 6.2 | 6.0 |
| 3 | 9.6 | 9.3 | 9.0 |
| 4 | 12.8 | 12.4 | 12.0 |
| 5 | 16.0 | 15.5 | 15.0 |
| 6 | 19.2 | 18.6 | 18.0 |
| 7 | 22.4 | 21.7 | 21.0 |
| 8 | 25.6 | 24.8 | 24.0 |
| 9 | 28.8 | 27.9 | 27.0 |

| N | L 0 | 1 | 2 | 3 | 4 | 5 | 6 | 7 | 8 | 9 |
|---|---|---|---|---|---|---|---|---|---|---|
| 150 | 17 609 | 638 | 667 | 696 | 725 | 754 | 782 | 811 | 840 | 869 |
| 151 | 898 | 926 | 955 | 984 | *013 | *041 | *070 | *099 | *127 | *156 |
| 152 | 18 184 | 213 | 241 | 270 | 298 | 327 | 355 | 384 | 412 | 441 |
| 153 | 469 | 498 | 526 | 554 | 583 | 611 | 639 | 667 | 696 | 724 |
| 154 | 752 | 780 | 808 | 837 | 865 | 893 | 921 | 949 | 977 | *005 |
| 155 | 19 033 | 061 | 089 | 117 | 145 | 173 | 201 | 229 | 257 | 285 |
| 156 | 312 | 340 | 368 | 396 | 424 | 451 | 479 | 507 | 535 | 562 |
| 157 | 590 | 618 | 645 | 673 | 700 | 728 | 756 | 783 | 811 | 838 |
| 158 | 866 | 893 | 921 | 948 | 976 | *003 | *030 | *058 | *085 | *112 |
| 159 | 20 140 | 167 | 194 | 222 | 249 | 276 | 303 | 330 | 358 | 385 |
| 160 | 412 | 439 | 466 | 493 | 520 | 548 | 575 | 602 | 629 | 656 |
| 161 | 683 | 710 | 737 | 763 | 790 | 817 | 844 | 871 | 898 | 925 |
| 162 | 952 | 978 | *005 | *032 | *059 | *085 | *112 | *139 | *165 | *192 |
| 163 | 21 219 | 245 | 272 | 299 | 325 | 352 | 378 | 405 | 431 | 458 |
| 164 | 484 | 511 | 537 | 564 | 590 | 617 | 643 | 669 | 696 | 722 |
| 165 | 748 | 775 | 801 | 827 | 854 | 880 | 906 | 932 | 958 | 985 |
| 166 | 22 011 | 037 | 063 | 089 | 115 | 141 | 167 | 194 | 220 | 246 |
| 167 | 272 | 298 | 324 | 350 | 376 | 401 | 427 | 453 | 479 | 505 |
| 168 | 531 | 557 | 583 | 608 | 634 | 660 | 686 | 712 | 737 | 763 |
| 169 | 789 | 814 | 840 | 866 | 891 | 917 | 943 | 968 | 994 | *019 |
| 170 | 23 045 | 070 | 096 | 121 | 147 | 172 | 198 | 223 | 249 | 274 |
| 171 | 300 | 325 | 350 | 376 | 401 | 426 | 452 | 477 | 502 | 528 |
| 172 | 553 | 578 | 603 | 629 | 654 | 679 | 704 | 729 | 754 | 779 |
| 173 | 805 | 830 | 855 | 880 | 905 | 930 | 955 | 980 | *005 | *030 |
| 174 | 24 055 | 080 | 105 | 130 | 155 | 180 | 204 | 229 | 254 | 279 |
| 175 | 304 | 329 | 353 | 378 | 403 | 428 | 452 | 477 | 502 | 527 |
| 176 | 551 | 576 | 601 | 625 | 650 | 674 | 699 | 724 | 748 | 773 |
| 177 | 797 | 822 | 846 | 871 | 895 | 920 | 944 | 969 | 993 | *018 |
| 178 | 25 042 | 066 | 091 | 115 | 139 | 164 | 188 | 212 | 237 | 261 |
| 179 | 285 | 310 | 334 | 358 | 382 | 406 | 431 | 455 | 479 | 503 |
| 180 | 527 | 551 | 575 | 600 | 624 | 648 | 672 | 696 | 720 | 744 |
| 181 | 768 | 792 | 816 | 840 | 864 | 888 | 912 | 935 | 959 | 983 |
| 182 | 26 007 | 031 | 055 | 079 | 102 | 126 | 150 | 174 | 198 | 221 |
| 183 | 245 | 269 | 293 | 316 | 340 | 364 | 387 | 411 | 435 | 458 |
| 184 | 482 | 505 | 529 | 553 | 576 | 600 | 623 | 647 | 670 | 694 |
| 185 | 717 | 741 | 764 | 788 | 811 | 834 | 858 | 881 | 905 | 928 |
| 186 | 951 | 975 | 998 | *021 | *045 | *068 | *091 | *114 | *138 | *161 |
| 187 | 27 184 | 207 | 231 | 254 | 277 | 300 | 323 | 346 | 370 | 393 |
| 188 | 416 | 439 | 462 | 485 | 508 | 531 | 554 | 577 | 600 | 623 |
| 189 | 646 | 669 | 692 | 715 | 738 | 761 | 784 | 807 | 830 | 852 |
| 190 | 875 | 898 | 921 | 944 | 967 | 989 | *012 | *035 | *058 | *081 |
| 191 | 28 103 | 126 | 149 | 171 | 194 | 217 | 240 | 262 | 285 | 307 |
| 192 | 330 | 353 | 375 | 398 | 421 | 443 | 466 | 488 | 511 | 533 |
| 193 | 556 | 578 | 601 | 623 | 646 | 668 | 691 | 713 | 735 | 758 |
| 194 | 780 | 803 | 825 | 847 | 870 | 892 | 914 | 937 | 959 | 981 |
| 195 | 29 003 | 026 | 048 | 070 | 092 | 115 | 137 | 159 | 181 | 203 |
| 196 | 226 | 248 | 270 | 292 | 314 | 336 | 358 | 380 | 403 | 425 |
| 197 | 447 | 469 | 491 | 513 | 535 | 557 | 579 | 601 | 623 | 645 |
| 198 | 667 | 688 | 710 | 732 | 754 | 776 | 798 | 820 | 842 | 863 |
| 199 | 885 | 907 | 929 | 951 | 973 | 994 | *016 | *038 | *060 | *081 |
| 200 | 30 103 | 125 | 146 | 168 | 190 | 211 | 233 | 255 | 276 | 298 |
| N | L 0 | 1 | 2 | 3 | 4 | 5 | 6 | 7 | 8 | 9 |

P P

| | 29 | 28 |
|---|---|---|
| 1 | 2.9 | 2.8 |
| 2 | 5.8 | 5.6 |
| 3 | 8.7 | 8.4 |
| 4 | 11.6 | 11.2 |
| 5 | 14.5 | 14.0 |
| 6 | 17.4 | 16.8 |
| 7 | 20.3 | 19.6 |
| 8 | 23.2 | 22.4 |
| 9 | 26.1 | 25.2 |

| | 27 | 26 |
|---|---|---|
| 1 | 2.7 | 2.6 |
| 2 | 5.4 | 5.2 |
| 3 | 8.1 | 7.8 |
| 4 | 10.8 | 10.4 |
| 5 | 13.5 | 13.0 |
| 6 | 16.2 | 15.6 |
| 7 | 18.9 | 18.2 |
| 8 | 21.6 | 20.8 |
| 9 | 24.3 | 23.4 |

| | 25 |
|---|---|
| 1 | 2.5 |
| 2 | 5.0 |
| 3 | 7.5 |
| 4 | 10.0 |
| 5 | 12.5 |
| 6 | 15.0 |
| 7 | 17.5 |
| 8 | 20.0 |
| 9 | 22.5 |

| | 24 | 23 |
|---|---|---|
| 1 | 2.4 | 2.3 |
| 2 | 4.8 | 4.6 |
| 3 | 7.2 | 6.9 |
| 4 | 9.6 | 9.2 |
| 5 | 12.0 | 11.5 |
| 6 | 14.4 | 13.8 |
| 7 | 16.8 | 16.1 |
| 8 | 19.2 | 18.4 |
| 9 | 21.6 | 20.7 |

| | 22 | 21 |
|---|---|---|
| 1 | 2.2 | 2.1 |
| 2 | 4.4 | 4.2 |
| 3 | 6.6 | 6.3 |
| 4 | 8.8 | 8.4 |
| 5 | 11.0 | 10.5 |
| 6 | 13.2 | 12.6 |
| 7 | 15.4 | 14.7 |
| 8 | 17.6 | 16.8 |
| 9 | 19.8 | 18.9 |

P P

| N | L 0 | 1 | 2 | 3 | 4 | 5 | 6 | 7 | 8 | 9 |
|---|---|---|---|---|---|---|---|---|---|---|
| 200 | 30 103 | 125 | 146 | 168 | 190 | 211 | 233 | 255 | 276 | 298 |
| 201 | 320 | 341 | 363 | 384 | 406 | 428 | 449 | 471 | 492 | 514 |
| 202 | 535 | 557 | 578 | 600 | 621 | 643 | 664 | 685 | 707 | 728 |
| 203 | 750 | 771 | 792 | 814 | 835 | 856 | 878 | 899 | 920 | 942 |
| 204 | 963 | 984 | *006 | *027 | *048 | *069 | *091 | *112 | *133 | *154 |
| 205 | 31 175 | 197 | 218 | 239 | 260 | 281 | 302 | 323 | 345 | 366 |
| 206 | 387 | 408 | 429 | 450 | 471 | 492 | 513 | 534 | 555 | 576 |
| 207 | 597 | 618 | 639 | 660 | 681 | 702 | 723 | 744 | 765 | 785 |
| 208 | 806 | 827 | 848 | 869 | 890 | 911 | 931 | 952 | 973 | 994 |
| 209 | 32 015 | 035 | 056 | 077 | 098 | 118 | 139 | 160 | 181 | 201 |
| 210 | 222 | 243 | 263 | 284 | 305 | 325 | 346 | 366 | 387 | 408 |
| 211 | 428 | 449 | 469 | 490 | 510 | 531 | 552 | 572 | 593 | 613 |
| 212 | 634 | 654 | 675 | 695 | 715 | 736 | 756 | 777 | 797 | 818 |
| 213 | 838 | 858 | 879 | 899 | 919 | 940 | 960 | 980 | *001 | *021 |
| 214 | 33 041 | 062 | 082 | 102 | 122 | 143 | 163 | 183 | 203 | 224 |
| 215 | 244 | 264 | 284 | 304 | 325 | 345 | 365 | 385 | 405 | 425 |
| 216 | 445 | 465 | 486 | 506 | 526 | 546 | 566 | 586 | 606 | 626 |
| 217 | 646 | 666 | 686 | 706 | 726 | 746 | 766 | 786 | 806 | 826 |
| 218 | 846 | 866 | 885 | 905 | 925 | 945 | 965 | 985 | *005 | *025 |
| 219 | 34 044 | 064 | 084 | 104 | 124 | 143 | 163 | 183 | 203 | 223 |
| 220 | 242 | 262 | 282 | 301 | 321 | 341 | 361 | 380 | 400 | 420 |
| 221 | 439 | 459 | 479 | 498 | 518 | 537 | 557 | 577 | 596 | 616 |
| 222 | 635 | 655 | 674 | 694 | 713 | 733 | 753 | 772 | 792 | 811 |
| 223 | 830 | 850 | 869 | 889 | 908 | 928 | 947 | 967 | 986 | *005 |
| 224 | 35 025 | 044 | 064 | 083 | 102 | 122 | 141 | 160 | 180 | 199 |
| 225 | 218 | 238 | 257 | 276 | 295 | 315 | 334 | 353 | 372 | 392 |
| 226 | 411 | 430 | 449 | 468 | 488 | 507 | 526 | 545 | 564 | 583 |
| 227 | 603 | 622 | 641 | 660 | 679 | 698 | 717 | 736 | 755 | 774 |
| 228 | 793 | 813 | 832 | 851 | 870 | 889 | 908 | 927 | 946 | 965 |
| 229 | 984 | *003 | *021 | *040 | *059 | *078 | *097 | *116 | *135 | *154 |
| 230 | 36 173 | 192 | 211 | 229 | 248 | 267 | 286 | 305 | 324 | 342 |
| 231 | 361 | 380 | 399 | 418 | 436 | 455 | 474 | 493 | 511 | 530 |
| 232 | 549 | 568 | 586 | 605 | 624 | 642 | 661 | 680 | 698 | 717 |
| 233 | 736 | 754 | 773 | 791 | 810 | 829 | 847 | 866 | 884 | 903 |
| 234 | 922 | 940 | 959 | 977 | 996 | *014 | *033 | *051 | *070 | *088 |
| 235 | 37 107 | 125 | 144 | 162 | 181 | 199 | 218 | 236 | 254 | 273 |
| 236 | 291 | 310 | 328 | 346 | 365 | 383 | 401 | 420 | 438 | 457 |
| 237 | 475 | 493 | 511 | 530 | 548 | 566 | 585 | 603 | 621 | 639 |
| 238 | 658 | 676 | 694 | 712 | 731 | 749 | 767 | 785 | 803 | 822 |
| 239 | 840 | 858 | 876 | 894 | 912 | 931 | 949 | 967 | 985 | *003 |
| 240 | 38 021 | 039 | 057 | 075 | 093 | 112 | 130 | 148 | 166 | 184 |
| 241 | 202 | 220 | 238 | 256 | 274 | 292 | 310 | 328 | 346 | 364 |
| 242 | 382 | 399 | 417 | 435 | 453 | 471 | 489 | 507 | 525 | 543 |
| 243 | 561 | 578 | 596 | 614 | 632 | 650 | 668 | 686 | 703 | 721 |
| 244 | 739 | 757 | 775 | 792 | 810 | 828 | 846 | 863 | 881 | 899 |
| 245 | 917 | 934 | 952 | 970 | 987 | *005 | *023 | *041 | *058 | *076 |
| 246 | 39 094 | 111 | 129 | 146 | 164 | 182 | 199 | 217 | 235 | 252 |
| 247 | 270 | 287 | 305 | 322 | 340 | 358 | 375 | 393 | 410 | 428 |
| 248 | 445 | 463 | 480 | 498 | 515 | 533 | 550 | 568 | 585 | 602 |
| 249 | 620 | 637 | 655 | 672 | 690 | 707 | 724 | 742 | 759 | 777 |
| 250 | 794 | 811 | 829 | 846 | 863 | 881 | 898 | 915 | 933 | 950 |
| N | L 0 | 1 | 2 | 3 | 4 | 5 | 6 | 7 | 8 | 9 |

P P

| | 22 | 21 |
|---|---|---|
| 1 | 2.2 | 2.1 |
| 2 | 4.4 | 4.2 |
| 3 | 6.6 | 6.3 |
| 4 | 8.8 | 8.4 |
| 5 | 11.0 | 10.5 |
| 6 | 13.2 | 12.6 |
| 7 | 15.4 | 14.7 |
| 8 | 17.6 | 16.8 |
| 9 | 19.8 | 18.9 |

| | 20 |
|---|---|
| 1 | 2.0 |
| 2 | 4.0 |
| 3 | 6.0 |
| 4 | 8.0 |
| 5 | 10.0 |
| 6 | 12.0 |
| 7 | 14.0 |
| 8 | 16.0 |
| 9 | 18.0 |

| | 19 |
|---|---|
| 1 | 1.9 |
| 2 | 3.8 |
| 3 | 5.7 |
| 4 | 7.6 |
| 5 | 9.5 |
| 6 | 11.4 |
| 7 | 13.3 |
| 8 | 15.2 |
| 9 | 17.1 |

| | 18 |
|---|---|
| 1 | 1.8 |
| 2 | 3.6 |
| 3 | 5.4 |
| 4 | 7.2 |
| 5 | 9.0 |
| 6 | 10.8 |
| 7 | 12.6 |
| 8 | 14.4 |
| 9 | 16.2 |

| | 17 |
|---|---|
| 1 | 1.7 |
| 2 | 3.4 |
| 3 | 5.1 |
| 4 | 6.8 |
| 5 | 8.5 |
| 6 | 10.2 |
| 7 | 11.9 |
| 8 | 13.6 |
| 9 | 15.3 |

250—300

| N | L 0 | 1 | 2 | 3 | 4 | 5 | 6 | 7 | 8 | 9 |
|---|---|---|---|---|---|---|---|---|---|---|
| 250 | 39 794 | 811 | 829 | 846 | 863 | 881 | 898 | 915 | 933 | 950 |
| 251 | 967 | 985 | *002 | *019 | *037 | *054 | *071 | *088 | *106 | *123 |
| 252 | 40 140 | 157 | 175 | 192 | 209 | 226 | 243 | 261 | 278 | 295 |
| 253 | 312 | 329 | 346 | 364 | 381 | 398 | 415 | 432 | 449 | 466 |
| 254 | 483 | 500 | 518 | 535 | 552 | 569 | 586 | 603 | 620 | 637 |
| 255 | 654 | 671 | 688 | 705 | 722 | 739 | 756 | 773 | 790 | 807 |
| 256 | 824 | 841 | 858 | 875 | 892 | 909 | 926 | 943 | 960 | 976 |
| 257 | 993 | *010 | *027 | *044 | *061 | *078 | *095 | *111 | *128 | *145 |
| 258 | 41 162 | 179 | 196 | 212 | 229 | 246 | 263 | 280 | 296 | 313 |
| 259 | 330 | 347 | 363 | 380 | 397 | 414 | 430 | 447 | 464 | 481 |
| 260 | 497 | 514 | 531 | 547 | 564 | 581 | 597 | 614 | 631 | 647 |
| 261 | 664 | 681 | 697 | 714 | 731 | 747 | 764 | 780 | 797 | 814 |
| 262 | 830 | 847 | 863 | 880 | 896 | 913 | 929 | 946 | 963 | 979 |
| 263 | 996 | *012 | *029 | *045 | *062 | *078 | *095 | *111 | *127 | *144 |
| 264 | 42 160 | 177 | 193 | 210 | 226 | 243 | 259 | 275 | 292 | 308 |
| 265 | 325 | 341 | 357 | 374 | 390 | 406 | 423 | 439 | 455 | 472 |
| 266 | 488 | 504 | 521 | 537 | 553 | 570 | 586 | 602 | 619 | 635 |
| 267 | 651 | 667 | 684 | 700 | 716 | 732 | 749 | 765 | 781 | 797 |
| 268 | 813 | 830 | 846 | 862 | 878 | 894 | 911 | 927 | 943 | 959 |
| 269 | 975 | 991 | *008 | *024 | *040 | *056 | *072 | *088 | *104 | *120 |
| 270 | 43 136 | 152 | 169 | 185 | 201 | 217 | 233 | 249 | 265 | 281 |
| 271 | 297 | 313 | 329 | 345 | 361 | 377 | 393 | 409 | 425 | .441 |
| 272 | 457 | 473 | 489 | 505 | 521 | 537 | 553 | 569 | 584 | 600 |
| 273 | 616 | 632 | 648 | 664 | 680 | 696 | 712 | 727 | 743 | 759 |
| 274 | 775 | 791 | 807 | 823 | 838 | 854 | 870 | 886 | 902 | 917 |
| 275 | 933 | 949 | 965 | 981 | 996 | *012 | *028 | *044 | *059 | *075 |
| 276 | 44 091 | 107 | 122 | 138 | 154 | 170 | 185 | 201 | 217 | 232 |
| 277 | 248 | 264 | 279 | 295 | 311 | 326 | 342 | 358 | 373 | 389 |
| 278 | 404 | 420 | 436 | 451 | 467 | 483 | 498 | 514 | 529 | 545 |
| 279 | 560 | 576 | 592 | 607 | 623 | 638 | 654 | 669 | 685 | 700 |
| 280 | 716 | 731 | 747 | 762 | 778 | 793 | 809 | 824 | 840 | 855 |
| 281 | 871 | 886 | 902 | 917 | 932 | 948 | 963 | 979 | 994 | *010 |
| 282 | 45 025 | 040 | 056 | 071 | 086 | 102 | 117 | 133 | 148 | 163 |
| 283 | 179 | 194 | 209 | 225 | 240 | 255 | 271 | 286 | 301 | 317 |
| 284 | 332 | 347 | 362 | 378 | 393 | 408 | 423 | 439 | 454 | 469 |
| 285 | 484 | 500 | 515 | 530 | 545 | 561 | 576 | 591 | 606 | 621 |
| 286 | 637 | 652 | 667 | 682 | 697 | 712 | 728 | 743 | 758 | 773 |
| 287 | 788 | 803 | 818 | 834 | 849 | 864 | 879 | 894 | 909 | 924 |
| 288 | 939 | 954 | 969 | 984 | *000 | *015 | *030 | *045 | *060 | *075 |
| 289 | 46 090 | 105 | 120 | 135 | 150 | 165 | 180 | 195 | 210 | 225 |
| 290 | 240 | 255 | 270 | 285 | 300 | 315 | 330 | 345 | 359 | 374 |
| 291 | 389 | 404 | 419 | 434 | 449 | 464 | 479 | 494 | 509 | 523 |
| 292 | 538 | 553 | 568 | 583 | 598 | 613 | 627 | 642 | 657 | 672 |
| 293 | 687 | 702 | 716 | 731 | 746 | 761 | 776 | 790 | 805 | 820 |
| 294 | 835 | 850 | 864 | 879 | 894 | 909 | 923 | 938 | 953 | 967 |
| 295 | 982 | 997 | *012 | *026 | *041 | *056 | *070 | *085 | *100 | *114 |
| 296 | 47 129 | 144 | 159 | 173 | 188 | 202 | 217 | 232 | 246 | 261 |
| 297 | 276 | 290 | 305 | 319 | 334 | 349 | 363 | 378 | 392 | 407 |
| 298 | 422 | 436 | 451 | 465 | 480 | 494 | 509 | 524 | 538 | 553 |
| 299 | 567 | 582 | 596 | 611 | 625 | 640 | 654 | 669 | 683 | 698 |
| 300 | 712 | 727 | 741 | 756 | 770 | 784 | 799 | 813 | 828 | 842 |
| N | L 0 | 1 | 2 | 3 | 4 | 5 | 6 | 7 | 8 | 9 |

P P

| 18 | | 17 | | 16 | | 15 | | 14 | |
|---|---|---|---|---|---|---|---|---|---|
| 1 | 1.8 | 1 | 1.7 | 1 | 1.6 | 1 | 1.5 | 1 | 1.4 |
| 2 | 3.6 | 2 | 3.4 | 2 | 3.2 | 2 | 3.0 | 2 | 2.8 |
| 3 | 5.4 | 3 | 5.1 | 3 | 4.8 | 3 | 4.5 | 3 | 4.2 |
| 4 | 7.2 | 4 | 6.8 | 4 | 6.4 | 4 | 6.0 | 4 | 5.6 |
| 5 | 9.0 | 5 | 8.5 | 5 | 8.0 | 5 | 7.5 | 5 | 7.0 |
| 6 | 10.8 | 6 | 10.2 | 6 | 9.6 | 6 | 9.0 | 6 | 8.4 |
| 7 | 12.6 | 7 | 11.9 | 7 | 11.2 | 7 | 10.5 | 7 | 9.8 |
| 8 | 14.4 | 8 | 13.6 | 8 | 12.8 | 8 | 12.0 | 8 | 11.2 |
| 9 | 16.2 | 9 | 15.3 | 9 | 14.4 | 9 | 13.5 | 9 | 12.6 |

### 300—350

| N | L 0 | 1 | 2 | 3 | 4 | 5 | 6 | 7 | 8 | 9 |
|---|---|---|---|---|---|---|---|---|---|---|
| 300 | 47 712 | 727 | 741 | 756 | 770 | 784 | 799 | 813 | 828 | 842 |
| 301 | 857 | 871 | 885 | 900 | 914 | 929 | 943 | 958 | 972 | 986 |
| 302 | 48 001 | 015 | 029 | 044 | 058 | 073 | 087 | 101 | 116 | 130 |
| 303 | 144 | 159 | 173 | 187 | 202 | 216 | 230 | 244 | 259 | 273 |
| 304 | 287 | 302 | 316 | 330 | 344 | 359 | 373 | 387 | 401 | 416 |
| 305 | 430 | 444 | 458 | 473 | 487 | 501 | 515 | 530 | 544 | 558 |
| 306 | 572 | 586 | 601 | 615 | 629 | 643 | 657 | 671 | 686 | 700 |
| 307 | 714 | 728 | 742 | 756 | 770 | 785 | 799 | 813 | 827 | 841 |
| 308 | 855 | 869 | 883 | 897 | 911 | 926 | 940 | 954 | 968 | 982 |
| 309 | 996 | *010 | *024 | *038 | *052 | *066 | *080 | *094 | *108 | *122 |
| 310 | 49 136 | 150 | 164 | 178 | 192 | 206 | 220 | 234 | 248 | 262 |
| 311 | 276 | 290 | 304 | 318 | 332 | 346 | 360 | 374 | 388 | 402 |
| 312 | 415 | 429 | 443 | 457 | 471 | 485 | 499 | 513 | 527 | 541 |
| 313 | 554 | 568 | 582 | 596 | 610 | 624 | 638 | 651 | 665 | 679 |
| 314 | 693 | 707 | 721 | 734 | 748 | 762 | 776 | 790 | 803 | 817 |
| 315 | 831 | 845 | 859 | 872 | 886 | 900 | 914 | 927 | 941 | 955 |
| 316 | 969 | 982 | 996 | *010 | *024 | *037 | *051 | *065 | *079 | *092 |
| 317 | 50 106 | 120 | 133 | 147 | 161 | 174 | 188 | 202 | 215 | 229 |
| 318 | 243 | 256 | 270 | 284 | 297 | 311 | 325 | 338 | 352 | 365 |
| 319 | 379 | 393 | 406 | 420 | 433 | 447 | 461 | 474 | 488 | 501 |
| 320 | 515 | 529 | 542 | 556 | 569 | 583 | 596 | 610 | 623 | 637 |
| 321 | 651 | 664 | 678 | 691 | 705 | 718 | 732 | 745 | 759 | 772 |
| 322 | 786 | 799 | 813 | 826 | 840 | 853 | 866 | 880 | 893 | 907 |
| 323 | 920 | 934 | 947 | 961 | 974 | 987 | *001 | *014 | *028 | *041 |
| 324 | 51 055 | 068 | 081 | 095 | 108 | 121 | 135 | 148 | 162 | 175 |
| 325 | 188 | 202 | 215 | 228 | 242 | 255 | 268 | 282 | 295 | 308 |
| 326 | 322 | 335 | 348 | 362 | 375 | 388 | 402 | 415 | 428 | 441 |
| 327 | 455 | 468 | 481 | 495 | 508 | 521 | 534 | 548 | 561 | 574 |
| 328 | 587 | 601 | 614 | 627 | 640 | 654 | 667 | 680 | 693 | 706 |
| 329 | 720 | 733 | 746 | 759 | 772 | 786 | 799 | 812 | 825 | 838 |
| 330 | 851 | 865 | 878 | 891 | 904 | 917 | 930 | 943 | 957 | 970 |
| 331 | 983 | 996 | *009 | *022 | *035 | *048 | *061 | *075 | *088 | *101 |
| 332 | 52 114 | 127 | 140 | 153 | 166 | 179 | 192 | 205 | 218 | 231 |
| 333 | 244 | 257 | 270 | 284 | 297 | 310 | 323 | 336 | 349 | 362 |
| 334 | 375 | 388 | 401 | 414 | 427 | 440 | 453 | 466 | 479 | 492 |
| 335 | 504 | 517 | 530 | 543 | 556 | 569 | 582 | 595 | 608 | 621 |
| 336 | 634 | 647 | 660 | 673 | 686 | 699 | 711 | 724 | 737 | 750 |
| 337 | 763 | 776 | 789 | 802 | 815 | 827 | 840 | 853 | 866 | 879 |
| 338 | 892 | 905 | 917 | 930 | 943 | 956 | 969 | 982 | 994 | *007 |
| 339 | 53 020 | 033 | 046 | 058 | 071 | 084 | 097 | 110 | 122 | 135 |
| 340 | 148 | 161 | 173 | 186 | 199 | 212 | 224 | 237 | 250 | 263 |
| 341 | 275 | 288 | 301 | 314 | 326 | 339 | 352 | 364 | 377 | 390 |
| 342 | 403 | 415 | 428 | 441 | 453 | 466 | 479 | 491 | 504 | 517 |
| 343 | 529 | 542 | 555 | 567 | 580 | 593 | 605 | 618 | 631 | 643 |
| 344 | 656 | 668 | 681 | 694 | 706 | 719 | 732 | 744 | 757 | 769 |
| 345 | 782 | 794 | 807 | 820 | 832 | 845 | 857 | 870 | 882 | 895 |
| 346 | 908 | 920 | 933 | 945 | 958 | 970 | 983 | 995 | *008 | *020 |
| 347 | 54 033 | 045 | 058 | 070 | 083 | 095 | 108 | 120 | 133 | 145 |
| 348 | 158 | 170 | 183 | 195 | 208 | 220 | 233 | 245 | 258 | 270 |
| 349 | 283 | 295 | 307 | 320 | 332 | 345 | 357 | 370 | 382 | 394 |
| 350 | 407 | 419 | 432 | 444 | 456 | 469 | 481 | 494 | 506 | 518 |
| N | L 0 | 1 | 2 | 3 | 4 | 5 | 6 | 7 | 8 | 9 |

**P P**

| 15 | |
|---|---|
| 1 | 1.5 |
| 2 | 3.0 |
| 3 | 4.5 |
| 4 | 6.0 |
| 5 | 7.5 |
| 6 | 9.0 |
| 7 | 10.5 |
| 8 | 12.0 |
| 9 | 13.5 |

| 14 | |
|---|---|
| 1 | 1.4 |
| 2 | 2.8 |
| 3 | 4.2 |
| 4 | 5.6 |
| 5 | 7.0 |
| 6 | 8.4 |
| 7 | 9.8 |
| 8 | 11.2 |
| 9 | 12.6 |

| 13 | |
|---|---|
| 1 | 1.3 |
| 2 | 2.6 |
| 3 | 3.9 |
| 4 | 5.2 |
| 5 | 6.5 |
| 6 | 7.8 |
| 7 | 9.1 |
| 8 | 10.4 |
| 9 | 11.7 |

| 12 | |
|---|---|
| 1 | 1.2 |
| 2 | 2.4 |
| 3 | 3.6 |
| 4 | 4.8 |
| 5 | 6.0 |
| 6 | 7.2 |
| 7 | 8.4 |
| 8 | 9.6 |
| 9 | 10.8 |

350—400

| N | L 0 | 1 | 2 | 3 | 4 | 5 | 6 | 7 | 8 | 9 | | P P |
|---|---|---|---|---|---|---|---|---|---|---|---|---|
| 350 | 54 407 | 419 | 432 | 444 | 456 | 469 | 481 | 494 | 506 | 518 | | |
| 351 | 531 | 543 | 555 | 568 | 580 | 593 | 605 | 617 | 630 | 642 | | |
| 352 | 654 | 667 | 679 | 691 | 704 | 716 | 728 | 741 | 753 | 765 | | |
| 353 | 777 | 790 | 802 | 814 | 827 | 839 | 851 | 864 | 876 | 888 | | **13** |
| 354 | 900 | 913 | 925 | 937 | 949 | 962 | 974 | 986 | 998 | *011 | | |
| 355 | 55 023 | 035 | 047 | 060 | 072 | 084 | 096 | 108 | 121 | 133 | | 1   1.3 |
| 356 | 145 | 157 | 169 | 182 | 194 | 206 | 218 | 230 | 242 | 255 | | 2   2.6 <br> 3   3.9 |
| 357 | 267 | 279 | 291 | 303 | 315 | 328 | 340 | 352 | 364 | 376 | | 4   5.2 |
| 358 | 388 | 400 | 413 | 425 | 437 | 449 | 461 | 473 | 485 | 497 | | 5   6.5 |
| 359 | 509 | 522 | 534 | 546 | 558 | 570 | 582 | 594 | 606 | 618 | | 6   7.8 |
| 360 | 630 | 642 | 654 | 666 | 678 | 691 | 703 | 715 | 727 | 739 | | 7   9.1 |
| 361 | 751 | 763 | 775 | 787 | 799 | 811 | 823 | 835 | 847 | 859 | | 8   10.4 <br> 9   11.7 |
| 362 | 871 | 883 | 895 | 907 | 919 | 931 | 943 | 955 | 967 | 979 | | |
| 363 | 991 | *003 | *015 | *027 | *038 | *050 | *062 | *074 | *086 | *098 | | |
| 364 | 56 110 | 122 | 134 | 146 | 158 | 170 | 182 | 194 | 205 | 217 | | |
| 365 | 229 | 241 | 253 | 265 | 277 | 289 | 301 | 312 | 324 | 336 | | |
| 366 | 348 | 360 | 372 | 384 | 396 | 407 | 419 | 431 | 443 | 455 | | **12** |
| 367 | 467 | 478 | 490 | 502 | 514 | 526 | 538 | 549 | 561 | 573 | | 1   1.2 |
| 368 | 585 | 597 | 608 | 620 | 632 | 644 | 656 | 667 | 679 | 691 | | 2   2.4 |
| 369 | 703 | 714 | 726 | 738 | 750 | 761 | 773 | 785 | 797 | 808 | | 3   3.6 |
| 370 | 820 | 832 | 844 | 855 | 867 | 879 | 891 | 902 | 914 | 926 | | 4   4.8 <br> 5   6.0 |
| 371 | 937 | 949 | 961 | 972 | 984 | 996 | *008 | *019 | *031 | *043 | | 6   7.2 |
| 372 | 57 054 | 066 | 078 | 089 | 101 | 113 | 124 | 136 | 148 | 159 | | 7   8.4 |
| 373 | 171 | 183 | 194 | 206 | 217 | 229 | 241 | 252 | 264 | 276 | | 8   9.6 <br> 9   10.8 |
| 374 | 287 | 299 | 310 | 322 | 334 | 345 | 357 | 368 | 380 | 392 | | |
| 375 | 403 | 415 | 426 | 438 | 449 | 461 | 473 | 484 | 496 | 507 | | |
| 376 | 519 | 530 | 542 | 553 | 565 | 576 | 588 | 600 | 611 | 623 | | |
| 377 | 634 | 646 | 657 | 669 | 680 | 692 | 703 | 715 | 726 | 738 | | |
| 378 | 749 | 761 | 772 | 784 | 795 | 807 | 818 | 830 | 841 | 852 | | **11** |
| 379 | 864 | 875 | 887 | 898 | 910 | 921 | 933 | 944 | 955 | 967 | | 1   1.1 |
| 380 | 978 | 990 | *001 | *013 | *024 | *035 | *047 | *058 | *070 | *081 | | 2   2.2 <br> 3   3.3 |
| 381 | 58 092 | 104 | 115 | 127 | 138 | 149 | 161 | 172 | 184 | 195 | | 4   4.4 |
| 382 | 206 | 218 | 229 | 240 | 252 | 263 | 274 | 286 | 297 | 309 | | 5   5.5 |
| 383 | 320 | 331 | 343 | 354 | 365 | 377 | 388 | 399 | 410 | 422 | | 6   6.6 |
| 384 | 433 | 444 | 456 | 467 | 478 | 490 | 501 | 512 | 524 | 535 | | 7   7.7 |
| 385 | 546 | 557 | 569 | 580 | 591 | 602 | 614 | 625 | 636 | 647 | | 8   8.8 |
| 386 | 659 | 670 | 681 | 692 | 704 | 715 | 726 | 737 | 749 | 760 | | 9   9.9 |
| 387 | 771 | 782 | 794 | 805 | 816 | 827 | 838 | 850 | 861 | 872 | | |
| 388 | 883 | 894 | 906 | 917 | 928 | 939 | 950 | 961 | 973 | 984 | | |
| 389 | 995 | *006 | *017 | *028 | *040 | *051 | *062 | *073 | *084 | *095 | | **10** |
| 390 | 59 106 | 118 | 129 | 140 | 151 | 162 | 173 | 184 | 195 | 207 | | 1   1.0 |
| 391 | 218 | 229 | 240 | 251 | 262 | 273 | 284 | 295 | 306 | 318 | | 2   2.0 <br> 3   3.0 |
| 392 | 329 | 340 | 351 | 362 | 373 | 384 | 395 | 406 | 417 | 428 | | 4   4.0 |
| 393 | 439 | 450 | 461 | 472 | 483 | 494 | 506 | 517 | 528 | 539 | | 5   5.0 |
| 394 | 550 | 561 | 572 | 583 | 594 | 605 | 616 | 627 | 638 | 649 | | 6   6.0 |
| 395 | 660 | 671 | 682 | 693 | 704 | 715 | 726 | 737 | 748 | 759 | | 7   7.0 |
| 396 | 770 | 780 | 791 | 802 | 813 | 824 | 835 | 846 | 857 | 868 | | 8   8.0 |
| 397 | 879 | 890 | 901 | 912 | 923 | 934 | 945 | 956 | 966 | 977 | | 9   9.0 |
| 398 | 988 | 999 | *010 | *021 | *032 | *043 | *054 | *065 | *076 | *086 | | |
| 399 | 60 097 | 108 | 119 | 130 | 141 | 152 | 163 | 173 | 184 | 195 | | |
| 400 | 206 | 217 | 228 | 239 | 249 | 260 | 271 | 282 | 293 | 304 | | |
| N | L 0 | 1 | 2 | 3 | 4 | 5 | 6 | 7 | 8 | 9 | | P P |

## 400—450

| N | L 0 | 1 | 2 | 3 | 4 | 5 | 6 | 7 | 8 | 9 | P P | |
|---|---|---|---|---|---|---|---|---|---|---|---|---|
| 400 | 60 206 | 217 | 228 | 239 | 249 | 260 | 271 | 282 | 293 | 304 | | |
| 401 | 314 | 325 | 336 | 347 | 358 | 369 | 379 | 390 | 401 | 412 | | |
| 402 | 423 | 433 | 444 | 455 | 466 | 477 | 487 | 498 | 509 | 520 | | |
| 403 | 531 | 541 | 552 | 563 | 574 | 584 | 595 | 606 | 617 | 627 | | |
| 404 | 638 | 649 | 660 | 670 | 681 | 692 | 703 | 713 | 724 | 735 | | |
| 405 | 746 | 756 | 767 | 777 | 788 | 799 | 810 | 821 | 831 | 842 | | |
| 406 | 853 | 863 | 874 | 885 | 895 | 906 | 917 | 927 | 938 | 949 | **11** | |
| 407 | 959 | 970 | 981 | 991 | *002 | *013 | *023 | *034 | *045 | *055 | 1 | 1.1 |
| 408 | 61 066 | 077 | 087 | 098 | 109 | 119 | 130 | 140 | 151 | 162 | 2 | 2.2 |
| 409 | 172 | 183 | 194 | 204 | 215 | 225 | 236 | 247 | 257 | 268 | 3 | 3.3 |
| 410 | 278 | 289 | 300 | 310 | 321 | 331 | 342 | 352 | 363 | 374 | 4 | 4.4 |
| | | | | | | | | | | | 5 | 5.5 |
| 411 | 384 | 395 | 405 | 416 | 426 | 437 | 448 | 458 | 469 | 479 | 6 | 6.6 |
| 412 | 490 | 500 | 511 | 521 | 532 | 542 | 553 | 563 | 574 | 584 | 7 | 7.7 |
| 413 | 595 | 606 | 616 | 627 | 637 | 648 | 658 | 669 | 679 | 690 | 8 | 8.8 |
| 414 | 700 | 711 | 721 | 731 | 742 | 752 | 763 | 773 | 784 | 794 | 9 | 9.9 |
| 415 | 805 | 815 | 826 | 836 | 847 | 857 | 868 | 878 | 888 | 899 | | |
| 416 | 909 | 920 | 930 | 941 | 951 | 962 | 972 | 982 | 993 | *003 | | |
| 417 | 62 014 | 024 | 034 | 045 | 055 | 066 | 076 | 086 | 097 | 107 | | |
| 418 | 118 | 128 | 138 | 149 | 159 | 170 | 180 | 190 | 201 | 211 | | |
| 419 | 221 | 232 | 242 | 252 | 263 | 273 | 284 | 294 | 304 | 315 | | |
| 420 | 325 | 335 | 346 | 356 | 366 | 377 | 387 | 397 | 408 | 418 | | |
| 421 | 428 | 439 | 449 | 459 | 469 | 480 | 490 | 500 | 511 | 521 | **10** | |
| 422 | 531 | 542 | 552 | 562 | 572 | 583 | 593 | 603 | 613 | 624 | 1 | 1.0 |
| 423 | 634 | 644 | 655 | 665 | 675 | 685 | 696 | 706 | 716 | 726 | 2 | 2.0 |
| 424 | 737 | 747 | 757 | 767 | 778 | 788 | 798 | 808 | 818 | 829 | 3 | 3.0 |
| 425 | 839 | 849 | 859 | 870 | 880 | 890 | 900 | 910 | 921 | 931 | 4 | 4.0 |
| 426 | 941 | 951 | 961 | 972 | 982 | 992 | *002 | *012 | *022 | *033 | 5 | 5.0 |
| | | | | | | | | | | | 6 | 6.0 |
| 427 | 63 043 | 053 | 063 | 073 | 083 | 094 | 104 | 114 | 124 | 134 | 7 | 7.0 |
| 428 | 144 | 155 | 165 | 175 | 185 | 195 | 205 | 215 | 225 | 236 | 8 | 8.0 |
| 429 | 246 | 256 | 266 | 276 | 286 | 296 | 306 | 317 | 327 | 337 | 9 | 9.0 |
| 430 | 347 | 357 | 367 | 377 | 387 | 397 | 407 | 417 | 428 | 438 | | |
| 431 | 448 | 458 | 468 | 478 | 488 | 498 | 508 | 518 | 528 | 538 | | |
| 432 | 548 | 558 | 568 | 579 | 589 | 599 | 609 | 619 | 629 | 639 | | |
| 433 | 649 | 659 | 669 | 679 | 689 | 699 | 709 | 719 | 729 | 739 | | |
| 434 | 749 | 759 | 769 | 779 | 789 | 799 | 809 | 819 | 829 | 839 | | |
| 435 | 849 | 859 | 869 | 879 | 889 | 899 | 909 | 919 | 929 | 939 | | |
| 436 | 949 | 959 | 969 | 979 | 988 | 998 | *008 | *018 | *028 | *038 | **9** | |
| 437 | 64 048 | 058 | 068 | 078 | 088 | 098 | 108 | 118 | 128 | 137 | 1 | 0.9 |
| 438 | 147 | 157 | 167 | 177 | 187 | 197 | 207 | 217 | 227 | 237 | 2 | 1.8 |
| 439 | 246 | 256 | 266 | 276 | 286 | 296 | 306 | 316 | 326 | 335 | 3 | 2.7 |
| 440 | 345 | 355 | 365 | 375 | 385 | 395 | 404 | 414 | 424 | 434 | 4 | 3.6 |
| | | | | | | | | | | | 5 | 4.5 |
| 441 | 444 | 454 | 464 | 473 | 483 | 493 | 503 | 513 | 523 | 532 | 6 | 5.4 |
| 442 | 542 | 552 | 562 | 572 | 582 | 591 | 601 | 611 | 621 | 631 | 7 | 6.3 |
| 443 | 640 | 650 | 660 | 670 | 680 | 689 | 699 | 709 | 719 | 729 | 8 | 7.2 |
| 444 | 738 | 748 | 758 | 768 | 777 | 787 | 797 | 807 | 816 | 826 | 9 | 8.1 |
| 445 | 836 | 846 | 856 | 865 | 875 | 885 | 895 | 904 | 914 | 924 | | |
| 446 | 933 | 943 | 953 | 963 | 972 | 982 | 992 | *002 | *011 | *021 | | |
| 447 | 65 031 | 040 | 050 | 060 | 070 | 079 | 089 | 099 | 108 | 118 | | |
| 448 | 128 | 137 | 147 | 157 | 167 | 176 | 186 | 196 | 205 | 215 | | |
| 449 | 225 | 234 | 244 | 254 | 263 | 273 | 283 | 292 | 302 | 312 | | |
| 450 | 321 | 331 | 341 | 350 | 360 | 369 | 379 | 389 | 398 | 408 | | |
| N | L 0 | 1 | 2 | 3 | 4 | 5 | 6 | 7 | 8 | 9 | P | P |

450—500

| N | L 0 | 1 | 2 | 3 | 4 | 5 | 6 | 7 | 8 | 9 |
|---|---|---|---|---|---|---|---|---|---|---|
| 450 | 65 321 | 331 | 341 | 350 | 360 | 369 | 379 | 389 | 398 | 408 |
| 451 | 418 | 427 | 437 | 447 | 456 | 466 | 475 | 485 | 495 | 504 |
| 452 | 514 | 523 | 533 | 543 | 552 | 562 | 571 | 581 | 591 | 600 |
| 453 | 610 | 619 | 629 | 639 | 648 | 658 | 667 | 677 | 686 | 696 |
| 454 | 706 | 715 | 725 | 734 | 744 | 753 | 763 | 772 | 782 | 792 |
| 455 | 801 | 811 | 820 | 830 | 839 | 849 | 858 | 868 | 877 | 887 |
| 456 | 896 | 906 | 916 | 925 | 935 | 944 | 954 | 963 | 973 | 982 |
| 457 | 992 | *001 | *011 | *020 | *030 | *039 | *049 | *058 | *068 | *077 |
| 458 | 66 087 | 096 | 106 | 115 | 124 | 134 | 143 | 153 | 162 | 172 |
| 459 | 181 | 191 | 200 | 210 | 219 | 229 | 238 | 247 | 257 | 266 |
| 460 | 276 | 285 | 295 | 304 | 314 | 323 | 332 | 342 | 351 | 361 |
| 461 | 370 | 380 | 389 | 398 | 408 | 417 | 427 | 436 | 445 | 455 |
| 462 | 464 | 474 | 483 | 492 | 502 | 511 | 521 | 530 | 539 | 549 |
| 463 | 558 | 567 | 577 | 586 | 596 | 605 | 614 | 624 | 633 | 642 |
| 464 | 652 | 661 | 671 | 680 | 689 | 699 | 708 | 717 | 727 | 736 |
| 465 | 745 | 755 | 764 | 773 | 783 | 792 | 801 | 811 | 820 | 829 |
| 466 | 839 | 848 | 857 | 867 | 876 | 885 | 894 | 904 | 913 | 922 |
| 467 | 932 | 941 | 950 | 960 | 969 | 978 | 987 | 997 | *006 | *015 |
| 468 | 67 025 | 034 | 043 | 052 | 062 | 071 | 080 | 089 | 099 | 108 |
| 469 | 117 | 127 | 136 | 145 | 154 | 164 | 173 | 182 | 191 | 201 |
| 470 | 210 | 219 | 228 | 237 | 247 | 256 | 265 | 274 | 284 | 293 |
| 471 | 302 | 311 | 321 | 330 | 339 | 348 | 357 | 367 | 376 | 385 |
| 472 | 394 | 403 | 413 | 422 | 431 | 440 | 449 | 459 | 468 | 477 |
| 473 | 486 | 495 | 504 | 514 | 523 | 532 | 541 | 550 | 560 | 569 |
| 474 | 578 | 587 | 596 | 605 | 614 | 624 | 633 | 642 | 651 | 660 |
| 475 | 669 | 679 | 688 | 697 | 706 | 715 | 724 | 733 | 742 | 752 |
| 476 | 761 | 770 | 779 | 788 | 797 | 806 | 815 | 825 | 834 | 843 |
| 477 | 852 | 861 | 870 | 879 | 888 | 897 | 906 | 916 | 925 | 934 |
| 478 | 943 | 952 | 961 | 970 | 979 | 988 | 997 | *006 | *015 | *024 |
| 479 | 68 034 | 043 | 052 | 061 | 070 | 079 | 088 | 097 | 106 | 115 |
| 480 | 124 | 133 | 142 | 151 | 160 | 169 | 178 | 187 | 196 | 205 |
| 481 | 215 | 224 | 233 | 242 | 251 | 260 | 269 | 278 | 287 | 296 |
| 482 | 305 | 314 | 323 | 332 | 341 | 350 | 359 | 368 | 377 | 386 |
| 483 | 395 | 404 | 413 | 422 | 431 | 440 | 449 | 458 | 467 | 476 |
| 484 | 485 | 494 | 502 | 511 | 520 | 529 | 538 | 547 | 556 | 565 |
| 485 | 574 | 583 | 592 | 601 | 610 | 619 | 628 | 637 | 646 | 655 |
| 486 | 664 | 673 | 681 | 690 | 699 | 708 | 717 | 726 | 735 | 744 |
| 487 | 753 | 762 | 771 | 780 | 789 | 797 | 806 | 815 | 824 | 833 |
| 488 | 842 | 851 | 860 | 869 | 878 | 886 | 895 | 904 | 913 | 922 |
| 489 | 931 | 940 | 949 | 958 | 966 | 975 | 984 | 993 | *002 | *011 |
| 490 | 69 020 | 028 | 037 | 046 | 055 | 064 | 073 | 082 | 090 | 099 |
| 491 | 108 | 117 | 126 | 135 | 144 | 152 | 161 | 170 | 179 | 188 |
| 492 | 197 | 205 | 214 | 223 | 232 | 241 | 249 | 258 | 267 | 276 |
| 493 | 285 | 294 | 302 | 311 | 320 | 329 | 338 | 346 | 355 | 364 |
| 494 | 373 | 381 | 390 | 399 | 408 | 417 | 425 | 434 | 443 | 452 |
| 495 | 461 | 469 | 478 | 487 | 496 | 504 | 513 | 522 | 531 | 539 |
| 496 | 548 | 557 | 566 | 574 | 583 | 592 | 601 | 609 | 618 | 627 |
| 497 | 636 | 644 | 653 | 662 | 671 | 679 | 688 | 697 | 705 | 714 |
| 498 | 723 | 732 | 740 | 749 | 758 | 767 | 775 | 784 | 793 | 801 |
| 499 | 810 | 819 | 827 | 836 | 845 | 854 | 862 | 871 | 880 | 888 |
| 500 | 897 | 906 | 914 | 923 | 932 | 940 | 949 | 958 | 966 | 975 |
| N | L 0 | 1 | 2 | 3 | 4 | 5 | 6 | 7 | 8 | 9 |

P P

**10**
| 1 | 1.0 |
| 2 | 2.0 |
| 3 | 3.0 |
| 4 | 4.0 |
| 5 | 5.0 |
| 6 | 6.0 |
| 7 | 7.0 |
| 8 | 8.0 |
| 9 | 9.0 |

**9**
| 1 | 0.9 |
| 2 | 1.8 |
| 3 | 2.7 |
| 4 | 3.6 |
| 5 | 4.5 |
| 6 | 5.4 |
| 7 | 6.3 |
| 8 | 7.2 |
| 9 | 8.1 |

**8**
| 1 | 0.8 |
| 2 | 1.6 |
| 3 | 2.4 |
| 4 | 3.2 |
| 5 | 4.0 |
| 6 | 4.8 |
| 7 | 5.6 |
| 8 | 6.4 |
| 9 | 7.2 |

500—550

| N | L 0 | 1 | 2 | 3 | 4 | 5 | 6 | 7 | 8 | 9 |
|---|---|---|---|---|---|---|---|---|---|---|
| 500 | 69 897 | 906 | 914 | 923 | 932 | 940 | 949 | 958 | 966 | 975 |
| 501 | 984 | 992 | *001 | *010 | *018 | *027 | *036 | *044 | *053 | *062 |
| 502 | 70 070 | 079 | 088 | 096 | 105 | 114 | 122 | 131 | 140 | 148 |
| 503 | 157 | 165 | 174 | 183 | 191 | 200 | 209 | 217 | 226 | 234 |
| 504 | 243 | 252 | 260 | 269 | 278 | 286 | 295 | 303 | 312 | 321 |
| 505 | 329 | 338 | 346 | 355 | 364 | 372 | 381 | 389 | 398 | 406 |
| 506 | 415 | 424 | 432 | 441 | 449 | 458 | 467 | 475 | 484 | 492 |
| 507 | 501 | 509 | 518 | 526 | 535 | 544 | 552 | 561 | 569 | 578 |
| 508 | 586 | 595 | 603 | 612 | 621 | 629 | 638 | 646 | 655 | 663 |
| 509 | 672 | 680 | 689 | 697 | 706 | 714 | 723 | 731 | 740 | 749 |
| 510 | 757 | 766 | 774 | 783 | 791 | 800 | 808 | 817 | 825 | 834 |
| 511 | 842 | 851 | 859 | 868 | 876 | 885 | 893 | 902 | 910 | 919 |
| 512 | 927 | 935 | 944 | 952 | 961 | 969 | 978 | 986 | 995 | *003 |
| 513 | 71 012 | 020 | 029 | 037 | 046 | 054 | 063 | 071 | 079 | 088 |
| 514 | 096 | 105 | 113 | 122 | 130 | 139 | 147 | 155 | 164 | 172 |
| 515 | 181 | 189 | 198 | 206 | 214 | 223 | 231 | 240 | 248 | 257 |
| 516 | 265 | 273 | 282 | 290 | 299 | 307 | 315 | 324 | 332 | 341 |
| 517 | 349 | 357 | 366 | 374 | 383 | 391 | 399 | 408 | 416 | 425 |
| 518 | 433 | 441 | 450 | 458 | 466 | 475 | 483 | 492 | 500 | 508 |
| 519 | 517 | 525 | 533 | 542 | 550 | 559 | 567 | 575 | 584 | 592 |
| 520 | 600 | 609 | 617 | 625 | 634 | 642 | 650 | 659 | 667 | 675 |
| 521 | 684 | 692 | 700 | 709 | 717 | 725 | 734 | 742 | 750 | 759 |
| 522 | 767 | 775 | 784 | 792 | 800 | 809 | 817 | 825 | 834 | 842 |
| 523 | 850 | 858 | 867 | 875 | 883 | 892 | 900 | 908 | 917 | 925 |
| 524 | 933 | 941 | 950 | 958 | 966 | 975 | 983 | 991 | 999 | *008 |
| 525 | 72 016 | 024 | 032 | 041 | 049 | 057 | 066 | 074 | 082 | 090 |
| 526 | 099 | 107 | 115 | 123 | 132 | 140 | 148 | 156 | 165 | 173 |
| 527 | 181 | 189 | 198 | 206 | 214 | 222 | 230 | 239 | 247 | 255 |
| 528 | 263 | 272 | 280 | 288 | 296 | 304 | 313 | 321 | 329 | 337 |
| 529 | 346 | 354 | 362 | 370 | 378 | 387 | 395 | 403 | 411 | 419 |
| 530 | 428 | 436 | 444 | 452 | 460 | 469 | 477 | 485 | 493 | 501 |
| 531 | 509 | 518 | 526 | 534 | 542 | 550 | 558 | 567 | 575 | 583 |
| 532 | 591 | 599 | 607 | 616 | 624 | 632 | 640 | 648 | 656 | 665 |
| 533 | 673 | 681 | 689 | 697 | 705 | 713 | 722 | 730 | 738 | 746 |
| 534 | 754 | 762 | 770 | 779 | 787 | 795 | 803 | 811 | 819 | 827 |
| 535 | 835 | 843 | 852 | 860 | 868 | 876 | 884 | 892 | 900 | 908 |
| 536 | 916 | 925 | 933 | 941 | 949 | 957 | 965 | 973 | 981 | 989 |
| 537 | 997 | *006 | *014 | *022 | *030 | *038 | *046 | *054 | *062 | *070 |
| 538 | 73 078 | 086 | 094 | 102 | 111 | 119 | 127 | 135 | 143 | 151 |
| 539 | 159 | 167 | 175 | 183 | 191 | 199 | 207 | 215 | 223 | 231 |
| 540 | 239 | 247 | 255 | 263 | 272 | 280 | 288 | 296 | 304 | 312 |
| 541 | 320 | 328 | 336 | 344 | 352 | 360 | 368 | 376 | 384 | 392 |
| 542 | 400 | 408 | 416 | 424 | 432 | 440 | 448 | 456 | 464 | 472 |
| 543 | 480 | 488 | 496 | 504 | 512 | 520 | 528 | 536 | 544 | 552 |
| 544 | 560 | 568 | 576 | 584 | 592 | 600 | 608 | 616 | 624 | 632 |
| 545 | 640 | 648 | 656 | 664 | 672 | 679 | 687 | 695 | 703 | 711 |
| 546 | 719 | 727 | 735 | 743 | 751 | 759 | 767 | 775 | 783 | 791 |
| 547 | 799 | 807 | 815 | 823 | 830 | 838 | 846 | 854 | 862 | 870 |
| 548 | 878 | 886 | 894 | 902 | 910 | 918 | 926 | 933 | 941 | 949 |
| 549 | 957 | 965 | 973 | 981 | 989 | 997 | *005 | *013 | *020 | *028 |
| 550 | 74 036 | 044 | 052 | 060 | 068 | 076 | 084 | 092 | 099 | 107 |

P P

| | 9 |
|---|---|
| 1 | 0.9 |
| 2 | 1.8 |
| 3 | 2.7 |
| 4 | 3.6 |
| 5 | 4.5 |
| 6 | 5.4 |
| 7 | 6.3 |
| 8 | 7.2 |
| 9 | 8.1 |

| | 8 |
|---|---|
| 1 | 0.8 |
| 2 | 1.6 |
| 3 | 2.4 |
| 4 | 3.2 |
| 5 | 4.0 |
| 6 | 4.8 |
| 7 | 5.6 |
| 8 | 6.4 |
| 9 | 7.2 |

| | 7 |
|---|---|
| 1 | 0.7 |
| 2 | 1.4 |
| 3 | 2.1 |
| 4 | 2.8 |
| 5 | 3.5 |
| 6 | 4.2 |
| 7 | 4.9 |
| 8 | 5.6 |
| 9 | 6.3 |

550—600

| N | L 0 | 1 | 2 | 3 | 4 | 5 | 6 | 7 | 8 | 9 |
|---|---|---|---|---|---|---|---|---|---|---|
| 550 | 74 036 | 044 | 052 | 060 | 068 | 076 | 084 | 092 | 099 | 107 |
| 551 | 115 | 123 | 131 | 139 | 147 | 155̄ | 162 | 170 | 178 | 186 |
| 552 | 194 | 202 | 210 | 218 | 225 | 233 | 241 | 249 | 257 | 265̄ |
| 553 | 273 | 280 | 288 | 296 | 304 | 312 | 320 | 327 | 335 | 343 |
| 554 | 351 | 359 | 367 | 374 | 382 | 390 | 398 | 406 | 414 | 421 |
| 555 | 429 | 437 | 445̄ | 453 | 461 | 468 | 476 | 484 | 492 | 500̄ |
| 556 | 507 | 515 | 523 | 531 | 539 | 547 | 554 | 562 | 570 | 578 |
| 557 | 586 | 593 | 601 | 609 | 617 | 624 | 632 | 640 | 648 | 656 |
| 558 | 663 | 671 | 679 | 687 | 695̄ | 702 | 710 | 718 | 726 | 733 |
| 559 | 741 | 749 | 757 | 764 | 772 | 780 | 788 | 796 | 803 | 811 |
| 560 | 819 | 827 | 834 | 842 | 850 | 858 | 865 | 873 | 881 | 889 |
| 561 | 896 | 904 | 912 | 920 | 927 | 935̄ | 943 | 950 | 958 | 966 |
| 562 | 974 | 981 | 989 | 997 | *005 | *012 | *020 | *028 | *035 | *043 |
| 563 | 75 051 | 059 | 066 | 074 | 082 | 089 | 097 | 105̄ | 113 | 120 |
| 564 | 128 | 136 | 143 | 151 | 159 | 166 | 174 | 182 | 189 | 197 |
| 565 | 205̄ | 213 | 220 | 228 | 236 | 243 | 251 | 259 | 266 | 274 |
| 566 | 282 | 289 | 297 | 305̄ | 312 | 320 | 328 | 335 | 343 | 351 |
| 567 | 358 | 366 | 374 | 381 | 389 | 397 | 404 | 412 | 420 | 427 |
| 568 | 435̄ | 442 | 450 | 458 | 465 | 473 | 481 | 488 | 496 | 504 |
| 569 | 511 | 519 | 526 | 534 | 542 | 549 | 557 | 565̄ | 572 | 580 |
| 570 | 587 | 595 | 603 | 610 | 618 | 626 | 633 | 641 | 648 | 656 |
| 571 | 664 | 671 | 679 | 686 | 694 | 702 | 709 | 717 | 724 | 732 |
| 572 | 740 | 747 | 755̄ | 762 | 770 | 778 | 785 | 793 | 800 | 808 |
| 573 | 815 | 823 | 831 | 838 | 846 | 853 | 861 | 868 | 876 | 884 |
| 574 | 891 | 899 | 906 | 914 | 921 | 929 | 937 | 944 | 952 | 959 |
| 575 | 967 | 974 | 982 | 989 | 997 | *005 | *012 | *020 | *027 | *035̄ |
| 576 | 76 042 | 050̄ | 057 | 065̄ | 072 | 080 | 087 | 095̄ | 103 | 110 |
| 577 | 118 | 125 | 133 | 140 | 148 | 155 | 163 | 170 | 178 | 185 |
| 578 | 193 | 200 | 208 | 215 | 223 | 230 | 238 | 245 | 253 | 260 |
| 579 | 268 | 275 | 283 | 290 | 298 | 305 | 313 | 320 | 328 | 335 |
| 580 | 343 | 350 | 358 | 365 | 373 | 380 | 388 | 395 | 403 | 410 |
| 581 | 418 | 425 | 433 | 440 | 448 | 455̄ | 462 | 470 | 477 | 485̄ |
| 582 | 492 | 500̄ | 507 | 515̄ | 522 | 530 | 537 | 545̄ | 552 | 559 |
| 583 | 567 | 574 | 582 | 589 | 597 | 604 | 612 | 619 | 626 | 634 |
| 584 | 641 | 649 | 656 | 664 | 671 | 678 | 686 | 693 | 701 | 708 |
| 585 | 716 | 723 | 730 | 738 | 745 | 753 | 760 | 768 | 775̄ | 782 |
| 586 | 790 | 797 | 805̄ | 812 | 819 | 827 | 834 | 842 | 849 | 856 |
| 587 | 864 | 871 | 879 | 886 | 893 | 901 | 908 | 916 | 923 | 930 |
| 588 | 938 | 945 | 953 | 960 | 967 | 975̄ | 982 | 989 | 997 | *004 |
| 589 | 77 012 | 019 | 026 | 034 | 041 | 048 | 056 | 063 | 070 | 078 |
| 590 | 085̄ | 093 | 100 | 107 | 115̄ | 122 | 129 | 137 | 144 | 151 |
| 591 | 159 | 166 | 173 | 181 | 188 | 195 | 203 | 210 | 217 | 225̄ |
| 592 | 232 | 240 | 247 | 254 | 262 | 269 | 276 | 283 | 291 | 298 |
| 593 | 305 | 313 | 320 | 327 | 335̄ | 342 | 349 | 357 | 364 | 371 |
| 594 | 379 | 386 | 393 | 401 | 408 | 415 | 422 | 430 | 437 | 444 |
| 595 | 452 | 459 | 466 | 474 | 481 | 488 | 495 | 503 | 510 | 517 |
| 596 | 525 | 532 | 539 | 546 | 554 | 561 | 568 | 576 | 583 | 590 |
| 597 | 597 | 605̄ | 612 | 619 | 627 | 634 | 641 | 648 | 656 | 663 |
| 598 | 670 | 677 | 685̄ | 692 | 699 | 706 | 714 | 721 | 728 | 735 |
| 599 | 743 | 750̄ | 757 | 764 | 772 | 779 | 786 | 793 | 801 | 808 |
| 600 | 815 | 822 | 830 | 837 | 844 | 851 | 859 | 866 | 873 | 880 |
| N | L 0 | 1 | 2 | 3 | 4 | 5 | 6 | 7 | 8 | 9 |

P P

**8**

| 1 | 0.8 |
|---|---|
| 2 | 1.6 |
| 3 | 2.4 |
| 4 | 3.2 |
| 5 | 4.0 |
| 6 | 4.8 |
| 7 | 5.6 |
| 8 | 6.4 |
| 9 | 7.2 |

**7**

| 1 | 0.7 |
|---|---|
| 2 | 1.4 |
| 3 | 2.1 |
| 4 | 2.8 |
| 5 | 3.5 |
| 6 | 4.2 |
| 7 | 4.9 |
| 8 | 5.6 |
| 9 | 6.3 |

## 600—650

| N | L 0 | 1 | 2 | 3 | 4 | 5 | 6 | 7 | 8 | 9 | | P P |
|---|---|---|---|---|---|---|---|---|---|---|---|---|
| 600 | 77 815 | 822 | 830 | 837 | 844 | 851 | 859 | 866 | 873 | 880 | | |
| 601 | 887 | 895 | 902 | 909 | 916 | 924 | 931 | 938 | 945 | 952 | | |
| 602 | 960 | 967 | 974 | 981 | 988 | 996 | *003 | *010 | *017 | *025 | | |
| 603 | 78 032 | 039 | 046 | 053 | 061 | 068 | 075 | 082 | 089 | 097 | | |
| 604 | 104 | 111 | 118 | 125 | 132 | 140 | 147 | 154 | 161 | 168 | | |
| 605 | 176 | 183 | 190 | 197 | 204 | 211 | 219 | 226 | 233 | 240 | | |
| 606 | 247 | 254 | 262 | 269 | 276 | 283 | 290 | 297 | 305 | 312 | | **8** |
| 607 | 319 | 326 | 333 | 340 | 347 | 355 | 362 | 369 | 376 | 383 | | 1   0.8 |
| 608 | 390 | 398 | 405 | 412 | 419 | 426 | 433 | 440 | 447 | 455 | | 2   1.6 |
| 609 | 462 | 469 | 476 | 483 | 490 | 497 | 504 | 512 | 519 | 526 | | 3   2.4 |
| 610 | 533 | 540 | 547 | 554 | 561 | 569 | 576 | 583 | 590 | 597 | | 4   3.2 <br> 5   4.0 |
| 611 | 604 | 611 | 618 | 625 | 633 | 640 | 647 | 654 | 661 | 668 | | 6   4.8 |
| 612 | 675 | 682 | 689 | 696 | 704 | 711 | 718 | 725 | 732 | 739 | | 7   5.6 |
| 613 | 746 | 753 | 760 | 767 | 774 | 781 | 789 | 796 | 803 | 810 | | 8   6.4 |
| 614 | 817 | 824 | 831 | 838 | 845 | 852 | 859 | 866 | 873 | 880 | | 9   7.2 |
| 615 | 888 | 895 | 902 | 909 | 916 | 923 | 930 | 937 | 944 | 951 | | |
| 616 | 958 | 965 | 972 | 979 | 986 | 993 | *000 | *007 | *014 | *021 | | |
| 617 | 79 029 | 036 | 043 | 050 | 057 | 064 | 071 | 078 | 085 | 092 | | |
| 618 | 099 | 106 | 113 | 120 | 127 | 134 | 141 | 148 | 155 | 162 | | |
| 619 | 169 | 176 | 183 | 190 | 197 | 204 | 211 | 218 | 225 | 232 | | |
| 620 | 239 | 246 | 253 | 260 | 267 | 274 | 281 | 288 | 295 | 302 | | |
| 621 | 309 | 316 | 323 | 330 | 337 | 344 | 351 | 358 | 365 | 372 | | **7** |
| 622 | 379 | 386 | 393 | 400 | 407 | 414 | 421 | 428 | 435 | 442 | | 1   0.7 |
| 623 | 449 | 456 | 463 | 470 | 477 | 484 | 491 | 498 | 505 | 511 | | 2   1.4 |
| 624 | 518 | 525 | 532 | 539 | 546 | 553 | 560 | 567 | 574 | 581 | | 3   2.1 |
| 625 | 588 | 595 | 602 | 609 | 616 | 623 | 630 | 637 | 644 | 650 | | 4   2.8 <br> 5   3.5 |
| 626 | 657 | 664 | 671 | 678 | 685 | 692 | 699 | 706 | 713 | 720 | | 6   4.2 |
| 627 | 727 | 734 | 741 | 748 | 754 | 761 | 768 | 775 | 782 | 789 | | 7   4.9 |
| 628 | 796 | 803 | 810 | 817 | 824 | 831 | 837 | 844 | 851 | 858 | | 8   5.6 |
| 629 | 865 | 872 | 879 | 886 | 893 | 900 | 906 | 913 | 920 | 927 | | 9   6.3 |
| 630 | 934 | 941 | 948 | 955 | 962 | 969 | 975 | 982 | 989 | 996 | | |
| 631 | 80 003 | 010 | 017 | 024 | 030 | 037 | 044 | 051 | 058 | 065 | | |
| 632 | 072 | 079 | 085 | 092 | 099 | 106 | 113 | 120 | 127 | 134 | | |
| 633 | 140 | 147 | 154 | 161 | 168 | 175 | 182 | 188 | 195 | 202 | | |
| 634 | 209 | 216 | 223 | 229 | 236 | 243 | 250 | 257 | 264 | 271 | | |
| 635 | 277 | 284 | 291 | 298 | 305 | 312 | 318 | 325 | 332 | 339 | | |
| 636 | 346 | 353 | 359 | 366 | 373 | 380 | 387 | 393 | 400 | 407 | | **6** |
| 637 | 414 | 421 | 428 | 434 | 441 | 448 | 455 | 462 | 468 | 475 | | 1   0.6 |
| 638 | 482 | 489 | 496 | 502 | 509 | 516 | 523 | 530 | 536 | 543 | | 2   1.2 |
| 639 | 550 | 557 | 564 | 570 | 577 | 584 | 591 | 598 | 604 | 611 | | 3   1.8 |
| 640 | 618 | 625 | 632 | 638 | 645 | 652 | 659 | 665 | 672 | 679 | | 4   2.4 <br> 5   3.0 |
| 641 | 686 | 693 | 699 | 706 | 713 | 720 | 726 | 733 | 740 | 747 | | 6   3.6 |
| 642 | 754 | 760 | 767 | 774 | 781 | 787 | 794 | 801 | 808 | 814 | | 7   4.2 |
| 643 | 821 | 828 | 835 | 841 | 848 | 855 | 862 | 868 | 875 | 882 | | 8   4.8 |
| 644 | 889 | 895 | 902 | 909 | 916 | 922 | 929 | 936 | 943 | 949 | | 9   5.4 |
| 645 | 956 | 963 | 969 | 976 | 983 | 990 | 996 | *003 | *010 | *017 | | |
| 646 | 81 023 | 030 | 037 | 043 | 050 | 057 | 064 | 070 | 077 | 084 | | |
| 647 | 090 | 097 | 104 | 111 | 117 | 124 | 131 | 137 | 144 | 151 | | |
| 648 | 158 | 164 | 171 | 178 | 184 | 191 | 198 | 204 | 211 | 218 | | |
| 649 | 224 | 231 | 238 | 245 | 251 | 258 | 265 | 271 | 278 | 285 | | |
| 650 | 291 | 298 | 305 | 311 | 318 | 325 | 331 | 338 | 345 | 351 | | |
| N | L 0 | 1 | 2 | 3 | 4 | 5 | 6 | 7 | 8 | 9 | | P P |

| N | L 0 | 1 | 2 | 3 | 4 | 5 | 6 | 7 | 8 | 9 |
|---|---|---|---|---|---|---|---|---|---|---|
| 650 | 81 291 | 298 | 305 | 311 | 318 | 325 | 331 | 338 | 345 | 351 |
| 651 | 358 | 365 | 371 | 378 | 385 | 391 | 398 | 405 | 411 | 418 |
| 652 | 425 | 431 | 438 | 445 | 451 | 458 | 465 | 471 | 478 | 485 |
| 653 | 491 | 498 | 505 | 511 | 518 | 525 | 531 | 538 | 544 | 551 |
| 654 | 558 | 564 | 571 | 578 | 584 | 591 | 598 | 604 | 611 | 617 |
| 655 | 624 | 631 | 637 | 644 | 651 | 657 | 664 | 671 | 677 | 684 |
| 656 | 690 | 697 | 704 | 710 | 717 | 723 | 730 | 737 | 743 | 750 |
| 657 | 757 | 763 | 770 | 776 | 783 | 790 | 796 | 803 | 809 | 816 |
| 658 | 823 | 829 | 836 | 842 | 849 | 856 | 862 | 869 | 875 | 882 |
| 659 | 889 | 895 | 902 | 908 | 915 | 921 | 928 | 935 | 941 | 948 |
| 660 | 954 | 961 | 968 | 974 | 981 | 987 | 994 | *000 | *007 | *014 |
| 661 | 82 020 | 027 | 033 | 040 | 046 | 053 | 060 | 066 | 073 | 079 |
| 662 | 086 | 092 | 099 | 105 | 112 | 119 | 125 | 132 | 138 | 145 |
| 663 | 151 | 158 | 164 | 171 | 178 | 184 | 191 | 197 | 204 | 210 |
| 664 | 217 | 223 | 230 | 236 | 243 | 249 | 256 | 263 | 269 | 276 |
| 665 | 282 | 289 | 295 | 302 | 308 | 315 | 321 | 328 | 334 | 341 |
| 666 | 347 | 354 | 360 | 367 | 373 | 380 | 387 | 393 | 400 | 406 |
| 667 | 413 | 419 | 426 | 432 | 439 | 445 | 452 | 458 | 465 | 471 |
| 668 | 478 | 484 | 491 | 497 | 504 | 510 | 517 | 523 | 530 | 536 |
| 669 | 543 | 549 | 556 | 562 | 569 | 575 | 582 | 588 | 595 | 601 |
| 670 | 607 | 614 | 620 | 627 | 633 | 640 | 646 | 653 | 659 | 666 |
| 671 | 672 | 679 | 685 | 692 | 698 | 705 | 711 | 718 | 724 | 730 |
| 672 | 737 | 743 | 750 | 756 | 763 | 769 | 776 | 782 | 789 | 795 |
| 673 | 802 | 808 | 814 | 821 | 827 | 834 | 840 | 847 | 853 | 860 |
| 674 | 866 | 872 | 879 | 885 | 892 | 898 | 905 | 911 | 918 | 924 |
| 675 | 930 | 937 | 943 | 950 | 956 | 963 | 969 | 975 | 982 | 988 |
| 676 | 995 | *001 | *008 | *014 | *020 | *027 | *033 | *040 | *046 | *052 |
| 677 | 83 059 | 065 | 072 | 078 | 085 | 091 | 097 | 104 | 110 | 117 |
| 678 | 123 | 129 | 136 | 142 | 149 | 155 | 161 | 168 | 174 | 181 |
| 679 | 187 | 193 | 200 | 206 | 213 | 219 | 225 | 232 | 238 | 245 |
| 680 | 251 | 257 | 264 | 270 | 276 | 283 | 289 | 296 | 302 | 308 |
| 681 | 315 | 321 | 327 | 334 | 340 | 347 | 353 | 359 | 366 | 372 |
| 682 | 378 | 385 | 391 | 398 | 404 | 410 | 417 | 423 | 429 | 436 |
| 683 | 442 | 448 | 455 | 461 | 467 | 474 | 480 | 487 | 493 | 499 |
| 684 | 506 | 512 | 518 | 525 | 531 | 537 | 544 | 550 | 556 | 563 |
| 685 | 569 | 575 | 582 | 588 | 594 | 601 | 607 | 613 | 620 | 626 |
| 686 | 632 | 639 | 645 | 651 | 658 | 664 | 670 | 677 | 683 | 689 |
| 687 | 696 | 702 | 708 | 715 | 721 | 727 | 734 | 740 | 746 | 753 |
| 688 | 759 | 765 | 771 | 778 | 784 | 790 | 797 | 803 | 809 | 816 |
| 689 | 822 | 828 | 835 | 841 | 847 | 853 | 860 | 866 | 872 | 879 |
| 690 | 885 | 891 | 897 | 904 | 910 | 916 | 923 | 929 | 935 | 942 |
| 691 | 948 | 954 | 960 | 967 | 973 | 979 | 985 | 992 | 998 | *004 |
| 692 | 84 011 | 017 | 023 | 029 | 036 | 042 | 048 | 055 | 061 | 067 |
| 693 | 073 | 080 | 086 | 092 | 098 | 105 | 111 | 117 | 123 | 130 |
| 694 | 136 | 142 | 148 | 155 | 161 | 167 | 173 | 180 | 186 | 192 |
| 695 | 198 | 205 | 211 | 217 | 223 | 230 | 236 | 242 | 248 | 255 |
| 696 | 261 | 267 | 273 | 280 | 286 | 292 | 298 | 305 | 311 | 317 |
| 697 | 323 | 330 | 336 | 342 | 348 | 354 | 361 | 367 | 373 | 379 |
| 698 | 386 | 392 | 398 | 404 | 410 | 417 | 423 | 429 | 435 | 442 |
| 699 | 448 | 454 | 460 | 466 | 473 | 479 | 485 | 491 | 497 | 504 |
| 700 | 510 | 516 | 522 | 528 | 535 | 541 | 547 | 553 | 559 | 566 |
| N | L 0 | 1 | 2 | 3 | 4 | 5 | 6 | 7 | 8 | 9 |

P P

| 7 | |
|---|---|
| 1 | 0.7 |
| 2 | 1.4 |
| 3 | 2.1 |
| 4 | 2.8 |
| 5 | 3.5 |
| 6 | 4.2 |
| 7 | 4.9 |
| 8 | 5.6 |
| 9 | 6.3 |

| 6 | |
|---|---|
| 1 | 0.6 |
| 2 | 1.2 |
| 3 | 1.8 |
| 4 | 2.4 |
| 5 | 3.0 |
| 6 | 3.6 |
| 7 | 4.2 |
| 8 | 4.8 |
| 9 | 5.4 |

700—750

| N | L 0 | 1 | 2 | 3 | 4 | 5 | 6 | 7 | 8 | 9 |
|---|---|---|---|---|---|---|---|---|---|---|
| 700 | 84 510 | 516 | 522 | 528 | 535 | 541 | 547 | 553 | 559 | 566 |
| 701 | 572 | 578 | 584 | 590 | 597 | 603 | 609 | 615 | 621 | 628 |
| 702 | 634 | 640 | 646 | 652 | 658 | 665 | 671 | 677 | 683 | 689 |
| 703 | 696 | 702 | 708 | 714 | 720 | 726 | 733 | 739 | 745 | 751 |
| 704 | 757 | 763 | 770 | 776 | 782 | 788 | 794 | 800 | 807 | 813 |
| 705 | 819 | 825 | 831 | 837 | 844 | 850 | 856 | 862 | 868 | 874 |
| 706 | 880 | 887 | 893 | 899 | 905 | 911 | 917 | 924 | 930 | 936 |
| 707 | 942 | 948 | 954 | 960 | 967 | 973 | 979 | 985 | 991 | 997 |
| 708 | 85 003 | 009 | 016 | 022 | 028 | 034 | 040 | 046 | 052 | 058 |
| 709 | 065 | 071 | 077 | 083 | 089 | 095 | 101 | 107 | 114 | 120 |
| 710 | 126 | 132 | 138 | 144 | 150 | 156 | 163 | 169 | 175 | 181 |
| 711 | 187 | 193 | 199 | 205 | 211 | 217 | 224 | 230 | 236 | 242 |
| 712 | 248 | 254 | 260 | 266 | 272 | 278 | 285 | 291 | 297 | 303 |
| 713 | 309 | 315 | 321 | 327 | 333 | 339 | 345 | 352 | 358 | 364 |
| 714 | 370 | 376 | 382 | 388 | 394 | 400 | 406 | 412 | 418 | 425 |
| 715 | 431 | 437 | 443 | 449 | 455 | 461 | 467 | 473 | 479 | 485 |
| 716 | 491 | 497 | 503 | 509 | 516 | 522 | 528 | 534 | 540 | 546 |
| 717 | 552 | 558 | 564 | 570 | 576 | 582 | 588 | 594 | 600 | 606 |
| 718 | 612 | 618 | 625 | 631 | 637 | 643 | 649 | 655 | 661 | 667 |
| 719 | 673 | 679 | 685 | 691 | 697 | 703 | 709 | 715 | 721 | 727 |
| 720 | 733 | 739 | 745 | 751 | 757 | 763 | 769 | 775 | 781 | 788 |
| 721 | 794 | 800 | 806 | 812 | 818 | 824 | 830 | 836 | 842 | 848 |
| 722 | 854 | 860 | 866 | 872 | 878 | 884 | 890 | 896 | 902 | 908 |
| 723 | 914 | 920 | 926 | 932 | 938 | 944 | 950 | 956 | 962 | 968 |
| 724 | 974 | 980 | 986 | 992 | 998 | *004 | *010 | *016 | *022 | *028 |
| 725 | 86 034 | 040 | 046 | 052 | 058 | 064 | 070 | 076 | 082 | 088 |
| 726 | 094 | 100 | 106 | 112 | 118 | 124 | 130 | 136 | 141 | 147 |
| 727 | 153 | 159 | 165 | 171 | 177 | 183 | 189 | 195 | 201 | 207 |
| 728 | 213 | 219 | 225 | 231 | 237 | 243 | 249 | 255 | 261 | 267 |
| 729 | 273 | 279 | 285 | 291 | 297 | 303 | 308 | 314 | 320 | 326 |
| 730 | 332 | 338 | 344 | 350 | 356 | 362 | 368 | 374 | 380 | 386 |
| 731 | 392 | 398 | 404 | 410 | 415 | 421 | 427 | 433 | 439 | 445 |
| 732 | 451 | 457 | 463 | 469 | 475 | 481 | 487 | 493 | 499 | 504 |
| 733 | 510 | 516 | 522 | 528 | 534 | 540 | 546 | 552 | 558 | 564 |
| 734 | 570 | 576 | 581 | 587 | 593 | 599 | 605 | 611 | 617 | 623 |
| 735 | 629 | 635 | 641 | 646 | 652 | 658 | 664 | 670 | 676 | 682 |
| 736 | 688 | 694 | 700 | 705 | 711 | 717 | 723 | 729 | 735 | 741 |
| 737 | 747 | 753 | 759 | 764 | 770 | 776 | 782 | 788 | 794 | 800 |
| 738 | 806 | 812 | 817 | 823 | 829 | 835 | 841 | 847 | 853 | 859 |
| 739 | 864 | 870 | 876 | 882 | 888 | 894 | 900 | 906 | 911 | 917 |
| 740 | 923 | 929 | 935 | 941 | 947 | 953 | 958 | 964 | 970 | 976 |
| 741 | 982 | 988 | 994 | 999 | *005 | *011 | *017 | *023 | *029 | *035 |
| 742 | 87 040 | 046 | 052 | 058 | 064 | 070 | 075 | 081 | 087 | 093 |
| 743 | 099 | 105 | 111 | 116 | 122 | 128 | 134 | 140 | 146 | 151 |
| 744 | 157 | 163 | 169 | 175 | 181 | 186 | 192 | 198 | 204 | 210 |
| 745 | 216 | 221 | 227 | 233 | 239 | 245 | 251 | 256 | 262 | 268 |
| 746 | 274 | 280 | 286 | 291 | 297 | 303 | 309 | 315 | 320 | 326 |
| 747 | 332 | 338 | 344 | 349 | 355 | 361 | 367 | 373 | 379 | 384 |
| 748 | 390 | 396 | 402 | 408 | 413 | 419 | 425 | 431 | 437 | 442 |
| 749 | 448 | 454 | 460 | 466 | 471 | 477 | 483 | 489 | 495 | 500 |
| 750 | 506 | 512 | 518 | 523 | 529 | 535 | 541 | 547 | 552 | 558 |
| N | L 0 | 1 | 2 | 3 | 4 | 5 | 6 | 7 | 8 | 9 |

P P

**7**

| 1 | 0.7 |
|---|---|
| 2 | 1.4 |
| 3 | 2.1 |
| 4 | 2.8 |
| 5 | 3.5 |
| 6 | 4.2 |
| 7 | 4.9 |
| 8 | 5.6 |
| 9 | 6.3 |

**6**

| 1 | 0.6 |
|---|---|
| 2 | 1.2 |
| 3 | 1.8 |
| 4 | 2.4 |
| 5 | 3.0 |
| 6 | 3.6 |
| 7 | 4.2 |
| 8 | 4.8 |
| 9 | 5.4 |

**5**

| 1 | 0.5 |
|---|---|
| 2 | 1.0 |
| 3 | 1.5 |
| 4 | 2.0 |
| 5 | 2.5 |
| 6 | 3.0 |
| 7 | 3.5 |
| 8 | 4.0 |
| 9 | 4.5 |

750—800

| N | L 0 | 1 | 2 | 3 | 4 | 5 | 6 | 7 | 8 | 9 | P P | |
|---|---|---|---|---|---|---|---|---|---|---|---|---|
| 750 | 87 506 | 512 | 518 | 523 | 529 | 535 | 541 | 547 | 552 | 558 | | |
| 751 | 564 | 570 | 576 | 581 | 587 | 593 | 599 | 604 | 610 | 616 | | |
| 752 | 622 | 628 | 633 | 639 | 645 | 651 | 656 | 662 | 668 | 674 | | |
| 753 | 679 | 685 | 691 | 697 | 703 | 708 | 714 | 720 | 726 | 731 | | |
| 754 | 737 | 743 | 749 | 754 | 760 | 766 | 772 | 777 | 783 | 789 | | |
| 755 | 79⁵ | 800 | 806 | 812 | 818 | 823 | 829 | 83⁵ | 841 | 846 | | |
| 756 | 852 | 858 | 864 | 869 | 875 | 881 | 887 | 892 | 898 | 904 | | |
| 757 | 910 | 915 | 921 | 927 | 933 | 938 | 944 | 95⁰ | 955 | 961 | | |
| 758 | 967 | 973 | 978 | 984 | 990 | 996 | *001 | *007 | *013 | *018 | | |
| 759 | 88 024 | 030 | 036 | 041 | 047 | 053 | 058 | 064 | 070 | 076 | | |
| 760 | 081 | 087 | 093 | 098 | 104 | 110 | 116 | 121 | 127 | 133 | | |
| 761 | 138 | 144 | 1⁵0 | 156 | 161 | 167 | 173 | 178 | 184 | 190 | | 6 |
| 762 | 195 | 201 | 207 | 213 | 218 | 224 | 230 | 235 | 241 | 247 | | |
| 763 | 252 | 258 | 264 | 270 | 275 | 281 | 287 | 292 | 298 | 304 | 1 | 0.6 |
| 764 | 309 | 315 | 321 | 326 | 332 | 338 | 343 | 349 | 35⁵ | 360 | 2 | 1.2 |
| 765 | 366 | 372 | 377 | 383 | 389 | 39⁵ | 400 | 406 | 412 | 417 | 3 | 1.8 |
| 766 | 423 | 429 | 434 | 440 | 446 | 451 | 457 | 463 | 468 | 474 | 4 | 2.4 |
| 767 | 480 | 485 | 491 | 497 | 502 | 508 | 513 | 519 | 525 | 530 | 5 | 3.0 |
| 768 | 536 | 542 | 547 | 553 | 559 | 564 | 570 | 576 | 581 | 587 | 6 | 3.6 |
| 769 | 593 | 598 | 604 | 610 | 615 | 621 | 627 | 632 | 638 | 643 | 7 | 4.2 |
| 770 | 649 | 65⁵ | 660 | 666 | 672 | 677 | 683 | 689 | 694 | 700 | 8 | 4.8 |
| | | | | | | | | | | | 9 | 5.4 |
| 771 | 705 | 711 | 717 | 722 | 728 | 734 | 739 | 74⁵ | 750 | 756 | | |
| 772 | 762 | 767 | 773 | 779 | 784 | 790 | 795 | 801 | 807 | 812 | | |
| 773 | 818 | 824 | 829 | 83⁵ | 840 | 846 | 852 | 857 | 863 | 868 | | |
| 774 | 874 | 880 | 885 | 891 | 897 | 902 | 908 | 913 | 919 | 92⁵ | | |
| 775 | 930 | 936 | 941 | 947 | 953 | 958 | 964 | 969 | 975 | 981 | | |
| 776 | 986 | 992 | 997 | *003 | *009 | *014 | *020 | *025 | *031 | *037 | | |
| 777 | 89 042 | 048 | 053 | 059 | 064 | 070 | 076 | 081 | 087 | 092 | | |
| 778 | 098 | 104 | 109 | 11⁵ | 120 | 126 | 131 | 137 | 143 | 148 | | |
| 779 | 154 | 159 | 16⁵ | 170 | 176 | 182 | 187 | 193 | 198 | 204 | | |
| 780 | 209 | 215 | 221 | 226 | 232 | 237 | 243 | 248 | 254 | 260 | | 5 |
| 781 | 265 | 271 | 276 | 282 | 287 | 293 | 298 | 304 | 310 | 315 | 1 | 0.5 |
| 782 | 321 | 326 | 332 | 337 | 343 | 348 | 354 | 360 | 365 | 371 | 2 | 1.0 |
| 783 | 376 | 382 | 387 | 393 | 398 | 404 | 409 | 41⁵ | 421 | 426 | 3 | 1.5 |
| 784 | 432 | 437 | 443 | 448 | 454⁻ | 459 | 46⁵ | 470 | 476 | 481 | 4 | 2.0 |
| 785 | 487 | 492 | 498 | 504 | 509 | 51⁵ | 520 | 526 | 531 | 537 | 5 | 2.5 |
| 786 | 542 | 548 | 553 | 559 | 564 | 570 | 575 | 581 | 586 | 592 | 6 | 3.0 |
| 787 | 597 | 603 | 609 | 614 | 620 | 625 | 631 | 636 | 642 | 647 | 7 | 3.5 |
| 788 | 653 | 658 | 664 | 669 | 67⁵ | 680 | 686 | 691 | 697 | 702 | 8 | 4.0 |
| 789 | 708 | 713 | 719 | 724 | 730 | 735 | 741 | 746 | 752 | 757 | 9 | 4.5 |
| 790 | 763 | 768 | 774 | 779 | 78⁵ | 790 | 796 | 801 | 807 | 812 | | |
| 791 | 818 | 823 | 829 | 834 | 840 | 845 | 851 | 856 | 862 | 867 | | |
| 792 | 873 | 878 | 883 | 889 | 894 | 900 | 905 | 911 | 916 | 922 | | |
| 793 | 927 | 933 | 938 | 944 | 949 | 95⁵ | 960 | 966 | 971 | 977 | | |
| 794 | 982 | 988 | 993 | 998 | *004 | *009 | *01⁵ | *020 | *026 | *031 | | |
| 795 | 90 037 | 042 | 048 | 053 | 059 | 064 | 069 | 07⁵ | 080 | 086 | | |
| 796 | 091 | 097 | 102 | 108 | 113 | 119 | 124 | 129 | 13⁵ | 140 | | |
| 797 | 146 | 151 | 157 | 162 | 168 | 173 | 179 | 184 | 189 | 19⁵ | | |
| 798 | 200 | 206 | 211 | 217 | 222 | 227 | 233 | 238 | 244 | 249 | | |
| 799 | 25⁵ | 260 | 266 | 271 | 276 | 282 | 287 | 293 | 298 | 304 | | |
| 800 | 309 | 314 | 320 | 325 | 331 | 336 | 342 | 347 | 352 | 358 | | |
| N | L 0 | 1 | 2 | 3 | 4 | 5 | 6 | 7 | 8 | 9 | P P | |

APPENDIX IV
800—850

| N | L 0 | 1 | 2 | 3 | 4 | 5 | 6 | 7 | 8 | 9 |
|---|---|---|---|---|---|---|---|---|---|---|
| 800 | 90 309 | 314 | 320 | 325 | 331 | 336 | 342 | 347 | 352 | 358 |
| 801 | 363 | 369 | 374 | 380 | 385 | 390 | 396 | 401 | 407 | 412 |
| 802 | 417 | 423 | 428 | 434 | 439 | 445 | 450 | 455 | 461 | 466 |
| 803 | 472 | 477 | 482 | 488 | 493 | 499 | 504 | 509 | 515 | 520 |
| 804 | 526 | 531 | 536 | 542 | 547 | 553 | 558 | 563 | 569 | 574 |
| 805 | 580 | 585 | 590 | 596 | 601 | 607 | 612 | 617 | 623 | 628 |
| 806 | 634 | 639 | 644 | 650 | 655 | 660 | 666 | 671 | 677 | 682 |
| 807 | 687 | 693 | 698 | 703 | 709 | 714 | 720 | 725 | 730 | 736 |
| 808 | 741 | 747 | 752 | 757 | 763 | 768 | 773 | 779 | 784 | 789 |
| 809 | 795 | 800 | 806 | 811 | 816 | 822 | 827 | 832 | 838 | 843 |
| 810 | 849 | 854 | 859 | 865 | 870 | 875 | 881 | 886 | 891 | 897 |
| 811 | 902 | 907 | 913 | 918 | 924 | 929 | 934 | 940 | 945 | 950 |
| 812 | 956 | 961 | 966 | 972 | 977 | 982 | 988 | 993 | 998 | *004 |
| 813 | 91 009 | 014 | 020 | 025 | 030 | 036 | 041 | 046 | 052 | ·057 |
| 814 | 062 | 068 | 073 | 078 | 084 | 089 | 094 | 100 | 105 | 110 |
| 815 | 116 | 121 | 126 | 132 | 137 | 142 | 148 | 153 | 158 | 164 |
| 816 | 169 | 174 | 180 | 185 | 190 | 196 | 201 | 206 | 212 | 217 |
| 817 | 222 | 228 | 233 | 238 | 243 | 249 | 254 | 259 | 265 | 270 |
| 818 | 275 | 281 | 286 | 291 | 297 | 302 | 307 | 312 | 318 | 323 |
| 819 | 328 | 334 | 339 | 344 | 350 | 355 | 360 | 365 | 371 | 376 |
| 820 | 381 | 387 | 392 | 397 | 403 | 408 | 413 | 418 | 424 | 429 |
| 821 | 434 | 440 | 445 | 450 | 455 | 461 | 466 | 471 | 477 | 482 |
| 822 | 487 | 492 | 498 | 503 | 508 | 514 | 519 | 524 | 529 | 535 |
| 823 | 540 | 545 | 551 | 556 | 561 | 566 | 572 | 577 | 582 | 587 |
| 824 | 593 | 598 | 603 | 609 | 614 | 619 | 624 | 630 | 635 | 640 |
| 825 | 645 | 651 | 656 | 661 | 666 | 672 | 677 | 682 | 687 | 693 |
| 826 | 698 | 703 | 709 | 714 | 719 | 724 | 730 | 735 | 740 | 745 |
| 827 | 751 | 756 | 761 | 766 | 772 | 777 | 782 | 787 | 793 | 798 |
| 828 | 803 | 808 | 814 | 819 | 824 | 829 | 834 | 840 | 845 | 850 |
| 829 | 855 | 861 | 866 | 871 | 876 | 882 | 887 | 892 | 897 | 903 |
| 830 | 908 | 913 | 918 | 924 | 929 | 934 | 939 | 944 | 950 | 955 |
| 831 | 960 | 965 | 971 | 976 | 981 | 986 | 991 | 997 | *002 | *007 |
| 832 | 92 012 | 018 | 023 | 028 | 033 | 038 | 044 | 049 | 054 | 059 |
| 833 | 065 | 070 | 075 | 080 | 085 | 091 | 096 | 101 | 106 | 111 |
| 834 | 117 | 122 | 127 | 132 | 137 | 143 | 148 | 153 | 158 | 163 |
| 835 | 169 | 174 | 179 | 184 | 189 | 195 | 200 | 205 | 210 | 215 |
| 836 | 221 | 226 | 231 | 236 | 241 | 247 | 252 | 257 | 262 | 267 |
| 837 | 273 | 278 | 283 | 288 | 293 | 298 | 304 | 309 | 314 | 319 |
| 838 | 324 | 330 | 335 | 340 | 345 | 350 | 355 | 361 | 366 | 371 |
| 839 | 376 | 381 | 387 | 392 | 397 | 402 | 407 | 412 | 418 | 423 |
| 840 | 428 | 433 | 438 | 443 | 449 | 454 | 459 | 464 | 469 | 474 |
| 841 | 480 | 485 | 490 | 495 | 500 | 505 | 511 | 516 | 521 | 526 |
| 842 | 531 | 536 | 542 | 547 | 552 | 557 | 562 | 567 | 572 | 578 |
| 843 | 583 | 588 | 593 | 598 | 603 | 609 | 614 | 619 | 624 | 629 |
| 844 | 634 | 639 | 645 | 650 | 655 | 660 | 665 | 670 | 675 | 681 |
| 845 | 686 | 691 | 696 | 701 | 706 | 711 | 716 | 722 | 727 | 732 |
| 846 | 737 | 742 | 747 | 752 | 758 | 763 | 768 | 773 | 778 | 783 |
| 847 | 788 | 793 | 799 | 804 | 809 | 814 | 819 | 824 | 829 | 834 |
| 848 | 840 | 845 | 850 | 855 | 860 | 865 | 870 | 875 | 881 | 886 |
| 849 | 891 | 896 | 901 | 906 | 911 | 916 | 921 | 927 | 932 | 937 |
| 850 | 942 | 947 | 952 | 957 | 962 | 967 | 973 | 978 | 983 | 988 |
| N | L 0 | 1 | 2 | 3 | 4 | 5 | 6 | 7 | 8 | 9 |

P P

| | 6 |
|---|---|
| 1 | 0.6 |
| 2 | 1.2 |
| 3 | 1.8 |
| 4 | 2.4 |
| 5 | 3.0 |
| 6 | 3.6 |
| 7 | 4.2 |
| 8 | 4.8 |
| 9 | 5.4 |

| | 5 |
|---|---|
| 1 | 0.5 |
| 2 | 1.0 |
| 3 | 1.5 |
| 4 | 2.0 |
| 5 | 2.5 |
| 6 | 3.0 |
| 7 | 3.5 |
| 8 | 4.0 |
| 9 | 4.5 |

850—900

| N | L 0 | 1 | 2 | 3 | 4 | 5 | 6 | 7 | 8 | 9 |
|---|---|---|---|---|---|---|---|---|---|---|
| 850 | 92 942 | 947 | 952 | 957 | 962 | 967 | 973 | 978 | 983 | 988 |
| 851 | 993 | 998 | *003 | *008 | *013 | *018 | *024 | *029 | *034 | *039 |
| 852 | 93 044 | 049 | 054 | 059 | 064 | 069 | 075 | 080 | 085 | 090 |
| 853 | 095 | 100 | 105 | 110 | 115 | 120 | 125 | 131 | 136 | 141 |
| 854 | 146 | 151 | 156 | 161 | 166 | 171 | 176 | 181 | 186 | 192 |
| 855 | 197 | 202 | 207 | 212 | 217 | 222 | 227 | 232 | 237 | 242 |
| 856 | 247 | 252 | 258 | 263 | 268 | 273 | 278 | 283 | 288 | 293 |
| 857 | 298 | 303 | 308 | 313 | 318 | 323 | 328 | 334 | 339 | 344 |
| 858 | 349 | 354 | 359 | 364 | 369 | 374 | 379 | 384 | 389 | 394 |
| 859 | 399 | 404 | 409 | 414 | 420 | 425 | 430 | 435 | 440 | 445 |
| 860 | 450 | 455 | 460 | 465 | 470 | 475 | 480 | 485 | 490 | 495 |
| 861 | 500 | 505 | 510. | 515 | 520 | 526 | 531 | 536 | 541 | 546 |
| 862 | 551 | 556 | 561 | 566 | 571 | 576 | 581 | 586 | 591 | 596 |
| 863 | 601 | 606 | 611 | 616 | 621 | 626 | 631 | 636 | 641 | 646 |
| 864 | 651 | 656 | 661 | 666 | 671 | 676 | 682 | 687 | 692 | 697 |
| 865 | 702 | 707 | 712 | 717 | 722 | 727 | 732 | 737 | 742 | 747 |
| 866 | 752 | 757 | 762 | 767 | 772 | 777 | 782 | 787 | 792 | 797 |
| 867 | 802 | 807 | 812 | 817 | 822 | 827 | 832 | 837 | 842 | 847 |
| 868 | 852 | 857 | 862 | 867 | 872 | 877 | 882 | 887 | 892 | 897 |
| 869 | 902 | 907 | 912 | 917 | 922 | 927 | 932 | 937 | 942 | 947 |
| 870 | 952 | 957 | 962 | 967 | 972 | 977 | 982 | 987 | 992 | 997 |
| 871 | 94 002 | 007 | 012 | 017 | 022 | 027 | 032 | 037 | 042 | 047 |
| 872 | 052 | 057 | 062 | 067 | 072 | 077 | 082 | 086 | 091 | 096 |
| 873 | 101 | 106 | 111 | 116 | 121 | 126 | 131 | 136 | 141 | 146 |
| 874 | 151 | 156 | 161 | 166 | 171 | 176 | 181 | 186 | 191 | 196 |
| 875 | 201 | 206 | 211 | 216 | 221 | 226 | 231 | 236 | 240 | 245 |
| 876 | 250 | 255 | 260 | 265 | 270 | 275 | 280 | 285 | 290 | 295 |
| 877 | 300 | 305 | 310 | 315 | 320 | 325 | 330 | 335 | 340 | 345 |
| 878 | 349 | 354 | 359 | 364 | 369 | 374 | 379 | 384 | 389 | 394 |
| 879 | 399 | 404 | 409 | 414 | 419 | 424 | 429 | 433 | 438 | 443 |
| 880 | 448 | 453 | 458 | 463 | 468 | 473 | 478 | 483 | 488 | 493 |
| 881 | 498 | 503 | 507 | 512 | 517 | 522 | 527 | 532 | 537 | 542 |
| 882 | 547 | 552 | 557 | 562 | 567 | 571 | 576 | 581 | 586 | 591 |
| 883 | 596 | 601 | 606 | 611 | 616 | 621 | 626 | 630 | 635 | 640 |
| 884 | 645 | 650 | 655 | 660 | 665 | 670 | 675 | 680 | 685 | 689 |
| 885 | 694 | 699 | 704 | 709 | 714 | 719 | 724 | 729 | 734 | 738 |
| 886 | 743 | 748 | 753 | 758 | 763 | 768 | 773 | 778 | 783 | 787 |
| 887 | 792 | 797 | 802 | 807 | 812 | 817 | 822 | 827 | 832 | 836 |
| 888 | 841 | 846 | 851 | 856 | 861 | 866 | 871 | 876 | 880 | 885 |
| 889 | 890 | 895 | 900 | 905 | 910 | 915 | 919 | 924 | 929 | 934 |
| 890 | 939 | 944 | 949 | 954 | 959 | 963 | 968 | 973 | 978 | 983 |
| 891 | 988 | 993 | 998 | *002 | *007 | *012 | *017 | *022 | *027 | *032 |
| 892 | 95 036 | 041 | 046 | 051 | 056 | 061 | 066 | 071 | 075 | 080 |
| 893 | 085 | 090 | 095 | 100 | 105 | 109 | 114 | 119 | 124 | 129 |
| 894 | 134 | 139 | 143 | 148 | 153 | 158 | 163 | 168 | 173 | 177 |
| 895 | 182 | 187 | 192 | 197 | 202 | 207 | 211 | 216 | 221 | 226 |
| 896 | 231 | 236 | 240 | 245 | 250 | 255 | 260 | 265 | 270 | 274 |
| 897 | 279 | 284 | 289 | 294 | 299 | 303 | 308 | 313 | 318 | 323 |
| 898 | 328 | 332 | 337 | 342 | 347 | 352 | 357 | 361 | 366 | 371 |
| 899 | 376 | 381 | 386 | 390 | 395 | 400 | 405 | 410 | 415 | 419 |
| 900 | 424 | 429 | 434 | 439 | 444 | 448 | 453 | 458 | 463 | 468 |
| N | L 0 | 1 | 2 | 3 | 4 | 5 | 6 | 7 | 8 | 9 |

P P

**6**

| 1 | 0.6 |
| 2 | 1.2 |
| 3 | 1.8 |
| 4 | 2.4 |
| 5 | 3.0 |
| 6 | 3.6 |
| 7 | 4.2 |
| 8 | 4.8 |
| 9 | 5.4 |

**5**

| 1 | 0.5 |
| 2 | 1.0 |
| 3 | 1.5 |
| 4 | 2.0 |
| 5 | 2.5 |
| 6 | 3.0 |
| 7 | 3.5 |
| 8 | 4.0 |
| 9 | 4.5 |

**4**

| 1 | 0.4 |
| 2 | 0.8 |
| 3 | 1.2 |
| 4 | 1.6 |
| 5 | 2.0 |
| 6 | 2.4 |
| 7 | 2.8 |
| 8 | 3.2 |
| 9 | 3.6 |

## 900—950

| N | L 0 | 1 | 2 | 3 | 4 | 5 | 6 | 7 | 8 | 9 |
|---|---|---|---|---|---|---|---|---|---|---|
| 900 | 95 424 | 429 | 434 | 439 | 444 | 448 | 453 | 458 | 463 | 468 |
| 901 | 472 | 477 | 482 | 487 | 492 | 497 | 501 | 506 | 511 | 516 |
| 902 | 521 | 525 | 530 | 535 | 540 | 545 | 550 | 554 | 559 | 564 |
| 903 | 569 | 574 | 578 | 583 | 588 | 593 | 598 | 602 | 607 | 612 |
| 904 | 617 | 622 | 626 | 631 | 636 | 641 | 646 | 650 | 655 | 660 |
| 905 | 665 | 670 | 674 | 679 | 684 | 689 | 694 | 698 | 703 | 708 |
| 906 | 713 | 718 | 722 | 727 | 732 | 737 | 742 | 746 | 751 | 756 |
| 907 | 761 | 766 | 770 | 775 | 780 | 785 | 789 | 794 | 799 | 804 |
| 908 | 809 | 813 | 818 | 823 | 828 | 832 | 837 | 842 | 847 | 852 |
| 909 | 856 | 861 | 866 | 871 | 875 | 880 | 885 | 890 | 895 | 899 |
| 910 | 904 | 909 | 914 | 918 | 923 | 928 | 933 | 938 | 942 | 947 |
| 911 | 952 | 957 | 961 | 966 | 971 | 976 | 980 | 985 | 990 | 995 |
| 912 | 999 | *004 | *009 | *014 | *019 | *023 | *028 | *033 | *038 | *042 |
| 913 | 96 047 | 052 | 057 | 061 | 066 | 071 | 076 | 080 | 085 | 090 |
| 914 | 095 | 099 | 104 | 109 | 114 | 118 | 123 | 128 | 133 | 137 |
| 915 | 142 | 147 | 152 | 156 | 161 | 166 | 171 | 175 | 180 | 185 |
| 916 | 190 | 194 | 199 | 204 | 209 | 213 | 218 | 223 | 227 | 232 |
| 917 | 237 | 242 | 246 | 251 | 256 | 261 | 265 | 270 | 275 | 280 |
| 918 | 284 | 289 | 294 | 298 | 303 | 308 | 313 | 317 | 322 | 327 |
| 919 | 332 | 336 | 341 | 346 | 350 | 355 | 360 | 365 | 369 | 374 |
| 920 | 379 | 384 | 388 | 393 | 398 | 402 | 407 | 412 | 417 | 421 |
| 921 | 426 | 431 | 435 | 440 | 445 | 450 | 454 | 459 | 464 | 468 |
| 922 | 473 | 478 | 483 | 487 | 492 | 497 | 501 | 506 | 511 | 515 |
| 923 | 520 | 525 | 530 | 534 | 539 | 544 | 548 | 553 | 558 | 562 |
| 924 | 567 | 572 | 577 | 581 | 586 | 591 | 595 | 600 | 605 | 609 |
| 925 | 614 | 619 | 624 | 628 | 633 | 638 | 642 | 647 | 652 | 656 |
| 926 | 661 | 666 | 670 | 675 | 680 | 685 | 689 | 694 | 699 | 703 |
| 927 | 708 | 713 | 717 | 722 | 727 | 731 | 736 | 741 | 745 | 750 |
| 928 | 755 | 759 | 764 | 769 | 774 | 778 | 783 | 788 | 792 | 797 |
| 929 | 802 | 806 | 811 | 816 | 820 | 825 | 830 | 834 | 839 | 844 |
| 930 | 848 | 853 | 858 | 862 | 867 | 872 | 876 | 881 | 886 | 890 |
| 931 | 895 | 900 | 904 | 909 | 914 | 918 | 923 | 928 | 932 | 937 |
| 932 | 942 | 946 | 951 | 956 | 960 | 965 | 970 | 974 | 979 | 984 |
| 933 | 988 | 993 | 997 | *002 | *007 | *011 | *016 | *021 | *025 | *030 |
| 934 | 97 035 | 039 | 044 | 049 | 053 | 058 | 063 | 067 | 072 | 077 |
| 935 | 081 | 086 | 090 | 095 | 100 | 104 | 109 | 114 | 118 | 123 |
| 936 | 128 | 132 | 137 | 142 | 146 | 151 | 155 | 160 | 165 | 169 |
| 937 | 174 | 179 | 183 | 188 | 192 | 197 | 202 | 206 | 211 | 216 |
| 938 | 220 | 225 | 230 | 234 | 239 | 243 | 248 | 253 | 257 | 262 |
| 939 | 267 | 271 | 276 | 280 | 285 | 290 | 294 | 299 | 304 | 308 |
| 940 | 313 | 317 | 322 | 327 | 331 | 336 | 340 | 345 | 350 | 354 |
| 941 | 359 | 364 | 368 | 373 | 377 | 382 | 387 | 391 | 396 | 400 |
| 942 | 405 | 410 | 414 | 419 | 424 | 428 | 433 | 437 | 442 | 447 |
| 943 | 451 | 456 | 460 | 465 | 470 | 474 | 479 | 483 | 488 | 493 |
| 944 | 497 | 502 | 506 | 511 | 516 | 520 | 525 | 529 | 534 | 539 |
| 945 | 543 | 548 | 552 | 557 | 562 | 566 | 571 | 575 | 580 | 585 |
| 946 | 589 | 594 | 598 | 603 | 607 | 612 | 617 | 621 | 626 | 630 |
| 947 | 635 | 640 | 644 | 649 | 653 | 658 | 663 | 667 | 672 | 676 |
| 948 | 681 | 685 | 690 | 695 | 699 | 704 | 708 | 713 | 717 | 722 |
| 949 | 727 | 731 | 736 | 740 | 745 | 749 | 754 | 759 | 763 | 768 |
| 950 | 772 | 777 | 782 | 786 | 791 | 795 | 800 | 804 | 809 | 813 |
| N | L 0 | 1 | 2 | 3 | 4 | 5 | 6 | 7 | 8 | 9 |

P P

**5**

| 1 | 0.5 |
|---|---|
| 2 | 1.0 |
| 3 | 1.5 |
| 4 | 2.0 |
| 5 | 2.5 |
| 6 | 3.0 |
| 7 | 3.5 |
| 8 | 4.0 |
| 9 | 4.5 |

**4**

| 1 | 0.4 |
|---|---|
| 2 | 0.8 |
| 3 | 1.2 |
| 4 | 1.6 |
| 5 | 2.0 |
| 6 | 2.4 |
| 7 | 2.8 |
| 8 | 3.2 |
| 9 | 3.6 |

950—1000

| N | L 0 | 1 | 2 | 3 | 4 | 5 | 6 | 7 | 8 | 9 |
|---|---|---|---|---|---|---|---|---|---|---|
| 950 | 97 772 | 777 | 782 | 786 | 791 | 795 | 800 | 804 | 809 | 813 |
| 951 | 818 | 823 | 827 | 832 | 836 | 841 | 845 | 850 | 855 | 859 |
| 952 | 864 | 868 | 873 | 877 | 882 | 886 | 891 | 896 | 900 | 905 |
| 953 | 909 | 914 | 918 | 923 | 928 | 932 | 937 | 941 | 946 | 950 |
| 954 | 955 | 959 | 964 | 968 | 973 | 978 | 982 | 987 | 991 | 996 |
| 955 | 98 000 | 005 | 009 | 014 | 019 | 023 | 028 | 032 | 037 | 041 |
| 956 | 046 | 050 | 055 | 059 | 064 | 068 | 073 | 078 | 082 | 087 |
| 957 | 001 | 096 | 100 | 105 | 109 | 114 | 118 | 123 | 127 | 132 |
| 958 | 137 | 141 | 146 | 150 | 155 | 159 | 164 | 168 | 173 | 177 |
| 959 | 182 | 186 | 191 | 195 | 200 | 204 | 209 | 214 | 218 | 223 |
| 960 | 227 | 232 | 236 | 241 | 245 | 250 | 254 | 259 | 263 | 268 |
| 961 | 272 | 277 | 281 | 286 | 290 | 295 | 299 | 304 | 308 | 313 |
| 962 | 318 | 322 | 327 | 331 | 336 | 340 | 345 | 349 | 354 | 358 |
| 963 | 363 | 367 | 372 | 376 | 381 | 385 | 390 | 394 | 399 | 403 |
| 964 | 408 | 412 | 417 | 421 | 426 | 430 | 435 | 439 | 444 | 448 |
| 965 | 453 | 457 | 462 | 466 | 471 | 475 | 480 | 484 | 489 | 493 |
| 966 | 498 | 502 | 507 | 511 | 516 | 520 | 525 | 529 | 534 | 538 |
| 967 | 543 | 547 | 552 | 556 | 561 | 565 | 570 | 574 | 579 | 583 |
| 968 | 588 | 592 | 597 | 601 | 605 | 610 | 614 | 619 | 623 | 628 |
| 969 | 632 | 637 | 641 | 646 | 650 | 655 | 659 | 664 | 668 | 673 |
| 970 | 677 | 682 | 686 | 691 | 695 | 700 | 704 | 709 | 713 | 717 |
| 971 | 722 | 726 | 731 | 735 | 740 | 744 | 749 | 753 | 758 | 762 |
| 972 | 767 | 771 | 776 | 780 | 784 | 789 | 793 | 798 | 802 | 807 |
| 973 | 811 | 816 | 820 | 825 | 829 | 834 | 838 | 843 | 847 | 851 |
| 974 | 856 | 860 | 865 | 869 | 874 | 878 | 883 | 887 | 892 | 896 |
| 975 | 900 | 905 | 909 | 914 | 918 | 923 | 927 | 932 | 936 | 941 |
| 976 | 945 | 949 | 954 | 958 | 963 | 967 | 972 | 976 | 981 | 985 |
| 977 | 989 | 994 | 998 | *003 | *007 | *012 | *016 | *021 | *025 | *029 |
| 978 | 99 034 | 038 | 043 | 047 | 052 | 056 | 061 | 065 | 069 | 074 |
| 979 | 078 | 083 | 087 | 092 | 096 | 100 | 105 | 109 | 114 | 118 |
| 980 | 123 | 127 | 131 | 136 | 140 | 145 | 149 | 154 | 158 | 162 |
| 981 | 167 | 171 | 176 | 180 | 185 | 189 | 193 | 198 | 202 | 207 |
| 982 | 211 | 216 | 220 | 224 | 229 | 233 | 238 | 242 | 247 | 251 |
| 983 | 255 | 260 | 264 | 269 | 273 | 277 | 282 | 286 | 291 | 295 |
| 984 | 300 | 304 | 308 | 313 | 317 | 322 | 326 | 330 | 335 | 339 |
| 985 | 344 | 348 | 352 | 357 | 361 | 366 | 370 | 374 | 379 | 383 |
| 986 | 388 | 392 | 396 | 401 | 405 | 410 | 414 | 419 | 423 | 427 |
| 987 | 432 | 436 | 441 | 445 | 449 | 454 | 458 | 463 | 467 | 471 |
| 988 | 476 | 480 | 484 | 489 | 493 | 498 | 502 | 506 | 511 | 515 |
| 989 | 520 | 524 | 528 | 533 | 537 | 542 | 546 | 550 | 555 | 559 |
| 990 | 564 | 568 | 572 | 577 | 581 | 585 | 590 | 594 | 599 | 603 |
| 991 | 607 | 612 | 616 | 621 | 625 | 629 | 634 | 638 | 642 | 647 |
| 992 | 651 | 656 | 660 | 664 | 669 | 673 | 677 | 682 | 686 | 691 |
| 993 | 695 | 699 | 704 | 708 | 712 | 717 | 721 | 726 | 730 | 734 |
| 994 | 739 | 743 | 747 | 752 | 756 | 760 | 765 | 769 | 774 | 778 |
| 995 | 782 | 787 | 791 | 795 | 800 | 804 | 808 | 813 | 817 | 822 |
| 996 | 826 | 830 | 835 | 839 | 843 | 848 | 852 | 856 | 861 | 865 |
| 997 | 870 | 874 | 878 | 883 | 887 | 891 | 896 | 900 | 904 | 909 |
| 998 | 913 | 917 | 922 | 926 | 930 | 935 | 939 | 944 | 948 | 952 |
| 999 | 957 | 961 | 965 | 970 | 974 | 978 | 983 | 987 | 991 | 996 |
| 1000 | 00 000 | 004 | 009 | 013 | 017 | 022 | 026 | 030 | 035 | 039 |
| N | L 0 | 1 | 2 | 3 | 4 | 5 | 6 | 7 | 8 | 9 |

P P

**5**

| | |
|---|---|
| 1 | 0.5 |
| 2 | 1.0 |
| 3 | 1.5 |
| 4 | 2.0 |
| 5 | 2.5 |
| 6 | 3.0 |
| 7 | 3.5 |
| 8 | 4.0 |
| 9 | 4.5 |

**4**

| | |
|---|---|
| 1 | 0.4 |
| 2 | 0.8 |
| 3 | 1.2 |
| 4 | 1.6 |
| 5 | 2.0 |
| 6 | 2.4 |
| 7 | 2.8 |
| 8 | 3.2 |
| 9 | 3.6 |

# V. International Atomic Weights (1956)

(Values in parentheses represent the most stable known isotopes.)

| Element | Symbol | Atomic No. | Atomic Weight | Element | Symbol | Atomic No. | Atomic Weight |
|---|---|---|---|---|---|---|---|
| Actinium | Ac | 89 | 227 | Mendelevium | Md | 101 | (256) |
| Aluminum | Al | 13 | 26.98 | Mercury | Hg | 80 | 200.61 |
| Americium | Am | 95 | (243) | Molybdenum | Mo | 42 | 95.95 |
| Antimony | Sb | 51 | 121.76 | Neodymium | Nd | 60 | 144.27 |
| Argon | A | 18 | 39.944 | Neon | Ne | 10 | 20.183 |
| Arsenic | As | 33 | 74.91 | Neptunium | Np | 93 | (237) |
| Astatine | At | 85 | (210) | Nickel | Ni | 28 | 58.71 |
| Barium | Ba | 56 | 137.36 | Niobium | Nb | 41 | 92.91 |
| Berkelium | Bk | 97 | (249) | Nitrogen | N | 7 | 14.008 |
| Beryllium | Be | 4 | 9.013 | Nobelium | No | 102 | (253) |
| Bismuth | Bi | 83 | 209.00 | Osmium | Os | 76 | 190.2 |
| Boron | B | 5 | 10.82 | Oxygen | O | 8 | 16.0000 |
| Bromine | Br | 35 | 79.916 | Palladium | Pd | 46 | 106.4 |
| Cadmium | Cd | 48 | 112.41 | Phosphorus | P | 15 | 30.975 |
| Calcium | Ca | 20 | 40.08 | Platinum | Pt | 78 | 195.09 |
| Californium | Cf | 98 | (249) | Plutonium | Pu | 94 | (242) |
| Carbon | C | 6 | 12.011 | Polonium | Po | 84 | 210 |
| Cerium | Ce | 58 | 140.13 | Potassium | K | 19 | 39.100 |
| Cesium | Cs | 55 | 132.91 | Praseodymium | Pr | 59 | 140.92 |
| Chlorine | Cl | 17 | 35.457 | Promethium | Pm | 61 | (145) |
| Chromium | Cr | 24 | 52.01 | Protactinium | Pa | 91 | 231 |
| Cobalt | Co | 27 | 58.94 | Radium | Ra | 88 | 226.05 |
| Copper | Cu | 29 | 63.54 | Radon | Rn | 86 | 222 |
| Curium | Cm | 96 | (245) | Rhenium | Re | 75 | 186.22 |
| Dysprosium | Dy | 66 | 162.51 | Rhodium | Rh | 45 | 102.91 |
| Einsteinium | Es | 99 | (255) | Rubidium | Rb | 37 | 85.48 |
| Erbium | Er | 68 | 167.27 | Ruthenium | Ru | 44 | 101.1 |
| Europium | Eu | 63 | 152.0 | Samarium | Sm | 62 | 150.35 |
| Fermium | Fm | 100 | (255) | Scandium | Sc | 21 | 44.96 |
| Fluorine | F | 9 | 19.00 | Selenium | Se | 34 | 78.96 |
| Francium | Fr | 87 | (223) | Silicon | Si | 14 | 28.09 |
| Gadolinium | Gd | 64 | 157.26 | Silver | Ag | 47 | 107.880 |
| Gallium | Ga | 31 | 69.72 | Sodium | Na | 11 | 22.991 |
| Germanium | Ge | 32 | 72.60 | Strontium | Sr | 38 | 87.63 |
| Gold | Au | 79 | 197.0 | Sulfur | S | 16 | 32.066 |
| Hafnium | Hf | 72 | 178.50 | Tantalum | Ta | 73 | 180.95 |
| Helium | He | 2 | 4.003 | Technetium | Tc | 43 | (99) |
| Holmium | Ho | 67 | 164.94 | Tellurium | Te | 52 | 127.61 |
| Hydrogen | H | 1 | 1.0080 | Terbium | Tb | 65 | 158.93 |
| Indium | In | 49 | 114.82 | Thallium | Tl | 81 | 204.39 |
| Iodine | I | 53 | 126.91 | Thorium | Th | 90 | 232.05 |
| Iridium | Ir | 77 | 192.2 | Thulium | Tm | 69 | 168.94 |
| Iron | Fe | 26 | 55.85 | Tin | Sn | 50 | 118.70 |
| Krypton | Kr | 36 | 83.80 | Titanium | Ti | 22 | 47.90 |
| Lanthanum | La | 57 | 138.92 | Tungsten | W | 74 | 183.86 |
| Lead | Pb | 82 | 207.21 | Uranium | U | 92 | 238.07 |
| Lithium | Li | 3 | 6.940 | Vanadium | V | 23 | 50.95 |
| Lutecium | Lu | 71 | 174.99 | Xenon | Xe | 54 | 131.30 |
| Magnesium | Mg | 12 | 24.32 | Ytterbium | Yb | 70 | 173.04 |
| Manganese | Mn | 25 | 54.94 | Yttrium | Y | 39 | 88.92 |
| | | | | Zinc | Zn | 30 | 65.38 |
| | | | | Zirconium | Zr | 40 | 91.22 |

# INDEX

# Index

## A

## B

## C